DATE	INVENTION	INVENTOR	
1816	Stethoscope	René Laënnec	
1821	Electric motor	Michael Faraday	
1823	'Difference engine'	Charles Babbage	
	Electromagnet	William Sturgeon	
1824	Portland cement	Joseph Aspdin	
1826	Reaper	Patrick Bell	
	Photography	Joseph-Nicéphore Niepce	France
	Water turbine	Benoît Fourneyron	France
1829	Sewing machine	Barthélemy Thimonnier	France
	Braille	Louis Braille	France
	Electromagnet	Joseph Henry	America
1832	Dynamo	Hippolyte Pixii	France
1834	Reaper	Cyrus McCormick	America
	Revolver	Samuel Colt	America
	'Analytical engine'	Charles Babbage	England
	Refrigeration	Jacob Perkins	America
1835	Daguerrotype photographs	Louis Daguerre	France
	Calotype photographs	W.H.Fox Talbot	England
1836	Screw propellor	Francis Pettit Smith	England
	Combine harvester	Hyram Moore/J. Hascall	America
	Primary cell	J.F.Daniell	England
1837	Electric telegraphy	C. Wheatstone/W. Cooke	England
	Screw propellor	John Ericsson	Sweden
1839	Steam hammer	James Nasmyth	Scotland
	Bicycle	Kirkpatrick Macmillan	Scotland
	Shorthand	Isaac Pitman	England
1840	Morse code	Samuel Morse	America
	Induction coil	Nicholas Callan	Ireland
1842	Anaesthetics	Horace Wells	America
	Vulcanization of rubber	Charles Goodyear	America
1846	Carbon-arc lamps	W.E.Staite	England
1850	Sewing machine	Isaac Merritt Singer	America
1851	Endoscopy	Hermann von Helmoltz	Germany
1852	Gyroscope	Léon Foucault	France
1853	Lift (elevator)	Elisha G. Otis	America
1855	Vacuum pump	Heinrich Geissler	Germany
	Bunsen burner	Robert Bunsen	Germany
	Steel converter	William Kelly	America
		Henry Bessemer	England
1856	Synthetic dye	W.H.Perkin	England
1859	Lead accumulator	Gaston Planté	France
	Gas engine	Étienne Lenoir	France
	Oil well drill	Edwin L. Drake	America
1860	Dynamo	Antonio Pacinotti	Italy
1861	Velocipede	Pierre and Ernest Michaux	France
1862	Parkesine plastic	Alexander Parkes	England
1863	T.N.T.	J.Wilbrand	Germany
1865	Vacuum pump	Hermann Sprengel	Germany
	Pasteurization	Louis Pasteur	France
	Antiseptic surgery	Joseph Lister	Scotland
1866	Fax machine	Giovanni Caselli	Italy
	Torpedo	Robert Whitehead	Austria
1867	Dynamite	Alfred Nobel	Sweden
	Clinical thermometer	Clifford Allbutt	England
1868	Typewriter	C.L.Sholes	America
	Primary cell	Georges Leclanché	France
1869	Air-brakes	George Westinghouse	America
1870	Celluloid	J.W.Hyatt	America
	Dynamo	Zénobe Gramme	Belgium
1874	Barbed wire	Joseph Glidden	America
1876	Telephone	Alexander Graham Bell	America
	4-stroke gas engine	Nikolaus August Otto	Germany
	Carpet sweeper	M.R.Bissell	America
1877	Phonograph (gramophone)	Thomas Alva Edison	America
	Microphone	Charles Cuttris	America
		Ernst Werner von Siemens	Germany
1878	Wimshurst machine	James Wimshurst	England
1879	Electric train	Ernst Werner von Siemens	Germany
1880	Filament lamps	Thomas Alva Edison	America
		J.W.Swan	England

THE GUINNESS HISTORY

of

INVENTIONS

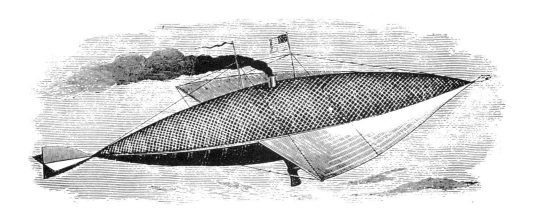

G. I. BROWN

GUINNESS PUBLISHING

Editor: Anne Marshall
Design: Alan Marshall
Diagrams: Peter Harper

The Work Copyright © G. I. Brown, 1996

The right of G. I. Brown to be identified as Author of this Work has been
asserted in accordance with the Copyright, Design and Patents Act, 1988

First published in 1996 by Guinness Publishing Ltd
Reprint 10 9 8 7 6 5 4 3 2 1 0

This Publication Copyright © Guinness Publishing Ltd, 1996
33 London Road, Enfield, Middlesex EN2 6DJ

'GUINNESS' is a registered trademark of Guinness Publishing Ltd

Printed and bound in Great Britain at The Bath Press, Bath

A catalogue record for this book is available from the British Library

ISBN 0-85112-546-8

PICTURE ACKNOWLEDGEMENTS

Apple Computers 202; British Museum p. 174; British Steel p. 13; BT Corporate Picture Library p. 188; Governing Body of Christ Church, Oxford p. 234; Civil Aviation Authority p. 150; Dunlop p. 38; Eastman Kodak Company p. 166, 167; EEV Limited p. 80; Eley Hawk Limited p. 27; GKN Westland p. 145; Hulton Deutsch Collection pp. 26, 101, 111, 115, 165, 185, 191, 223, 225, 237 (left), 249; The Imperial War Museum pp. 235, 237 (right), 240; Kia Cars UK Limited p. 78; John Laing plc p. 121; Lion Laboratories plc p. 140; Gary Marshall; Mary Evans Picture Library pp. 7, 8, 15, 28, 58, 61, 67, 69, 71, 83, 95, 96, 99, 103, 124, 125, 127, 129, 136, 141, 142, 153, 155, 159, 169, 171, 177, 182, 193, 197, 221, 222, 233, 238, 246; Massey Ferguson p. 211; National Motor Museum p. 133; Nuclear Electric/Ian Sadler p. 91; PA News p. 34; The Patent Office pp. 64, 118; Public Record Office FO 850/234 p. 201; Reflecting Roadstuds Ltd p. 9; G.A. Robinson p. 46; The Science Museum/Science & Society Picture Library pp. 29, 42, 49, 53, 94, 110, 179, 210; Science Photo Library p. 157 (Roger Ressmeyer, Starlight), p. 162 (Ray Ellis), p. 204 (J. Bernholc et al, North Carolina State University), p. 205 (US Department of Energy), p. 230 (Simon Fraser/Coronary Care Unit/Hexham General Hospital), p. 251 (John Frassanito, NASA); Singer UK Ltd p. 117; Slingsby Amphibious Hovercraft p. 126; Sotheby's p. 23; VSEL (part of GEC Marine) p. 239; Whatman International Limited p. 43. *Colour section*: Fibre optics (Adam Hart-Davis/Science Photo Library); Tutankhamen (Hulton Deutsch Collection); Plate mill (British Steel); Atomic clock (Courtesy of the National Physical Laboratory ©Crown 1996, reproduced by permission of the Controller of HMSO); Solar energy complex (Lowell Georgia/Science Photo Library); Static electricity (US Department of Energy/Science Photo Library); Gas turbine engine (Rolls-Royce plc); Welding (Rover Group Ltd; Elisha Otis (Otis plc); Virtual reality (James King-Holmes/W Industries/Science Photo Library); CAD (Otis plc); MRI scanner (Hank Morgan/Science Photo Library); Hubble telescope (NASA/Science Photo Library).
Front cover illustrations (clockwise from left): Thomas Edison (Hulton Deutsch); drugs in pill and capsule form (Daily Telegraph Colour Library and Tony Stone Images); 1914 Model T Ford and new Zetec-SE four-cylinder six-valve car engine (Ford Motor Co.); Apple PowerBook computer (Apple); Leonardo da Vinci's helicopter drawing; James Watt's rotative beam engine (1788). *Back cover*: Gillette razor (Patent Office); combine harvester (Peter Harper).

ACKNOWLEDGEMENTS

The author would like to thank the following organizations for their help and assistance in providing information: Alternative Vehicles Technology (AVT), Apple Computer UK Ltd, BBC Education, The British Agrochemicals Association, British Glass, The British Plastics Federation, The British Printing Industries Federation, British Steel plc, British Telecommunications plc, The British Wind Energy Association, The Centre for Alternative Technology, Chubb Locks Ltd, The Crown Cork Co. Ltd, Duracell, E.H. Industries Ltd, The Electric Vehicles Association, Eton College librarians, Goodfellow, Imperial War Museum, The Institute of Materials, Intel Corporation (UK) Ltd, International Business Machines (IBM), International Computers Ltd (ICL), Leica Camera Ltd, Lion Laboratories plc, Medical Research Council, Meiko, Meteorological Office, Microsoft Corporation Motorola, National Army Museum, National Physical Laboratory, National Power, The National Radiological Protection Board (NRPB), Novell, Nuclear Electric plc, Otis Elevator Co., The Patent Office, Pilkington plc, Polaroid (UK) Ltd, Reflecting Roadstuds Ltd, Science Museum Library, Shell UK Ltd, Singer UK Ltd, Slough Library, Telecom Australia, Vodafone Ltd.

CONTENTS

1

THE ART *of* INVENTION

'...there is nothing more difficult...than to take the lead in the introduction
of a new order of things. Because the innovator has for enemies
all those who have done well under the old conditions and lukewarm
defenders in those who may do well under the new.'

NICCOLO MACHIAVELLI (1469–1527),
Italian statesman

THE ART OF INVENTION

INVENTION IS AS OLD AS THE HILLS. Many things that we take entirely for granted, such as the wheel, the needle and the plough were in fact invented many thousands of years ago. Early civilizations did not have a DIY store or supermarket to satisfy their everyday needs. They had to set about developing new techniques and fashioning new materials, as best they could, to satisfy their needs – necessity was the mother of invention. That so much was achieved, given the paucity of resources, is quite remarkable.

INVENTION AND DISCOVERY

This book is about invention, which involves making something that is completely new, and only indirectly about discovery, which is finding, by chance or diligent search, something that already exists. For example, natural gas and penicillin were discovered, whereas the vacuum cleaner and steam engine were invented. There is, however, a fascinating relationship between the two processes because they feed on each other, with one invention or discovery leading to another.

For example, gunpowder was invented probably in China in the middle of the 9th century, but it did not appear in the West until about 1260. It not only led to the invention of all manner of weapons of war, but, more surprisingly, also begat the steam engine via an earlier unsuccessful gunpowder engine – and the steam engine was at the very heart of the Industrial Revolution, and at the birth of the railways.

Uranium, discovered in 1789, led to the discovery of radioactivity, in 1896; to the elucidation of the structure of the atom, some 15 years later; and to the invention of the atomic bomb and the use of atomic power, during and after World War II.

The discovery and exploitation of electricity, around 1800, led to the invention of the dynamo and the motor; it was the start of the electrical industry. The discovery of coal gas from coal, and then petrol from crude oil, led to the invention of the internal combustion engine and, subsequently to the motor car and the aeroplane.

And so, with one thing leading to another, inventing has mushroomed into a vast industry. It began slowly enough in prehistoric days, accelerated in the 16th and 17th centuries when increasingly more came to be known about science and technology, and began its golden age around the middle of the 18th century.

One invention followed another and generated still more. Highlights between 1750 to 1800 include the spinning jenny, Watt's steam engine, the first iron ship, the power loom and gaslighting. The period 1800 to 1850 saw the invention of the electric battery, the steam train, photography, the dynamo, the bicycle and telegraphy. The Bessemer process for making steel, synthetic dyes, dynamite, the telephone, the record-player, the electric light, the motor car, radio and X-rays evolved between 1850 and 1900. And the 20th century has seen the inventions of aeroplanes, motion pictures, television, rockets, jet engines, atom bombs and atomic power stations, silicon chips, computers, laser beams and space travel.

Inventions, on a smaller scale, include the safety pin, sliced bread, Sellotape, barbed wire, Monopoly, Scrabble, the zip fastener, Velcro, the ballpoint pen, parking meters, wheel clamps, baked beans, the blackboard, Spam, tea-bags, the paper clip, Meccano, Lego, Elastoplast, the mouse trap, false eyelashes, the Workmate, fish fingers, crossword puzzles, football pools, disposable nappies - to name but a few!

INVENTORS

All an inventor has to do is to 'see what everyone else has seen, but think what no one else has thought'. Many, indeed,

> **6** *"Necessity is the mother of invention" is a silly proverb. "Necessity is the mother of futile dodges" is much nearer to the truth.* **9**
>
> *A.N. WHITEHEAD (1861–1947), English mathematician*

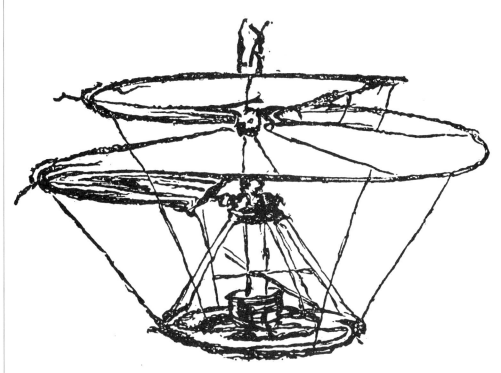

Leonardo's drawing of a helicopter, c. 1480. He hoped that it might rise from the ground if the corkscrew-like framework at the top was covered with starched linen and could be rapidly rotated, perhaps by pulling on a rope wrapped round the central shaft

must have said: 'That is a good idea; I could have thought of it myself.' The idea, however, is only the start. It must, certainly, be original but to succeed as an invention it must also be translated into practical reality. That might require a fair share of luck and involve years of hard work and frustration, together with financial and legal wranglings. There are no well-trodden paths for inventors to follow; success, and even fame, can be achieved in many ways by many different people.

The dreamer

Leonardo da Vinci (1452–1519) was born in Vinci, between Pisa and Florence, the illegitimate son of a notary and a peasant girl. If simply having ideas makes a good inventor then Leonardo might well rank as one of the best because he certainly had a fertile imagination. His notebooks, written in mirror writing, contain a wealth of sketched designs for aeroplanes, helicopters, tanks, pistols, roller bearings, gears, parachutes, diving suits, lock gates, centrifugal pumps, hydraulic presses, lathes, and machines for weaving, spinning, grinding, rope making, and cutting files.

Leonardo was, however, well ahead of his times, and very few of his ideas were put into practice because there was no real demand for what he proposed and, even if there had been, the technology and materials of the day would have been found wanting.

So he is best remembered for all his other remarkable activities. He was, predominantly, a painter, with *The Mona Lisa* and *The Last Supper* as examples of his talent; he had a wide knowledge of all the sciences; he left remarkable collections of drawings, which include some astonishingly accurate anatomical ones; and made his living, for some time, as an architect and military engineer. Few have achieved so much in so many fields and he must be considered to be one of the greatest geniuses of all time.

The professional

Thomas Alva Edison (1847–1931) was born in Milan, Ohio. His genius is of a different order from Leonardo's because he was solely an inventor, but in that field he is one of the world's greatest.

He was one of seven children of a general trader and his wife, a former school teacher. Illness delayed the young Thomas's formal schooling until he was eight years old and then it only lasted for three months because he walked out when a teacher told him his brain was 'addled'. Thereafter he was taught by his

> **Two men look out through the same bars; One sees the mud, and one the stars.**
>
> *FREDERICK LANGBRIDGE (1849–1923), English poet*

Thomas Edison after working for three days and nights on his phonograph

indignant mother who quickly unearthed a formidable interest in learning.

Thomas undertook odd jobs from the age of 11 and he did particularly well by selling newspapers on the Grand Trunk Railroad, but his big break came when, aged 15, he saved the life of the 2¹/₂-year-old stationmaster's son by snatching him away from a moving wagon. The grateful father rewarded Edison by training him as a telegraph operator in the station office, and he honed his skills in other establishments until he went to work for the Western Union Telegraph Co. in Boston, Massachusetts, in 1868, at the age of 21.

Two years later, he took out his first patent – a press-button device for members of Congress to record their votes – but it did not appeal to the conservative politicians. Fortunately, Edison's second invention – an automatic ticker-tape machine for transmitting gold and stock exchange prices – was more successful. So much so that he sold the seven patents involved to the Western Union for $40,000 and used the money to set up the firm of Edison and Unger. He also got married, on Christmas Day, 1871, and this eventually allowed him to perpetuate his debt to telegraphy when he nicknamed his two children Dot and Dash, after the Morse Code (⇒p. 180).

Before Edison, inventing had been a largely individual, one-off activity, but he transformed it into a business. The workshops, which he set up in New Jersey, gave him a base from which to operate, and money made from one invention was immediately invested in developing another.

When the work-force increased to 150, he controlled a technical power-house, the like of which had never been seen before.

Over the next 55 years, Edison was granted over 1000 patents. These included an automatic telegraph recorder in which Morse code characters were punched into a paper tape (1872); quadruplex telegraphy, which enabled four messages to be passed along one line (1874); the phonograph, which became the gramophone (1877); an incandescent light bulb with a platinum filament, and an improved transmitter for the telephone (1878); an improved light bulb, with a carbon filament (1879); a movie camera, called the kinetograph, which could make short films, and the kinetoscope, a coin-operated slot-machine on which they could be viewed (1889); the alkaline, nickel-iron battery (1909); the first talking moving picture (1912); and a substitute for rubber (1927).

Between times, he had moved twice to larger premises, first in 1876 to Menlo Park and, then, in 1887 to West Orange. He remarried, in 1886, after the death of his first wife, and suffered severe financial set-backs, involving lengthy litigation over patent rights. Seven of his factories were burnt down in 1914, and, since an accident in his early teens, he had been deaf.

Edison said that genius was 'one per cent inspiration and 99 per cent perspiration' and wrote that 'when it comes to problems of a mechanical nature, I want to tell you that all I've ever tackled and solved have been done by hard, logical thinking'. An outside commentator put his success down to 'breathtaking resourcefulness'.

Edison became a multi-millionaire; a popular poll, in 1922, rated him as the 'greatest living American'; and he controlled his companies until he was 80 years old. Two years later, he collapsed at a celebration given for him by his friend Henry Ford, who had been one of his early employees, and he never fully recovered. He died on 18 October 1931. His obituary in the *New York Times* occupied $4\frac{1}{2}$ pages, and, on the day of his funeral, the lights all over America were dimmed for one minute in his honour.

The man in the street

Percy Shaw (1890–1976), was born in Halifax, England, and in 1934 invented the cat's eyes, which mark the centre of a road at night by reflecting the light from a headlamp back to the driver. They consist of two aluminium-backed lenses positioned in a rubber pad inside a cast-iron casing set into the road. The secret of their success is that the surfaces of the lenses are cleaned whenever their rubber pad is depressed by traffic.

The tale is told that Shaw used to be guided by the sheen of the centrally placed, metal tramlines when driving home on a foggy night from his local inn. When the tramlines were removed, to make way for buses, he missed them, but remembered seeing the reflection of his headlamps from the eyes of a cat sitting on a wall.

The son of a labourer, Shaw left school at 13 and, after a variety of jobs, built up

Percy Shaw OBE, founder of the Reflecting Roadstuds Co.

a road repair business before founding his Reflecting Roadstuds Co. in Halifax in 1935; it now produces over one million cat's eyes every year. He was an eccentric bachelor who lived till he was 86 in Boothtown Mansion, adjacent to his factory, which had been his home since the age of two. He became very rich and had a Rolls-Royce but no carpets or curtains; he liked to watch wrestling on television and he was awarded the OBE, in 1965.

GETTING A PATENT

All serious inventors need to protect their rights to the exclusive use of their ideas by taking out legally binding patents. The first patent was granted by the Italian state of Florence in 1421 to Filippo Brunelleschi, the builder of the Palazzo Pitti and the Cathedral dome. It related to the invention of a barge with special lifting gear to carry marble; it was intended to prevent the inventor from being 'robbed of the reward of his labours'; and it lasted for three years. In the UK, the first patent was granted by

> *❛Genius is the capacity for seeing relationships where lesser men see none.❜*
>
> WILLIAM JAMES (1842–1910), American philosopher

> 6 *Everything that can be invented has been invented.* 9

CHARLES H. DUELL,
Director, US Patents Office, 1899

Henry VI, in 1449, to John of Utyman for making coloured glass for the windows of Eton College chapel. Today, patents are granted in the UK by The Patent Office under the Patents Act 1977; they protect an invention and provide monopoly rights to its use for up to 20 years. Other countries have their own, similar legislation.

To be granted a patent, an idea must be novel and must not be obvious to someone with a good knowledge of the area involved. It must also be capable of being made or used in industry – which includes agriculture, but rules out literary, dramatic or artistic work; games; new business schemes; computer programs; scientific theories; mathematical methods; and perpetual motion machines.

When applying for a patent, full details of what is proposed have to be submitted, and these are then examined to see whether the idea is patentable. Because official forms and legal jargon are involved it may be necessary to seek assistance from a professional patent agent. This can be a lengthy and expensive business and can take anything up to 4½ years. It will cost several hundred pounds for a patent to be granted, and annual renewal fees will have to be paid in order to maintain the patent in force from the beginning of the fifth year.

To obtain patent protection overseas, it is necessary to apply to the patent offices of individual countries. This procedure can be simplified by using the Patent Cooperation Treaty under which an international application can be made in the 48 participating countries. Alternatively, an application can be made in the 16 European states within the European Patent Convention.

In 1994, the UK Patent Office received 26,465 applications and 9920 patents were granted.

It is estimated that worldwide around 1500 patent applications are submitted daily. Most will involve minor improvements in a product or process; some will be more hopeful than realistic; some will never be heard of again; a very small number will be a great commercial success; but, occasionally, one will turn up which makes history and affects all our lives.

COPYRIGHT OR TRADE MARKS

When it is not possible to get a patent, some protection is afforded by either a copyright or a registered trade mark.

A copyright is granted for original literary, dramatic, musical and artistic work, sound recording, broadcasts and films, or computer programs. It allows the owner of the copyright, whose name is commonly preceded by a symbol ©, to exercise some control over the ways in which the original work can be used. For example, the author of a book can prevent it from being improperly copied or adapted, and the maker of a film can prevent it from being exhibited without permission. It is possible to take legal action if there are serious copyright infringements but many problems that arise are settled by negotiation.

Copyright protection in this country is automatic and does not have to be appplied or paid for. For published or unpublished literary, musical, or artistic work, the copyright lasts until 50 years after the death of the creator. The copyright protection will normally apply in most overseas countries because the UK is a member of international organizations such as the Berne Convention for the Protection of Literary and Artistic Works and the Universal Copyright Convention.

A trade mark is used to distinguish one manufacturer's goods from another. Examples are provided by Kodak for cameras, Singer for sewing machines and Toblerone for chocolate. The name may be marked with ® or ™.

To obtain a trade mark in this country, application has to be made to the Trade Marks Registry, which is a branch of the Patent Office. If there is no valid objection when the suggested name is advertised in the Trade Marks Journal, it is officially registered. The procedure takes about two years. There is an original application fee of £170 and renewal fees after, first, seven years, and then after 14-year periods. Separate applications have to be made in each country to obtain the necessary marks overseas.

Legal action can be taken against anyone infringing a registered mark by seeking to use it or anything that resembles it too closely.

2

MATERIALS

'Gold is for the mistress – silver for the maid –
Copper for the craftsman cunning in his trade.'
'Good!' said the Baron, sitting in his hall,
'But Iron – Cold Iron – is master of them all.'

RUDYARD KIPLING (1856–1936),
English writer

MATERIALS

EVERYTHING HAS TO BE MADE FROM SOMETHING, and the progress of invention has gone hand in hand with man's ability to imitate natural materials, to improve upon them, to find completely new ones, and to find how to handle and use them all. The study of materials has become a science in its own right and it is now possible, in many cases, to tailor-make a material for a specific purpose.

METALS

At first, our ancestors knew of only three metals – gold, silver and copper – because they are the only ones which occur naturally. However, the number went up to seven when they found that tin, lead, mercury and iron could be made by heating their naturally occurring oxide or sulphide ores with charcoal (smelting). The discovery of tin was particularly important because it alloyed with copper to make bronze. Hence the Bronze Age which replaced the Stone Age around 3000 BC.

The Iron Age took over from the Bronze Age around 1200 BC, the time delay being due to the fact that it requires a much higher temperature to smelt iron than tin or copper. Thereafter, until the discovery of new ores and the development of better techniques for extracting metals from them, not much progress was made. By 1750, there were still only 13 known metals; by 1850, 43; and by 1950, 74. Today there are 83, of which 15 are man-made. Very few of these metals are much used in their pure form, but there are several thousand alloys, made by blending pure metals together, in everyday, commercial use

❜ He who holds the iron of the world will rule the world. ❞

Chinese proverb

IRON

Iron is the most important metal. It was originally made by heating an ore such as haematite, which contains iron oxide (Fe_2O_3), in a charcoal fire. When the fire died down, a spongy mass of iron remained which could be hammered into shape. Eventually, bellows were used to raise the temperature in the fire to speed up the process, and in the 15th century cylindrical furnaces were built and cold air was pumped in at the base. These were the forerunners of modern blast furnaces. The temperature was high enough to melt the iron so that it could be run off from the bottom of the furnace as what came to be known as pig or cast iron. It had the disadvantage of being very brittle because it contained 3 to 5 per cent of carbon and other impurities which had dissolved in the iron from the ore and the charcoal. Nevertheless, it was useful because in its molten form it could easily be cast into moulds.

Increased production was threatened by a shortage of charcoal so an English ironmaster, Dud Dudley, attempted to replace charcoal by coal, in 1619, but this was not successful because the coal was too impure. The breakthrough did not come until 1709 when Abraham Darby used coke – it was the start of the modern Iron Age. Darby, who came from a Quaker family, served an apprenticeship as a smith in Birmingham before founding a small brassworks in Bristol in 1699. He moved to Coalbrookdale in Shropshire where he made his important invention and where his pioneering work was continued by his son and grandson.

Wrought iron

Brittle pig-iron is suitable for making castings for stoves, cookers, manhole covers, cylinder blocks and machine stands, but for other purposes such as railway lines, chains, horseshoes, anchors, ornamental work and 'iron' ships, it was originally converted into wrought iron, which is malleable and ductile. This was done by removing most of the carbon and other impurities by repeated hammering – hence the term 'wrought'. It was a laborious business, fortunately replaced in 1783 by a puddling process patented by an Englishman, Henry Cort. This process involved heating the pig-iron with haematite whilst stirring (puddling) the mixture with long iron rods. As the impurities were removed, the melting point of the mixture rose until it became pasty. At that stage, it was removed, hammered, and rolled into shape. Cort's invention was as important as that of Darby and it greatly increased the use of iron. Alas, Cort got into debt in trying to build up his business and his patents were confiscated by the government. With 12 childen to support, he was ruined, until eventually he was granted a small pension.

THE BLAST FURNACE

A modern blast furnace consists of a steel cylinder, which can be 30 m (33 yd) high and 10 m (10.7 yd) in diameter at its widest point. The steel is about 40 mm (1.6 in) thick and it is lined with firebrick about 1 m thick which is cooled by

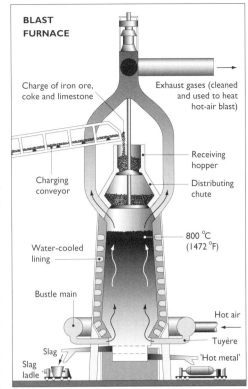

BLAST FURNACE

Charge of iron ore, coke and limestone

Exhaust gases (cleaned and used to heat hot-air blast)

Charging conveyor

Receiving hopper

Distributing chute

Water-cooled lining

800 °C (1472 °F)

Bustle main

Hot air

Slag

Tuyère

Slag ladle

'Hot metal'

The essential features of a typical blast furnace. The hot exhaust gases are used to heat the air coming into the bustle main in large heat exchangers. The temperature inside the furnace at the bottom is close to 2000°C (3530°F)

A blast furnace at British Steel's Teesside works at Redcar

passing water through embedded piping. The charge of oxide iron ore (mainly haematite), coke and limestone is fed in at the top through a hopper arrangement which allows entry into the furnace without letting any gases out. Hot dry air, enriched with oxygen and, possibly, with fuel oil, is passed into the bottom of the furnace through small pipes, known as tuyères, which lead off from a large circulating bustle pipe which runs round the base of the furnace.

The oxide ore is converted into molten iron and the impurities form a molten slag with the limestone. Both slag and iron sink to the bottom or hearth of the furnace where the slag floats on top of the iron. They are periodically tapped off through the slag notch and the tap hole respectively, as new raw materials are fed in at the top. The whole process is continuous and may go on for over ten years before the furnace needs relining.

MAKING STEEL

Making steel involves lowering the carbon content of pig-iron to below $1\frac{1}{2}$ per cent and controlling the other impurities. This was first done successfully by Benjamin Huntsman, an English clockmaker, in 1742. He melted wrought iron in a clay crucible and added the required amount of carbon, but his method was very expensive and could only be carried out on a small scale. It was replaced by a process invented independently in the 1850s, first by an American, William Kelly, and later by an Englishman, Sir Henry Bessemer. It came to be known as the Bessemer process because Kelly's development work was hindered by financial difficulties in 1857. Around 1864, Frenchman Pierre Martin, and a naturalized Briton who was born in Germany, Sir William Siemens, invented the open-hearth process. Both processes lasted for close on 100 years but were then replaced by the basic oxygen process for making bulk steel and an electrical process for making special, higher-quality steels.

The basic oxygen process

This process uses a cylindrical steel, refractory-lined furnace, which can be rotated into horizontal or vertical positions. A typical furnace is 9 m (9.8 yd) across and 10 m (10.9 yd) high. Whilst in a tilted position, it is charged with up to 30 per cent scrap metal and 'hot metal' from a blast furnace. It is then moved into a vertical position and a high-speed jet of oxygen is directed on to the surface of the charge through a water-cooled lance. Some of the carbon in the charge is converted into gaseous oxides which escape from the furnace through a hood. Other impurities also form oxides and these react with added lime to form a slag. After the 'blow', the furnace is tipped into a horizontal position so that the molten steel can be run off through the tap-hole. The correct amounts of carbon and other elements are then added to give the type of steel required. The furnace is then inverted to pour away the slag. A large furnace can produce 350 tonnes of steel in 40 minutes.

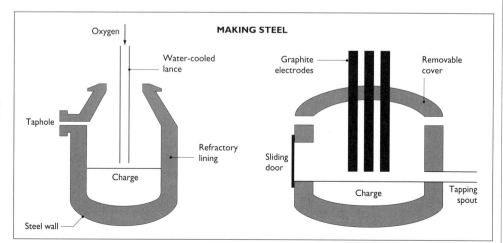

A basic oxygen furnace (left) and an electric arc furnace (right)

SIR HENRY BESSEMER
(1813–98)

BESSEMER, born in Charlton in Hertfordshire, England, was a prolific inventor in many fields with more than 150 patents to his name. These included a method of making corduroy velvet, a machine for franking stamps, and new methods of rolling and cutting glass, of silvering mirrors and of extracting the juice from sugar canes.

He made enough money by manufacturing a bronze gilding powder to set up a small iron-works in St Pancras, London and he turned to steel making in 1854, at the start of the Crimean War, when he found that existing gun barrels were not strong enough to fire a new rifled shell he had designed. Bessemer's process, very similar to that of William Kelly in America, was not unlike today's basic oxygen process. He used a converter, shaped like a concrete-mixer, instead of the cylindrical furnace, and air, bubbled up through the charge, took the place of the jet of oxygen.

The use of Bessemer converters was not immediately successful in Great Britain, but they were adopted in the 1860s by Andrew Carnegie the Scottish-born American industrialist and philanthropist, who made his fortune out of them. Later, Bessemer himself received due reward. He became very rich, was knighted and made a Fellow of the Royal Society in 1879. However, he had to live down one disastrous invention. Having suffered from sea-sickness all his life, he built a ship in 1874 called the SS *Bessemer* in which the passenger saloon was kept horizontal in any sea by a hydraulic mechanism. Alas, it failed miserably and the venture lost him £35,000. Fortunately, it did little damage to his reputation as, in Carnegie's words, 'the great king of steel'.

> *I had nothing to unlearn. My mind was open and free to receive any new impressions…*
>
> *SIR HENRY BESSEMER (1813–98), English engineer*

Sir Henry Bessemer's cross-channel steamer was designed to prevent bouts of sea-sickness. The idea of the SS Bessemer *was that its saloon, balanced amidships on a central pivot, would remain on an even keel. It failed, however, and the ship was adapted into a conventional steamer*

The electric arc process

This process uses a cylindrical vessel made of steel and lined with refractory material. It is, typically, 7 m (7.6 yd) across and 5 m (5.5 yd) high, and has a movable lid through which three graphite electrodes can be lowered into the vessel. The charge is made up almost entirely of scrap steel and it is heated by forming arcs between the ends of the electrodes and the surface of the charge. Oxygen is blown into the melt, if necessary, and lime, fluorspar and iron oxide are added to form a slag with the impurities and to give a steel of the required composition. The slag is raked or poured from the surface, and the steel is run out through the tapping spout by tilting the furnace. A large furnace can make 150 tonnes of steel in about 30 minutes.

Types of steel

There are hundreds of different types of steel. Mild steels, containing 0.1 to 0.25 per cent of carbon, are soft, malleable and ductile. They are used in making tinplate, corrugated iron sheets, ships' plates, car bodies, rolled steel joists and steel pipes and take the place, today, of wrought iron. Medium steels (0.25 to 0.6 per cent carbon) and hard steels (0.6 to 1.5 per cent carbon) are harder than mild steels and are used for making tools and most alloy steels. These alloy steels vary widely. Incorporation of chromium and nickel gives stainless steels; cobalt gives a highly magnetic steel; tungsten gives very hard steels used for making cutting tools; manganese steels are hard and tough and are used in rock drills; and silicon gives spring steels.

Many of the steels can also have their properties enhanced by heat treatments. On heating to red heat and quenching in oil or water they may become brittle, but this brittleness can be removed by tempering. This is done by reheating and then recooling; different degrees and rates of heating and cooling give different products.

In case hardening, steel is hardened on the surface by heating in a pack of charcoal (carburizing); carbon diffuses into the steel surface and hardens it by forming carbides. Alternatively, steel can be heated in an atmosphere of ammonia (nitriding); nitrogen from the decomposition of the ammonia forms surface nitrides. Case hardened steels are used in such articles as gear wheels.

Annealing is a process in which steels are maintained at a temperature of about 1000°C for some time and then allowed to cool very slowly; a soft steel which can be machined very easily results.

ELECTRICAL METHODS OF EXTRACTION

The ores of reactive metals cannot be obtained by simple smelting processes. It is necessary to use electrical energy which only became possible just after 1800 when the Voltaic pile (⇒p. 68) provided a good source of current. In 1807, Sir Humphrey Davy used a large pile at the Royal Institution in London to make sodium by passing a current through molten sodium chloride (common salt). He wrote in his notebook that it was a 'capital experiment'. It certainly provided a powerful method of extracting metals, and within the next two years he had made potassium, calcium, strontium, barium and magnesium.

Making aluminium on a large scale took much longer even though it is the most abundant metal in the Earth's crust. It occurs as the oxide, Al_2O_3, in bauxite, but this cannot be smelted with carbon except at an impossibly high temperature; nor can it be melted so that a current can be passed through it. The difficulty was overcome in 1886 by two 23 year olds – the American Charles Hall and the Frenchman Paul Héroult. They found, independently, that a mixture of aluminium oxide with a mineral called cryolite, which occurred naturally in Greenland, would melt at around 1000°C. Passing an electric current through the molten mixture not only kept it liquid but also produced molten aluminium which could be run off from the bottom of the cell.

Because of the high electrical cost, aluminium is not cheap but its low density makes it an invaluable metal and it is widely used when alloyed with magnesium as, for example, in Duralumin which was first made by a German mettalurgist, Alfred Wilm, around 1909. It is used in making aeroplanes.

❛ These materials would appear specially suited for the manufacture of...certain items of cutlery. ❜

HARRY BREARLEY, inventor of stainless steel, 1912

SHAPING METALS

Casting

Molten metals can be cast into shape. The melting is usually carried out in a crucible made of a high-melting material such as carbon, and the molten metal is poured into a mould made out of a stiff mixture of sand and oils. In die-casting, metal moulds made in two halves are used. The molten metal is fed into them by gravity or forced in under pressure. Many alloys with low melting points are shaped in this way.

In centrifugal casting, a molten metal is poured into a metal mould which is spun at a high speed. The metal is flung on to the inner faces of the mould and takes up its shape. If the mould is cylindrical, for example, a pipe will result. In investment casting, a pattern is made out of wax or plastic. It is then covered with a slurry of a refractory material and, when this sets, the inner wax or plastic is removed by melting or dissolving. The resulting mould can be filled with molten metal, or it can be used for centrifugal casting as, for example, in making 'hollow' jewellery.

Hammering and forging

Many metals can be shaped by hammering when they are hot; the craft is traditionally carried out by hand by blacksmiths. In drop-forging, a hot piece of metal is secured above a die on an anvil and a second, heavy die is allowed to fall down on to it between vertical guides. Alternatively, the hammer is forced down on to the metal under pressure.

Extrusion and drawing

Some pipes and tubes are made by extruding a hot metal, under pressure, through round holes or ring apertures respectively. Other shapes, such as curtain rails, are made in a similar way by extrusion through shaped dies. Thin rods and wire are made by pulling, or drawing, a thicker rod of hot metal through a series of smaller and smaller dies.

Rolling

Large ingots of steel and some other metals can be squeezed into shape by passing through rollers which are held close together under pressure. This process can be applied to cold or hot steel. Hot rolling is easier, but cold rolling gives a better finished surface. It is possible to make a variety of shapes, for example, beams and railway lines, by using shaped rollers.

Turning, milling and drilling

All these operations use hard, sharp cutting tools to remove metal. Drilling makes holes; in turning, on a lathe, a stationary tool is used to shape a rotating piece of metal; in milling, grooves or slots are cut into a flat metal surface by a rotating cutting tool.

Hard steels were used at first for the tips of cutting tools, but they were replaced in about 1900 by an alloy steel, developed by Fred W. Taylor and Maunsel White in the USA. It contained vanadium, tungsten and chromium. In turn, it gave way in 1926 to a material developed in laboratories at the German firms of Krupp's in Germany and General Motors in the USA. It was made of tungsten carbide bonded with cobalt. Nowadays, titanium and tantalum carbides may be added.

Grinding

In grinding, metal is scraped away from a surface by a hard, abrasive powder held by a bonding agent on a wheel. At first, naturally occurring powders such as sand, emery and even diamond were used, but now silicon carbide (carborundum) or tungsten carbide are used.

Powder metallurgy

English chemist William Hyde Wollaston found, in around 1800, that powdered platinum could be beaten into shape when it was hot, and his success in making platinum crucibles in this way brought the metal into more widespread use and enabled him at the age of 34 to give up his medical practice and concentrate on scientific research. It was an early application of powder metallurgy. Today, the method is used for shaping many metals and metallic carbides. The powder is placed in a metal or graphite die, heated and subjected to a high pressure.

'We must beat the iron while it is hot, but we may polish it at leisure.'

JOHN DRYDEN (1631–1700), English poet

JOINING METALS

Metals can be joined by screws or bolts, rivets ($\Rightarrow$p. 61), soldering, brazing, welding, or adhesives. In soldering, the two pieces to be joined are abutted or overlapped and solder, liquefied by a blow lamp or a soldering iron, is allowed to run over the join. A chemical such as zinc chloride is used (it is known as a flux) to keep the surfaces clean. A typical 'soft' solder, melting at around 200°C, contains 60 per cent tin and 40 per cent lead. Brazing uses a 'hard' solder containing about 60 per cent zinc with 40 per cent copper. It melts at around 850°C and gives a stronger joint than a 'soft' solder, but needs a gas torch to apply it.

In welding, two adjoining pieces of metal are heated by an oxy-acetylene flame which is also used to melt metal from a welding-rod held nearby. This metal is allowed to flow into, and over, the gap between the two metal pieces. When it sets it forms a join. Alternatively, there are a number of electrical welding techniques. In arc welding, a current is passed between the welding-rod and the joint to be made; when an arc forms it produces enough heat to effect the weld. In spot welding, two pieces of metal are overlapped with pointed electrodes positioned opposite each other on both sides. When the two electrodes are pressed together, the current which passes heats the metals and produces a localized, spot weld. The electrodes are then moved to a different position nearby. In seam-welding, a continous weld is obtained, in the same sort of way, by moving the two pieces of metal between two rolling discs serving as electrodes.

LEATHER

The ancient art of making leather from animal hides involves the removal of the hairy outer layer and the inner fleshy one, followed by a preserving process known as tanning. Today, the layers are generally removed by treating the skin with milk of lime, scraping and washing. Vegetable tanning, the oldest method, involves soaking the skins in aqueous extracts from the roots and barks of many trees and plants. They contain tannins which react with the collagen of which the leather is mainly composed. In chrome tanning, introduced towards the end of the 19th century, chromium salts are used, and, since the 1920s, special chemicals (syntans) have been synthesized to do the job.

Tanning may be followed by many finishing processes and it is possible to make a wide variety of leathers by using the skins from different animals, or different parts of the same animal, and by varying or combining the tanning and finishing processes.

Tough, hard leather for the soles of shoes is made from cowhide and it is treated with waxes to make it waterproof. Chamois leather is oil-tanned sheepskin. Suede is made by buffing leather on an emery wheel to loosen the surface. Patent leather is made by treating the leather surface with synthetic plastics. There are also many substitutes for leather which are made by coating fabrics with plastic finishes.

So I wish him joy where'er he dwell, That first found out the leather bottel.

Anon

GLASS

The simplest type of clear glass – soda glass – is made by heating a mixture of white sand, sodium carbonate and calcium carbonate in a furnace to a temperature of around 1400°C. At that temperature glass is a viscous semi-liquid, like a hot syrup, but it solidifies on cooling. It is a particularly versatile material because it can be shaped by pressing, drawing, moulding, blowing or rolling, and the addition of other chemicals to its basic ingredients can change its nature very considerably. Many chemicals, for example, produce coloured glasses.

The first use of glass, or glass-like substances, was in the glazing of soap-stone beads or ornaments around 4000

BC, but objects made entirely of glass, such as small beads, were not made until around 3000 BC. Small vessels began to appear around 1500 BC. They were made by dipping a shaped core of sand and/or clay into molten glass and removing the core when the glass had solidified on cooling. The vessels could be made of coloured glass and decorated by adding blobs or threads of different colours. Solid figures and articles were made by casting molten glass into clay moulds or by sculpting pieces of solid glass by grinding and carving.

The invention of glass-blowing, probably in Syria, towards the end of the 1st century BC, had a revolutionary impact. The glass-blower picked up a blob of molten glass on the end of an iron tube. He had to keep spinning the tube, to prevent the blob from sagging, but by blowing, with or without the help of moulds and tools, the skilled craftsman could make a wide range of vases, bowls, and bottles.

GLASS BOTTLES

By the middle of the 17th century, handmade bottles had largely replaced stoneware for storing wines and ales but it was not until 1887 that a machine, invented by John Ashley in Yorkshire, England, was operated commercially. It enabled two men to produce 200 bottles an hour but it was only semi-automatic because molten glass was fed into its mould by hand. The first fully automatic machine, invented by M.J. Owens in America in 1898, could produce 2500 bottles an hour. It transferred the correct amount of molten glass into revolving moulds by suction and it was widely used until replaced by the IS (individual section) machine invented by an American Henry W. Ingle, in 1925. This had a gravity feed for the molten glass and could produce bottles more quickly than Owens's machine. Thereafter, design changes meant that lighter bottles could be made and, today, they are commonly strengthened by the application of external coatings. When titanium compounds are used the process is known as titanizing.

Corks were introduced in the 17th century. The internal screw top came in 1879, the external screw top in 1889, and the crown top, as on many beer bottles, in 1892.

SHEET GLASS

The oldest method of making sheet glass, which survived until well into the 20th century, was to pour molten glass into a flat, clay mould and let it solidify. The surface of the glass was then improved by grinding and polishing. There have since been several developmental stages in the manufacture of sheet glass.

Crown and cylinder glass

Small sheets of glass were made during the 14th century by blowing a bubble of glass on the end of a blowing iron and then spinning it round as rapidly as possible. The glass spread out, and was flattened under the centrifugal force, and it could then be cut away from the rod and allowed to cool into a circular piece of glass. It had a characteristic 'bull's-eye' or 'crown' in the middle, which is why it came to be known as crown-glass. It was widely used in early stained glass windows and samples of it can still be seen in old churches and houses.

For larger sheets, a blob of molten glass was blown into a bubble which was elongated into a cylinder by swinging it, pendulum-wise, in a pit. The cylinder was then cut down one side, whilst still hot, opened up and rolled flat.

Blowing and swinging glass into a cylinder for making sheet glass

The product, known as cylinder or broad glass, was probably first made in Britain in 1567.

Rolled glass

In 1884, Chance Brothers in England invented a process in which molten glass was poured on to an inclined plane, passed through a pair of rollers, and then ground and polished. Textured glass could be made by using patterned rollers. The method was improved in 1923 by Pilkington Brothers Ltd, another English firm, in collaboration with the Ford Motor Company. By 1937, the process had been developed so that, after forming, both sides of the glass could be ground and polished simultaneously. It was widely used until float glass was invented in the 1950s (see below).

Drawn glass

In 1903, John Lubbbers in the USA made a large cylinder of glass, 40 ft (12.2 m) high and 3 ft (0.9 m) in diameter, by drawing it upwards on a ring out of a pot of molten glass. Early attempts to make a sheet of plate glass by the same method were frustrated because the edges of the glass sagged, but by 1913 the difficulties had been overcome. A sheet of metal was dipped into a vat of molten glass and it was slowly withdrawn, pulling the glass up with it. The edges of this sheet of glass were cooled to prevent them from sagging and once they had solidified sufficiently they were gripped by rollers which withdrew the sheet of glass further.

Float glass

The method of making float glass was patented by Pilkington Brothers Ltd in 1957 and is now used all over the world. Molten glass is poured on to a pool of molten tin, and allowed to flow continuously along the surface of the metal. This ensures that the lower surface of the glass has a good finish. The process is carried out in an inert atmosphere so that the upper surface is not oxidized. The glass is kept sufficiently hot to ensure that it is fluid enough to set itself exactly parallel to the lower surface. The sheet of glass passes from the tin bath through annealing chambers in which it is slowly cooled. When solidified it is cut as required.

It was a stroke of luck that the glass was of the right thickness to meet the major demand. Nevertheless, seven years and around £11 million was invested in perfecting the process.

GLASS TUBING

Glass tubing was originally made by one worker blowing a hole into a blob of glass on a blowing iron. A second worker, facing the first, took hold of the blob with another iron and the two stretched the blob out into a tube by walking backwards, away from each other.

Today, tubing is made by running a steady stream of molten glass down the outside of a vertical, metal tube through which a current of air is passing. As the glass is pulled off at the bottom, it solidifies into a tube.

SPECIAL GLASSES

Flint glass

The Venetians were, for many years, supreme in the art of glass-making. That is why the Glass-Sellers Co. in England began in 1673 to try to find a better product. This led to the invention of flint glass by George Ravenscroft. It was made by heating a mixture of white sand, flints (an impure form of silica), potassium carbonate and lead oxide. The glass produced was much more brilliant – more diamond-like – than soda glass and it was much sought after for making decorative tableware, particularly when it was cut to enhance its natural sparkle. Bohemian crystal-glass, which was very similar, was developed at about the same time.

Quartz glass

This glass is made from pure silica. It requires a particularly high temperature to melt the silica but the product is useful, both because it has a remarkably low coefficient of expansion and and is very transparent to infra-red and ultraviolet light. It is used in making optical equipment and apparatus which needs to withstand severe temperature changes.

Heat resisting glass

Glass often breaks, on sudden heating or

'Glass must be made entirely of holes; otherwise, you couldn't see through it.'

ANONYMOUS
SCHOOLBOY

cooling, because one surface expands or contracts more than the other. The Corning Glass Co. in the United States discovered in 1912 that the addition of 10 to 15 per cent of boron oxide produced a glass, for example Pyrex, which has a much lower coefficient of expansion than soda glass. It can, therefore, withstand sudden temperature changes more readily. As it also has a higher softening temperature and is more resistant to chemical attack it is widely used in making cooking utensils and laboratory equipment.

Safety glass

This is made by sandwiching a sheet of transparent plastic between two sheets of glass. It was first patented by Frenchman Edouard Benedictus in 1909, and used in car windscreens from 1920. Today, that requirement is met by using sheet glass that has been heat treated (tempered) so that it crumbles, rather than shatters when it breaks. The process was patented in France as early as 1874 by François Royer de la Bastie.

Strong safety glass has also been made since 1898 by incorporating metal wiring between two sheets of glass, but the product is not fully transparent.

Glass fibres

A hot rod of glass can be drawn out into a fine fibre by stretching it, and similar fibres have been manufactured since 1908 by feeding molten glass through a spinneret. The fibres can then be spun together and woven into glass cloth which is useful in heat- and sound-proofing and in electrical insulation. The fibres are also blended with plastics to make fibreglass which is used in making boat hulls and car bodies. Fibres made from very pure glass are used in fibre optics ($\Rightarrow$p. 183).

Glass ceramics

Silver chloride, which darkens on exposure to light, as in photographic film, can be added to glass to make a product which darkens in the light, and conversely lightens in the dark. It is said to be photochromic and is used in making sunglasses.

An important, accidental discovery came out of the work on these photosensitive glasses when it was found in 1957 that they became permanently opaque and virtually unbreakable when they were heated. The new products were referred to as glass ceramics and they have replaced normal glass in many uses where transparency is unnecessary. A typical modern formulation contains silica, aluminium oxide, titanium oxide and lithium oxide but there is an almost endless number of possibilities to cover such uses as ovenware, electrical insulators, rocket nose-cones and space-vehicle tiles.

Soluble glass

A glass which dissolves slowly in water can be made by using phosphorus oxide instead of silicon dioxide. It might be possible to incorporate chemicals into pellets of such a glass and use them for slowly releasing the chemical into soil or a water supply.

PAPER

The word paper is derived from papyrus, a tall reed once very common in Egypt. It was used to make ropes and boats, and around 3000 BC for making a sort of paper by hammering together strips of its pith laid criss-cross on a flat surface; it was called papyrus. Tradition has it that something akin to modern paper was first made in China by Ts'ai Lun, a member of the Imperial court in Peking, in AD 105. He made it by steeping and crushing old rags and the bark of mulberry trees in water to get a porridge-like pulp. He then shook this into an even layer on a flat sieve and, after draining the water away, dried the resulting sheet. The process, which spread slowly into Europe, remains basically the same today though it uses different raw materials and has been automated.

Rags, augmented by a wide variety of other fibrous materials such as straw, continued as the main source of paper until the middle of the 19th century when methods of obtaining a satisfactory pulp from wood chippings were invented.

❛ Paper is more important than petrol. ❜

ANON

At first they were mashed with water mechanically. Then, a few years later, chemical processes which involved heating them with solutions of an alkali or a bisulphite took over. They are still in use today, but concern about the large number of trees being felled to meet the demand for paper has led to much increased recycling of waste paper.

The rise in literacy and the start of newspapers increased the demand for paper and led to the invention of new methods of manufacture. Nicholas-Louis Robert patented a machine in 1799 in France, and Bryan Donkin, a Bermondsey engineer, designed one in 1803 in England. His machine, which is still used, was called a Fourdrinier machine after the two English brothers, Henry and Sealey, who financed him. In outline, the wood pulp, with suitable additives, is fed on to a moving mesh belt and most of the water drains away. The sheet of flimsy, wet paper then goes through a series of rollers to remove more water. It then passes through heated cylinders to dry it, and finally through more heated rollers (calenders) to give it the required surface.

Writing paper has to be sized so that it is not porous like blotting paper. This is done by adding chemicals to the original pulp mixture or by spraying the surface of the paper. Fillers, such as china clay, have also to be added to make high-quality paper. Carbon paper, for copying, was invented in 1906 by an Englishman, R. Wedgewood; paper cups were first made in 1908; paper handkerchiefs in 1924; and paperback books in 1936.

Papier mâché articles are made by sticking pieces of paper together over a mould. When the glue has set, the shape is removed and painted. This method was first used by the Egyptians for making mummy cases.

The paper-clip, consisting of a double loop of springy wire, was invented by a Norwegian, Johann Vaaler, in 1900. For more sheets, a spring-loaded bulldog clip can be used, or a treasury tag, a short piece of cord with a tag at both ends, can be inserted through holes punched into a pile of papers.

POTTERS

> ❛Time's wheel runs back or stops: potter and clay endure.❜
>
> ROBERT BROWNING (1812–89), English poet

The art of making pots probably began in China – hence the term 'china' given to much domestic pottery – and was practised in the near East around 7000 BC. It involves shaping a pliable mixture of wet clay, followed by drying, firing and, if necessary, glazing. Because there are so many different types of clay, so many different additives that can be incorporated, and so many ways of firing, there are many final products which range from the humble plate to the heat shields in spacecraft. They are sometimes known, collectively, as ceramics.

THE BASIC PROCESS

Originally, shaping was done with fingers and thumbs; by coiling long 'ropes' of clay and then smoothing the surface; or by using moulds. Making round objects by manipulating the clay whilst it was being rotated (throwing) began about 3500 BC when the first primitive potter's wheel was invented. More modern methods include pressing between dies, working on a lathe, and extruding through holes or annular rings.

Firing was done at first in open fires but then, from around 5000 BC, in special ovens called kilns. The temperatures used nowadays vary between 500 and 2000°C and in a modern plant the firing is carried out continuously with the piece getting hotter and hotter as it passes through a kiln which may be 100 m (109 yd) long.

If the pottery is porous, it can be made waterproof by glazing. This involves coating the surface with a material which fuses into a hard, glass-like glaze when it is refired. Using salt is a cheap way of glazing, but mixtures of metallic oxides and silica give better coloured finishes which can be decorated in all sorts of ways by using different mixtures.

PORCELAIN

The earliest material, made from clay fired at about 500°C, was known as earthenware or, if red clay was used, terracotta. It was porous and had to be glazed if required for storing liquids. Later, around 1500 BC, the Chinese used a more sandy clay, which, when fired at about 1100°C, produced stoneware. This was harder than earthenware and non-porous.

Everything began to change during the 14th century with the arrival of porcelain from China. It had been made there since around AD 800, from a particularly pure form of clay known as kaolin or china clay to which feldspar had been added. This had to be fired at 1200 to 1400°C but it made a very hard and translucent form of pottery the like of which had never been seen in the West.

It triggered off a race to try to reproduce something of the same quality. Majolica, an earthenware coated with a white tin glaze, was made in Italy and, later, in Delft in Holland, but the first European porcelain was made in Meissen in Germany in about 1711. China clay had been discovered in those parts in 1698, and Johann Böttger found quite by accident how to use it to make porcelain. He was an alchemist still striving, like many before him, to convert base metals into gold. Whilst trying to make better crucibles in which to heat his magic mixtures he found that heating a mixture of china clay and quartz produced porcelain. The elector of Saxony, who had previously imprisoned Böttger for being an alchemist, made him a Baron and established the first porcelain factory in Europe. Others followed at Limoges and Sèvres, in France, and William Cookworthy, a Quaker pharmacist from Plymouth in England, discovered the local deposits of china clay in 1756 and set up a factory to manufacture porcelain.

During the 18th century, European porcelain came to rival that from China but it remained a luxury until it was brought into more general use, mainly by two Englishmen – Josiah Wedgwood (1730–95) and Josiah Spode (1754–1827). Wedgwood came from a Staffordshire family of potters and began his apprenticeship aged nine, after the death of his father. In 1754, he established his own pottery and set about trying to make cheap earthenware which could compete with porcelain. In 1763, he patented cream-coloured queen's-ware, and followed it with blue jasper-

A pair of Meissen Hausmaler plates, c. 1750

ware ornamented with clasical reliefs, and with black basalt ware. In 1769 he built a new factory, called Etruria, near Hanley, where he practised mass-production methods to make basic crockery for everyday use. His work was supplemented by Josiah Spode's invention of bone china in 1800. This was made from a mixture of china clay, feldspar and bone ash (which contains phosphates). The product looked not unlike porcelain but it was much cheaper and stronger. It became widely used, and was popularized by Spode's use of the willow pattern.

INDUSTRIAL CERAMICS

A whole new range of ceramic-like materials have been made in recent years from oxides of aluminium and zirconium, silicon carbide and nitride, and synthetic materials known as sialons, first made at the University of Newcastle upon Tyne in England in 1972. They are made by baking powders (sintering) in high-temperature kilns, under pressure if necessary, and are shaped by abrasives.

The materials are extremely hard, resistant to corrosion and highly refractory, and many of them have exceptional electrical, magnetic and optical properties. They are used in making cutting tools, bearings, false teeth, hip-replacement joints, furnace linings, heat-shields for spacecraft (to withstand the high temperatures reached on re-entering the Earth's atmosphere), optical fibres, electrical insulators, recording heads, turbine blades (to enable an engine to run at a higher temperature), rocket jets and superconductors (⇒p. 81).

Cermets are composite materials containing a hard ceramic with a metal such as cobalt. They are easier to manufacture than an ordinary ceramic but have similar properties and uses. They are particularly valuable in making cutting tools.

PAINTS

Paints have long been used for decoration (some cave paintings are 15,000 years old) and, much more recently, to protect surfaces. At first, naturally occurring coloured substances such as ochres, siennas and umbers were used, and they were mixed with water, egg-white, egg-yolk gums or hot waxes so that they could be applied easily. Nowadays, the solid colour is known as the pigment; the liquid as the medium or vehicle.

In the 15th century, Dutch painters, particularly Jan van Eyck, began to use linseed oil as the vehicle, and paints came to be classified as oil-based or water-based.

Until the 1950s, oil-paints used mainly linseed or tung oils, which 'dried' because the oil reacted with oxygen in the air and then polymerized to form a hard, slightly flexible film. Water-based paints were exemplified by whitewash, a suspension of slaked lime in water, which 'dried' by the evaporation of the water.

Other paints called distempers were developed from that simple formula by incorporating coloured substances and binders, such as glue or water glass, to give better adhesion. They were used in scene-painting and internal wall decoration.

The composition of paints changed in the 1950s when the oils in oil-paints were largely replaced by alkyd resins (⇒p. 35), and the distempers gave way to latex or emulsion paints in which polymers, such as polyvinyl acetate or acrylic resins (⇒p. 34) were suspended in water. Non-drip paints were also an important addition to the range. They contain a polymer formed from alkyd resins and polyamides which is thixotropic. That is, it is normally gel-like, with a high viscosity, but flows, with a lower viscosity, under the pressure of a brush.

Varnishes and lacquers are solutions of natural resins, such as shellac or copal, or synthetic plastics, such as polyurethane and cellulose nitrates, in a solvent.

DYES

The first dyes to be used were all naturally occurring substances such as alizarin (from madder), indigo (from woad) and Tyrian purple (from a sea-snail), but William Henry Perkin (1838–1907) changed that when he made the first synthetic dye in 1856. It was an accidental discovery made at the age of 18 when he was an assistant at the Royal College of Chemistry in London. Whilst trying to make the white solid, quinine, he ended up with a blackish mess, from which he extracted a purple substance.

When he found that it would dye silk very successfully, he patented his product, persuaded his father and brother to back him, and began to manufacture the dye. It was the start of a new industry, and the dye, known as mauve, was widely used. Queen Victoria wore a dress dyed with it and the penny purple postage stamps issued in 1881 owe their colour to it.

Many more dyes followed. In 1859, Peter Griess, a German chemist working in a brewery at Burton-on-Trent in England, invented a process for making new azo dyes from aniline. In 1869, Perkin synthesized alizarin, the natural dye of the madder plant, and, in 1880, synthetic indigo was made by Adolf von Baeyer, professor of chemistry at Munich University. And so it went on, with many of the growers of the natural products being ruined in the process.

BUILDING MATERIALS

Bricks were in use at least 8000 years ago. They were made at first by hand moulding mud or clay and letting the ovoid shape dry out in the sun. Soon after, they were shaped in rectangular moulds before sun-drying, but by 3500 BC they were being fired in a kiln, which made them stronger. Chopped straw was sometimes added to bind them together - Hence the comment about building bricks without straw: see Exodus 5.

These early bricks were used only in important buildings and did not come into common usage until the Industrial Revolution when manual processes were replaced by automation. At the same time, special clays began to be used. Breeze-blocks were first made in Britain during the 1930s from furnace ashes (breeze) and cement. They are cheaper, lighter and weaker than clay bricks but satisfactory for internal walling.

MORTAR AND PLASTER

Mud, clay and bitumen were used for bonding bricks or stones together until the Romans introduced a mortar consisting of lime (obtained by heating limestone), sand and water, which hardens on drying. It was used for many years until replaced by a mix containing cement, sand and water.

Mortars can also be used for surfacing walls but plaster of Paris is usually preferred. It is made by driving some of the water off from naturally occurring gypsum and is applied as a stiff, watery paste, by hand, or by nailing preformed plasterboards in position.

CEMENT AND CONCRETE

The first cement was made in Italy by mixing a naturally occurring volcanic ash, known as pozzuolana, with lime. The mixture set into something much harder and stronger than mortar. When mixed with sand and broken stones, the cement formed an early sort of concrete which set under water, and which was used by the Romans in many of their fine buildings.

The use of concrete declined after the fall of the Roman Empire but it was resurrected by an English civil engineer, John Smeaton, for building the fourth Eddystone Lighthouse off the south west coast of England between 1756 and 1759. He made his cement by heating clay-containing limestone rock which occurs quite widely. Others made similar products but in 1824 Joseph Aspdin, an English bricklayer, patented a process for making cement by heating a powdered

> *Our national flower is the concrete clover leaf.*
>
> LEWIS MUMFORD (1895–1990), American author

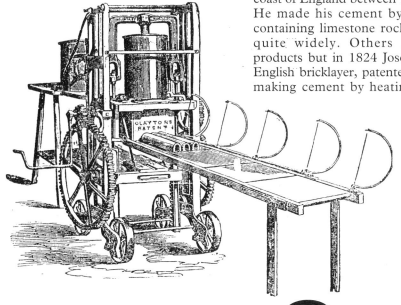

Clayton's tile-, brick- and pipe-making machine, patented in 1858

Concrete in the modern world – the New York waterfront

mixture of pure limestone or chalk with selected clays. It was called Portland cement because it resembled natural stone found on the Isle of Portland, England, when it set. Today, it is made by passing a slurry of the powdered mixture and water down a slanting and rotating cylinder, fitted with baffles, up which flames are passing. The resulting cement is then finely powdered in a ball-mill which consists of a horizontal, cylindrical container which can be rotated and which contains steel balls.

Concrete is normally used in conjunction with embedded steel rods or frameworks, as reinforced concrete. Pre-stressed concrete is also common. It is made by allowing concrete to set in a mould containing tightly stretched steel wires. When it is set, the tension in the wires is released and this compresses the concrete. The product can be made in a variety of shapes and is both strong and springy. It is the use of concrete and steel together which has made so many modern construction projects possible.

EXPLOSIVES

> *❝The invention of gunpowder hath quite altered the condition of Martial Affairs over the world, both by sea and land.❞*
>
> ROBERT BOYLE (1627–91), Irish chemist

Most people associate explosives with the death and destruction of warfare, but they are also used in making fireworks and in civil engineering, quarrying, mining, and shooting for sport. They have provided the world's most powerful source of portable energy for almost a millennium, and played an immense role in shaping history.

GUNPOWDER

Gunpowder, which looks rather like soot, contains about 75 per cent potassium nitrate, 10 per cent sulphur and 15 per cent wood charcoal. It was probably first made in China in the middle of the 9th century and was introduced to the western world through an English philosopher, Roger Bacon, in the 13th century. He was a clever Franciscan monk with a talent not far short of that of Leonardo (⇒p. 7); so much so that he gained the title of Doctor Mirabilis.

Gunpowder was the only practical explosive available for more than 500 years and, over that time, it had a revolutionary impact. It was used in fireworks, in early military rockets, as a propellant in guns, for blasting in mines, and for filling bombs and shells until replaced, for most purposes, around 1875. It was also the early base, in many countries, from which their wider chemical industries grew. The vast du Pont organization, for example, began as a gunpowder manufacturing company set up in Wilmington, Delaware, USA, by Eleuthère Irénée du Pont de Nemours in 1802, two years after he had emigrated from France.

NITROCELLULOSE AND NITROGLYCERINE

Nitrocellulose, a white fibrous solid, was first made in 1845 by C.F. Schönbein, a German professor at the University of Basle in Switzerland. Two years later, Ascanio Sobrero, professor of applied chemistry at Turin University in Italy, made nitroglycerine, a yellow, oily liquid. They are both explosive, but too unpredictable for safe use in their pure forms.

Nitrocellulose, under the name of gun-cotton, only became reliably useful when Sir Frederick Abel, the chief chemist to the British War Office, patented a modified form in 1865. Nitroglycerine was tamed by Alfred Nobel in 1867 by mixing three parts of it with one part of a naturally occurring, porous substance called kieselguhr; the resulting product was called dynamite. In 1875, Nobel made blasting gelatine by blending 7 to 8 per cent of nitrocellulose with nitroglycerine, and gelignite by incorporating potassium nitrate and wood-pulp into that mixture.

These new explosives soon began to replace gunpowder for blasting, but it remained as a propellant, even though it was very smoky, because both gun-cotton and dynamite were too powerful for that purpose. It was, however, a great improvement when gunpowder was replaced by a smokeless powder invented by a French professor of chemistry, Paul Vielle, in 1886. It was white and was called Poudre B (blanche) to distinguish it from gunpowder, known in France as Poudre N (noir). Similar alternatives, containing nitrocellulose and nitroglycerine, were made by Nobel in 1888 (ballistite); Abel in 1889 (cordite); and an American explosives expert, Charles E. Munroe, in 1891 (indurite).

MODERN EXPLOSIVES

Trinitrotoluene (TNT), first made in 1863 by a German chemist, J. Wilbrand, was adopted as a shell-filling in his country in 1902 and in 1914 by Britain. It is a yellow solid which is very safe to store and use, and which can be easily melted for pouring into shells and bombs. During World War II it was supplemented by pentaerythritol-tetranitrate (PETN), first made in Germany in 1894, and by RDX, which contains cyclotrimethylenetrinitramine in a plastic form. Semtex is a modern version of it.

In the 1950s, ANFOs were developed for civilian use, particularly in the USA. Made up of a mixture of around 94 per cent *a*mmonium *n*itrate and 6 per cent *f*uel *o*ils, they are not unlike a gunpowder mixture with the potassium nitrate replaced by ammonium nitrate and the sulphur and carbon by fuel oils. They can be delivered ready mixed or for mixing on site. They are also made into slurries or water-gels by mixing with water and thickening agents to which TNT or PETN can be added.

❛...it is a misfortune to make a discovery which has a practical importance; it disturbs your peace of mind to the utmost.❜

C. F. SCHÖNBEIN
(1799–1868), who first
made gun-cotton

Paper or polyethylene case protected by water-resistant varnish

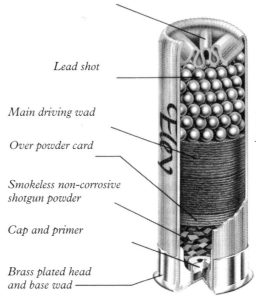

Lead shot

Main driving wad

Over powder card

Smokeless non-corrosive shotgun powder

Cap and primer

Brass plated head and base wad

Inside an Eley Grand Prix shot gun cartridge for game shooting

ALFRED NOBEL
(1833–96)

An early cartridge of Nobel's dynamite

ALFRED NOBEL was born in Stockholm but was educated in Russia where his father, Immanuel, had gone to find work after an early bankruptcy in Sweden. The family flourished when a mine, invented by Immanuel, was adopted by the Russians during the Crimean War, but a second bankruptcy at the end of the war drove most of them back to Stockholm where Alfred and his father set up a small laboratory in 1859.

The enterprise was almost ruined by a disastrous explosion in 1864 which wrecked the laboratory, killed five people including the Nobels' youngest son, and maimed Immanuel for life. One of Alfred's brothers advised him to 'abandon the damned career of an inventor, which merely brings disaster in its train'. But Alfred was no quitter. Making nitroglycerine within the city of Stockholm was banned, but he began

again in the middle of a lake outside the city boundaries. In 1867, he invented dynamite; in 1888, gelignite; and in 1888 ballistite.

Nobel was not only a great inventor, but a tireless worker and a brilliant salesman and organizer. He founded the British Dynamite Co. Ltd in 1871, and began to make explosives at Ardeer, in Scotland. The factory is now part of Imperial Chemical Industries. When he died, aged 63, he had 93 factories throughout the world and 123 British patents to his name. He left about £2 million sterling, which was used to found the famous Nobel Prizes.

His success was almost matched by that of his two surviving brothers, Robert and Ludvig, out of an original family of eight. They had stayed behind in Russia in 1859 and came to play a major part in the establishment of the oil industry in the Baku region.

DETONATORS AND FUSES

Gunpowder could be ignited by a flame or a spark, but that would not suffice for gun-cotton or dynamite, and Nobel pioneered the use of detonators. His first, patented in 1864, for detonating nitroglycerine, consisted of gunpowder packed into a small glass or wood tube. Later, he replaced the gunpowder by mercury fulminate, and, today, a mixture of lead azide and lead styphnate is most common.

The mixture is contained in an aluminium tube, about $1\frac{1}{2}$ in (38 mm) long and $\frac{1}{4}$ in (6 mm) diameter, closed at

one end. A length of safety fuse which burns at a steady rate is inserted into the open end. It was invented in 1831 by an English leather salesman, William Bickford, and consists of a thin trail of gunpowder passing through the centre of a thin rope.

Alternatively, an electric detonator is fired by passing a current through a fine wire embedded in the mixture in the detonator.

Detonating fuse, for example Cordtex and Nonel, used for connecting charges so that they can be exploded simultaneously, contains a trail of PETN or RDX within an outer covering.

FUELS

COAL

For many years, wood was the main solid fuel for heating and cooking but, in most parts of the world, there are now better uses for it and it has been largely replaced by coal.

Historians can trace its use as a fuel back to 370 BC but it only began to be

used efficiently towards the end of the 18th century when an American, Benjamin Thompson, later Count Rumford, invented improved grates, and chimneys and cookers in which to burn it.

The safety lamp
Deep mining of coal has long been a dirty and dangerous occupation. The danger

was caused by methane gas seeping from the coal and forming an explosive mixture with air (fire-damp) which could be ignited by a spark. After an appalling number of disasters, in 1815 miners in the north of England sought help from Sir Humphry Davy, and within three months he had invented his safety lamp. The trick was to surround the light from an oil lamp by a cylinder of fine wire gauze. The metal gauze spread out the heat from the light inside so that the surface of the lamp never reached a temperature high enough to explode fire-damp. Mr Buddle, the mine manager who had originally explained the requirement to Davy and had tested his first lamp, commented that 'we have subdued the monster'. Davy refused to patent his invention. He wrote: 'I have never received so much pleasure from the result of any of my chemical labours; I trust the cause of humanity will gain something by it.'

Early miner's safety lamps

Heating coal

When the the Revd John Clayton heated coal in a retort in 1685 he reported that 'at first there came over only Phlegm, afterwards a black Oil, and then likewise a Spirit arose, which I could noway condense'. The Phlegm is now recognized as ammoniacal liquor, the Oil as coal tar, and the Spirit as coal gas. The grey-black solid remaining in the retort was coke.

All four materials came into prominence during the 19th century. Coke replaced charcoal for smelting; ammoniacal liquor and coal tar were used for making a wide variety of chemicals; and coal gas came to be used, first for lighting and then for heating and cooking. The coal was heated in two ways. In a coke-oven, the conditions chosen for heating it were designed to give the best quality coke; coal gas was a by-product. At a gas works, the main aim was to produce good quality coal gas, and the coke was the by-product.

Smokeless fuels

It has been recognized for a long time that burning coal in an open grate is both wasteful and causes pollution. Wasteful because the products that can be obtained by heating it are destroyed, and causing pollution because of the smoke and harmful gases which escape up the chimney into the atmosphere. An Englishman, T. Parker, took out a patent in 1890 for a process in which coal was heated to about 500°C instead of the 1200°C used in coke ovens and gas works. This allowed many of the useful products to be collected but still left a good solid fuel. It became known as a smokeless fuel; Coalite, based on Parker's patent, is a typical example.

COAL GAS

The inflammable gas given off when coal is heated was used for lighting the offices of Lord Lonsdale's coal mine near Whitehaven in England in 1765, and William Murdock, a Cornish engineer and inventor, used it to light his own house in 1792. James Watt and Matthew Boulton found out about this when they employed him to install their steam engines in Cornish mines, and as a result they invited him to fit gas into their factory in Soho in 1802. This was so successful that by 1804 they were selling complete gas-lighting installations, and street lighting was in use in London by 1809. By 1812, 52 English towns had gas works; by 1850, there were nearly 1000.

❛No man ever had genius who did not aim to execute more than he was able.❜

SIR HUMPHRY DAVY (1778–1829), English chemist

The rise of gas in private houses was, nevertheless, slow. The gas burnt with a luminous flame, like that of a candle, but it was smoky and smelly; the hole at which it burnt kept getting blocked up; prospective users were suspicious of it because they knew it was both explosive and poisonous; and it had to be piped to any user. So, until about 1840, candles, or oil lamps using vegetable or animal oils, were the main source of light in most homes.

The uses of lamps, candles and coal gas were all boosted by inventions between 1850 and 1860. In 1854, a Canadian, Dr Abraham Gesner, patented a process for making what he called kerosene by heating naturally occurring asphalt, and between 1847 and 1850 in Scotland James Young had made a similar liquid, which he called paraffin, by heating oily shales. Both liquids, which came to be known as mineral oils, provided a better and cheaper fuel for oil lamps than the vegetable and animal oils already in use. They could also be used in heating stoves. From 1859, better supplies of kerosene (paraffin) were obtained from crude oil (see below) and this also provided paraffin wax which made better candles than the existing animal and vegetable products, such as tallow.

In 1855 Robert Bunsen, a distinguished German chemist, invented the Bunsen burner in which coal gas was passed through a fine jet and across an air hole through which it could suck in air. Subsequent burning of the mixture of gas and air gave a hotter, non-luminous flame which was not smoky. It could be used for heating, so that coal gas cookers and fires became possible for the first time. Gas lighting was given a prolonged life by the invention of the gas mantle in 1885 by an Austrian, Carl Auer, later Baron von Welsbach. The mantle consisted of a loosely woven silk or cotton thimble, which became incandescent when fitted over a hot, non-luminous flame because it was impregnated with thorium oxide together with a little cerium oxide. It provided a much more efficient source of light than the previous luminous flame.

Oil lamps, candles and coal gas were all used for lighting until well into the 19th century before they were finally replaced, in advanced countries, by electricity. Kerosene (paraffin) and gas are both still widely used, alongside electricity, for heating and in the case of gas for cooking. But in Britain it is now town gas – a mixture of natural (North Sea) gas with smaller amounts of coal gas originating from coke ovens. The older gas works and the associated gasometers or gas holders which dominated many areas until well into the 19th century have gone.

CRUDE OIL

This black, sticky liquid is found in many parts of the world trapped in pockets of porous rocks. In some places, as around the Persian Gulf, it seeps to the surface. Such seepage occurs at Oil Creek in Pennsylvania, and it was there in 1859 that 'Colonel' Edwin L. Drake struck oil when he drilled a well down to 69 ft (21 m). He was an unemployed railroad conductor, backed by a group of investors, and the 'Colonel' title was invented to impress the local people.

Drilling

Edwin Drake drilled his well by an old method first used in China for obtaining underground brine. An iron bar hanging from a cable was wrapped around a capstan at the top of a wooden derrick which was turned by a steam engine. The iron bar was repeatedly raised and then allowed to fall to hack out the hole.

The modern method of rotary drilling was patented in 1884 by an Englishman, Robert Beart. In its modern form, a drilling bit is fitted at the end of a hollow steel pipe which is rotated from within a derrick. Drilling mud is pumped down the pipe to cool the bit, to carry debris up the hole, to line it, and to prevent the rapid escape of gas or oil when it is first struck. As the hole gets deeper, further lengths of pipe are screwed on at the top as necessary.

There have been many improvements in this basic technique. Sharper and tougher drill bits are now available; the direction of drilling can be changed by inserting a wedge or a whipstock into the hole; the first underwater wells were drilled, from piers, around 1900; and

The first oil well, drilled by Edwin L. Drake in Pennsylvania in 1859. Within a year there were over 70 wells in the region yielding 1200 barrels of oil a day

deep-sea drilling from floating rigs, begun in the Gulf of Mexico just after the end of World War II, is now commonplace.

Refining

Crude oil is of little use in its raw state but it can be separated into its component parts (refined) by making use of the fact that they all have different boiling points. The crude oil is heated to about 400°C and the resulting mixture of liquids and vapours is passed into the bottom of a fractionating tower which is divided into a number of compartments by trays. They contain holes which are covered by what are known as a 'bubble-caps' and overflow pipes. The temperature within the tower falls from about 400°C at the bottom to about 40°C at the top. Each tray is kept at a different temperature, so that different liquids (fractions) condense in them and can be tapped off periodically. The separation is assisted by the upwards flow of vapours, and the downwards flow of liquids, in the tower.

The main products are fuel gases, petrol or gasoline, kerosene or paraffin oil, diesel oil, lubricating oils, paraffin wax and bitumen. Originally, it was the kerosene (paraffin) and the paraffin wax which mattered because they were needed for oil lamps, heating stoves and candles. At that time, the gasoline was burnt to get rid of it!

To meet today's different requirements, the fractions collected from the fractionating tower undergo different treatments. The most important is known as cracking which involves breaking down the large molecules in fuel oils into the smaller molecules in petrol. It was originally done by heating to a high temperature under pressure (thermal cracking), but the more common process nowadays uses a catalyst (catalytic cracking). Other processes – alkylation, reforming, polymerization, reforming and isomerization – are also used. Many of them produce by-products which are themselves useful as fuels, for example Calor gas (from the Latin, *calor* = heat), or for making many other chemicals.

FRACTIONAL DISTILLATION

The operation of a fractionating tower in which crude oil is separated into its useful components (fractions), each with different boiling points

DETERGENTS

Soap, which has been known for some 5000 years, is the traditional example of a detergent (cleansing agent).

In the past, it was made by heating animal oils or fats with the ashes from burnt wood or seaweed which are now known to contain the mild alkalis, potassium or sodium carbonate. Today it is made from stronger alkalis – sodium or potassium hydroxide – and fats and oils such as tallow, coconut oil, palm oil, whale oil and olive oil. Glycerine is a valuable by-product.

Water, by itself, is a very limited cleansing agent because it contains polar molecules which will not mix with the non-polar molecules in oils or greases. It therefore runs off them, just as it does off the oily feathers on a duck's back, without washing them away. Added soap acts as a go-between, bringing the water and the oils and greases together in an emulsion which can be washed away. It can do this because its long-chain

❝*Cleanliness is, indeed, next to godliness.*❞

JOHN WESLEY (1703–91), founder of Methodism

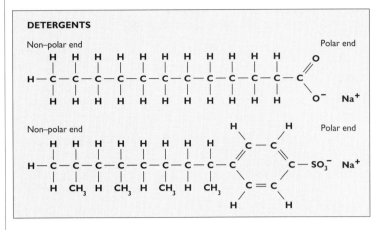

DETERGENTS

Non–polar end   Polar end

Non–polar end   Polar end

Soap molecule – sodium laurate (top) and a detergent molecule – an alkylbenzene sulphonate (bottom)

molecules are polar at one end and non-polar at the other. The polar end 'attracts' water whilst the non-polar end 'attracts' oils and greases.

Soap, however, is not entirely satisfactory, particularly when used in hard or acidic water, and it has been replaced to some extent by synthetic detergents which like soap have molecules with one polar and one non-polar end. Detergents are usually more soluble in water than soap is; they do not form a scum with hard water; they enable water to spread and penetrate more fully over or through a fabric being washed; and they can generally be used equally well under acidic or alkaline conditions. They are also generally made from petrochemicals, and this solved the problem of how to cope with an impending shortage of naturally occurring oils and fats which first became apparent around 1900. Development work was started then but synthetic detergents only came to the fore after the end of World War II, during which soap

had been rationed in both Germany and Britain.

The manufacture in 1942 of Teepol by a subsidiary of the Shell Oil Company, from an unwanted by-product of oil refining, was an important turning point. It opened the door to thousands of substances which have been made, patented and marketed ever since. At first, the new detergents were not broken up by bacteria, as soap was, and they caused serious pollution in rivers. That problem was overcome by adapting the shape of the detergent molecules; these modern products are said to be biodegradable.

They are generally made in powder form by mixing the ingredients into a slurry and pumping a spray of it into the top of a tower up which hot air is passed. The slurry contains not only the detergent but many additives: sodium perborate acts as a mild bleach; sodium silicate prevents the powder from sticking together in lumps; phosphates act as water softeners and help to disperse dirt; fluorescent materials, a replacement for the old-fashioned dolly-blue, act as whiteners; and enzymes remove biological stains by reacting with the proteins concerned.

Not all products are new. Persil, first marketed in 1907, owes its name to the addition of sodium *per*borate and sodium *sil*icate, and the addition of enzymes was first patented in 1913. By now, however, they have become commonplace and the manufacture of synthetic detergents outstrips that of soap. A select few have become household names.

PLASTICS

The cellulose molecule is made up of thousands of cyclic ($C_6H_{10}O_5$) units linked together in a long chain. Two such units are shown here

The term plastic, coined in about 1930, covers a wide field of natural and synthetic materials which can be moulded into shape. They are generally

carbon compounds with very large molecules (macromolecules) made up of recurring smaller molecules. They are known as polymers (Greek: *poly* = many, *meros* = parts) and they are marketed under a bewildering array of trade names.

CELLULOSE PRODUCTS

Cellulose is the commonest naturally occurring polymer. It is the main constituent of cotton, flax, hemp and jute,

STRUCTURE OF CELLULOSE

and also occurs, together with lignins and resins, in wood. Its molecule is made up of thousands of ß-glucose units.

In 1890 Frenchman Louis Despeissis found that cellulose would dissolve in a solution of copper sulphate and ammonia, and in 1892 two Englishmen, E.J. Bevan and C.F. Cross, also found that it could be dissolved by a mixture of carbon disulphide and sodium hydroxide. Cellulose fibres could be formed from these solutions by forcing them through a spinneret, a disc with fine holes in it. These were the first examples of what came to be known as artifical silks or rayons. The French process was called the cuprammonium process; the English, the viscose process. The latter could also be used to make sheets of Cellophane by extruding the solution through a narrow slit.

Cellulose acetate
Cellulose will react with acetic anhydride to form cellulose acetate, which will dissolve in propanone. The solution can be passed through a spinneret into hot air to make fibres, for example Celanese, used in varnishes or lacquers, or extruded through a slit into sheets or films. The process was pioneered by two Swiss brothers, Henri and Camille Dreyfus, during and after World War I. Their first use of the acetate solution was for covering the fabric of aircraft wings during the war.

Cellulose nitrate
Cellulose reacts with a mixture of nitric and sulphuric acids under different conditions, to form a number of different cellulose nitrates, commonly, but wrongly, called nitrocelluloses. Those containing around 11 per cent nitrogen will dissolve in mixtures of ether and alcohol, and the solution can be used to make fibres of artificial silk or rayon by using a spinneret. The process was originated by a French chemist, the Comte Hilaire de Chardonnet, in 1884, and started commercially in 1891.

Alexander Parkes, an English chemist, also found in 1862 that the nitrate could be converted into an ivory-like substance, which he called Parkesine, by treating it with camphor. The material could be worked into any shape whilst it was hot,

but Parkes could not exploit it successfully – that was left to J.W. Hyatt in the USA. He was a successful inventor and called the new material celluloid. Hyatt used it for making billiard balls, table tennis balls and spectacle frames. Later, it was used in photographic film. Celluloid is now classified as a thermoplastic because it can be repeatedly softened by heating and hardened by cooling.

THERMOPLASTICS

Polyethene
Polyethene (PE), known in Britain under the trade name Polythene, is a milky-white, waxy solid which was made in 1933 by R.O. Gibson and E.W. Fawcett in the research laboratories of Imperial Chemical Industries in England. They were heating ethene gas at about 200°C under a pressure of about 1000 atmospheres when they discovered that the small ethene molecule, C_2H_4, linked with itself into a long-chain polymer. It is now known that it can do this because the molecule contains a double bond which can open up. It is rather like adjacent pairs of identical twins holding hands; when they let go they can all link up together in a long chain. Ethene is called the monomer, and the polymer it forms is called polyethene. The process by which it forms is called addition polymerization.

The invention of polyethene was very timely because when production began in 1939 it met the urgent need for an electrical insulator in radar (⇒p. 149) equipment. Later it was used for making tubes, pipes, sheeting, bottles, kitchenware and toys.

6 But only God can make a tree. 9

JOYCE KILMER
(1888–1918),
English poet

Many molecules of ethene link together to form one giant molecule of polyethene

ADDITION POLYMERIZATION

Other examples

Many other molecules with double bonds can undergo addition polymerization to give a wide variety of useful products. Polyvinyl chloride is used in packaging film, electrical fittings, window frames and bottles. Polymethylmethacrylate, under a number of trade names such as Perspex, Plexiglas, Lucite and Oroglas as an unbreakable substitute for glass. Polystyrene in foam packing, seed trays and building insulation. Polytetrafluoroethene in surface coatings for bearings and non-stick pans; Fluon and Teflon are typical trade names. Polypropene in food packaging, bottle crates and domestic appliances. Polyacrylonitryl in fabrics such as Orlon or in making carbon fibre (⇒p. 38). Polyvinyl acetate is used in paints and adhesives.

Two or more different monomers may also link together to form co-polymers. Typical examples are Buna S, a synthetic rubber made from butadiene and styrene; and ABS, made from acrylonitrile, butadiene and styrene, and used in computer and telephone casings.

An international squash tournament, held in May 1996, is played in a court made of transparent Perspex at the foot of the Gaza Pyramid in Egypt

Ziegler catalysts

In 1953 German Karl Ziegler found that it was possible to make polyethene at about 60°C and five atmospheres pressure if what came to be known as a Ziegler catalyst was present. His product, called high-density polyethene (HDPE), was stronger, less elastic, and had a higher softening temperature than the older variety (low-density polyethene (LDPE)). This use of catalysts for polymerization was developed by an Italian, Giulio Natta, and the two workers shared the Nobel Prize for Chemistry in 1963.

THERMOSETTING PLASTICS

Thermosetting plastics can be moulded into shape when hot but not resoftened once they have cooled. This is because extensive cross-linking builds up between the molecules during the hot moulding.

Bakelite

This was patented in 1909 by Dr Leo Baekeland, a Belgian living in the USA. He made it from a reaction between

phenol and formaldehyde (methanal). It was a powder which could be moulded into shape when hot. Because it was a good insulator and was not affected by heat or oil, it found immediate use in making the electrical equipment which was being fitted into cars.

Baekeland was a distinguished inventor with over 100 patents to his name, but he is lucky to be referred to as 'the father of the plastics industry' because he only patented his invention one day before an Englishman, James Swinburne, submitted a rival application.

Thermosetting plastics, similar to Bakelite, can be made from formaldehyde (methanal) and either carbamide (urea) or melamine. Melaware, Beetle and Formica are typical. They are stronger than Bakelite and can also be made in a wider range of colours. Formaldehyde also forms hard, horn-like plastics with casein, obtained from cow's milk, known as casein. The process was first patented in Germany in 1899 and the material known as a casein plastic, is used in buttons and buckles.

Other examples

Alkyd resins are made from dicarboxylic acids, which have two — COOH groups in their molecules, and diols or triols, with two or three — OH groups. Their name derives from *al*cohol-ac*id* and they are widely used in 'oil' paints. Polyurethanes were first made from diisocyanates and diols or triols by a German, Otto Bayer, in 1937. From the 1950s they have been used in floor finishings and hard-wearing paints, and, in the form of a foam, for making pillows, packaging and insulating materials. Epoxy resins, first made in 1946 from epichlorohydrin and bisphenols, are used in making adhesives, surface coatings and laminates. Polycarbonates, made from carbonyl chloride and phenols, are stronger than polymethylmethacrylate (⇒p. 34) and have a higher melting point. They are used in making car windows, bulletproof shields and compact discs.

SYNTHETIC FIBRES

The first artificial fibres made from cellulose have been supplemented in recent years by many completely synthetic products.

Nylon

Nylon is one of a number of polyamides which can be made from dicarboxylic acids with — COOH groups at each end of their molecules and diamine with —NH$_2$ groups at their ends. The two substances can react to form long-chain molecules, held together by — CO —NH — bonds, because each — COOH group can link to each — NH$_2$ group with the elimination of a water, H$_2$O, molecule. The process is known as condensation polymerization.

Nylon 66, the commonest form of nylon, is a white, horny material which is relatively cheap, very resistant to rotting, and combines great tensile strength with low density. It can be converted into fibres by pressing through fine holes when molten. The threads are then stengthened by stretching (cold-drawing). It was invented by an American, W.H. Carothers, who began his working life as a university teacher before joining the American du Pont company. Whilst there, he invented nylon 66 in 1935 as well as the synthetic rubber, neoprene (⇒p. 36). In spite of this success, he suffered from depression because he thought he had not achieved much, and he committed suicide in 1937 at the age of 41. Nylon was first manufactured in the USA in 1939 and within the first year about 64 million pairs of nylon stockings were sold. The fibres are also used for making bristles, surgical sutures and fishing nets. Today, less nylon is used for making fabrics but it has become popular for hinges, bearings and gear wheels.

Polyamides similar to nylon, known as Kevlars, were developed by the du Pont company in the late 1960s. They contain aromatic, carbon-ring groups between

Molecules of hexanedioic acid and hexane-1,6-diamine link together with the elimination of water, H$_2$O, molecules to form nylon

> ❝ *The synthetic polyamide stockings cling properly and do not become baggy.* ❞

from W. H. CAROTHERS's original patent, 1937

the — CO — NH — links and make strong, stiff fibres with a low density.

Polyethene terephthalate (PET)

This is made from terephthalic acid, whch has — COOH groups at each end of its molecule, and glycol which has —OH groups at its ends. As with nylon, the two react together with the elimination of water to form long-chain molecules. The plastic, first made by two English chemists, J.R. Whinfield and J.T. Dickson in 1940, is particularly strong and resistant to attack by moisture or insects. It is used under the trade names of Terylene and Dacron, for making tent or tarpaulin fabrics, sails, ropes and clothing.

RUBBER

Rubber is obtained from the milky juice, latex, which can be tapped off from tropical trees of the species *Hevea*. It has been known for many years but it was not, at first, very useful because it became sticky in hot weather and brittle in cold. A Scot, Charles Macintosh, was one of the first to try and exploit it, and in 1923 he patented a method of applying it to fabric to make waterproof clothing which eventually came to be called 'mackintoshes'.

It was a good idea but only became really successful following Charles Goodyear's invention in the USA in 1844 of the process of vulcanization. He had failed as an iron-maker but after ten years of research, dogged by poverty and ridicule, he found that rubber became more elastic, tougher, and usable over a wider range of temperature if about 2 per cent of sulphur was incorporated. Adding about 30 per cent made a black, brittle product called Ebonite or Vulcanite.

It was imagination which gave us wings.

Otto Bayer
(1902–82),
German chemist

It is now known that rubber is a natural polymer made up of isoprene C_3H_8 monomers. Incorporation of small amounts of sulphur introduces some degree of cross-linking.

Synthetic rubber

Because the isoprene molecule contains two double bonds it can undergo addition polymerization ($\Rightarrow$p. 33), using a Ziegler catalyst, to give a synthetic product very much like natural rubber. Cheaper materials can be made, however, using other monomers. Neoprene, first made by the American W.H. Carothers, is made from chloroprene; buna rubbers are made from butadiene or butadiene and styrene. For some purposes synthetic rubbers are better than the natural product.

SILICONES

These are polymers based on a framework of silicon and oxygen atoms. Their manufacture and use was pioneered by the Corning Glass Works, the Dow Chemical Co. and the General Electric Co. in the USA in the 1940s. They were first made in Britain in 1954.

They are made in the form of fluids, rubbers and resins. The fluids are oily liquids used as lubricants, hydraulic fluids, non-stick agents and water repellants; they can be converted into greases by adding soaps. The rubbers maintain their elasticity over a wider temperature range than ordinary rubber. They are used in oven door seals, in cable insulation, and in medical components and spare parts; bouncing putty is a novelty form. The resins are used as water repellants and release agents.

ADHESIVES

Most substances that are tacky and can be spread can function as adhesives. When applied to two surfaces, which are then pressed together, they dry out and bond the surfaces together. Many different substances have been used over the past 5000 years. At first, adhesives were made from plant or animal products such as starch from flour, resins and gums from trees, casein from milk, egg-white and blood. A large number of gelatine glues could also be made by boiling hoofs, hides, bones and horns. They were used either in their pure state or in solution in a solvent, commonly water. When spread thinly over two surfaces to be bonded they slowly dried out, or the solvent evaporated. A variety of glues was required because different surfaces needed different products to stick them together effectively.

Since the 1930s, however, synthetic adhesives involving plastics have largely taken over. Materials such as cellulose nitrate, polyvinyl acetate, synthetic rubbers, polystyrene and urea-formaldehyde resins are used in solutions or emulsions.

Other plastics are used in what are known as reaction adhesives. A two-part glue, such as Araldite, is made from two components which are mixed just prior to use. One component may be an epoxy resin with the other a catalyst to harden it. In a superglue, a cyanoacrylate is prevented from polymerizing by the addition of an acid stabilizer. It will only harden when it comes into contact with moisture in the air or on the surface to be bonded. Other glues harden on heating.

It is an indication of the greatly improved quality of these glues that they were used in the 1940s for sticking plywood together in the 7781 Mosquito aeroplanes made by the de Havilland company, and that they are still used today for bonding aeroplane components made of aluminium alloys.

❛Carbon is the joker in the pack of chemical elements. ❜

ANON

ABRASIVES

Abrasives are hard substances used for removing unwanted material by scratching it away. Their comparative hardness is measured against ten standard minerals on Mohs' scale, invented by Friedrich Mohs, a German mineralogist.

In use the chosen minerals are 1. talc: 2. gypsum: 3. calcite: 4. fluorite: 5, apatite: 6. orthoclase: 7. quartz: 8. topaz: 9. corundum: 10. diamond.

For example, an abrasive with a hardness of 8 will scratch quartz but be scratched by corundum.

The chosen abrasive is crushed into a powder which is then seived to obtain the required particle size. It is then glued on to paper or cloth, or mixed with a binding agent and compressed into blocks or wheels.

Mild abrasives, low down on Mohs' scale, are used in kitchen and bathroom cleaning powders and metal polishes; powdered silica, feldspar, limestone and pumice are common ingredients. Jeweller's rouge is used for polishing gemstones. Sand, flint, alumina and emery are used in sandpapers and emery papers and in grinding wheels. But for most industrial purposes synthetic diamonds (see below) or silicon carbide (carborundum) are used.

Attempts are being made to make superhard abrasives to replace diamond but progress is slow. Maybe 'diamonds *are* for ever'.

Below left: *Diamond – each C atom is linked to four others arranged tetrahedrally.*
Centre: *Graphite – the atoms are linked together in layers with only weak forces holding the layers together.*
Right: *A bucky ball – one molecule of C_{60}*

FORMS OF CARBON

ALLOTROPES

Graphite and diamond are the two naturally occurring forms (allotropes) of carbon and, after many unsuccessful attempts, graphite was converted into diamond in 1957 by the General Electric Co. in the USA. A very high temperature and pressure were required and the artificial diamonds which were made were only small. They have, nevertheless, many industrial applications.

It was something of a surprise when a third allotrope of carbon was made in 1985 by Harold Kroto at Sussex

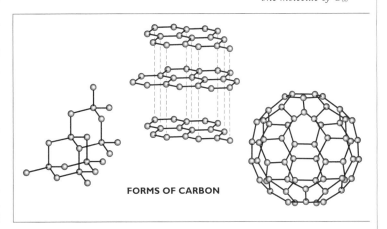

FORMS OF CARBON

Many modern tennis rackets and golf clubs are made from materials containing carbon fibres

University in England. When he subjected graphite to irradiation by a laser beam ($\Rightarrow$p. 160), in an atmosphere of helium, he found that C_{60} molecules were formed. Their shape resembled the huge geodesic domes used in roofs by the American engineer Buckminster Fuller so they were called buckminsterfullerenes or, because they were also shaped like soccer balls, bucky balls. Other allotropes, C_{170}, C_{240} and C_{540} have also been made; they are known collectively as fullerenes, and the molecules have 12 five-membered rings of carbon atoms with different numbers of six-membered ones.

CARBON FIBRES

These consist of long chains of carbon atoms; they are thinner than human hair, but stronger than steel. They were first made by Bill Watt at the Royal Aircraft Establishment at Farnborough, England, by carefully heating stretched polyacrylonitrile ($\Rightarrow$p. 34) fibres in the absence of air, in about 1964. They are incorporated into plastics to make strong, low-density materials used, for example, in making aeroplane parts, tennis racket frames or golf club shafts.

COMPOSITES

Composite materials contain more than one component. Papier mâché ($\Rightarrow$p. 22) and cermets ($\Rightarrow$p. 24) are typical examples, but many others consist of plastic mouldings or laminates.

The Belgian-born chemist Dr Leo Baekeland ($\Rightarrow$p. 34) was the first to exploit this field when he made successful and cheap mouldings from a mixture of Bakelite with wood-flour or sawdust. More recently, fibres of glass, nylon, boron, carbon, and Kevlar 49, invented in 1965 by a du Pont research worker, Stephanie Kwoleck, have been embedded in a variety of plastics. It is also possible, though very expensive, to grow long thin crystals (whiskers) of such substances as silicon carbide and aluminium oxide. These may, one day, become very useful

components of composite materials.

Laminates are made by bonding thin layers together; plywood provides one of the commonest examples. It is made by gluing together, in a press, an odd number of thin sheets (veneers) of wood with their grains crossed. The first glues which were used provided no resistance to moisture, but modern resins can make plywood very suitable for building boats. It can be manufactured in large sheets and in curved shapes.

Sheets of asbestos, cloth or paper can also be impregnated with a thermosetting plastic and formed into laminates in a heated press. They are used as electrical insulators, for turning into small machine parts, such as gears, and for work surfaces in kitchens.

MEASUREMENT

'Every science has some instrument of precision...enabling observers to express their results as measured quantities. In astronomy we have the divided circle, in chemistry the balance, in heat the thermometer, while the whole system of civilised life may be fitly symbolised by a foot rule, a set of weights and a clock.'

JAMES CLERK MAXWELL (1831–79),
Scottish physicist

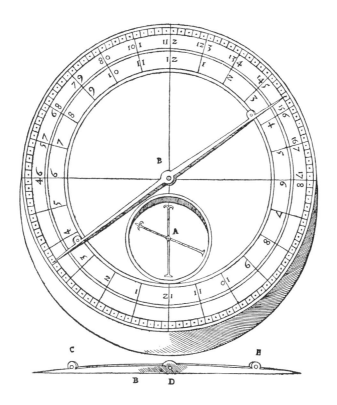

MEASUREMENT

MODERN MEASUREMENTS *are based on SI units (Système Internationale d'Unités) first proposed in 1960 and now widely accepted. Basic definitions are laid down for seven units covering length, mass, time, electric current, temperature, luminous intensity and amount of substance. SI units took the place of the older French metric system and the British imperial system both introduced to bring some order to the haphazard arrangements that existed.*

The metric system was based on definitions of the metre, the kilogram and the second. It was adopted in France in 1795 and enforced after 1834. Many other countries, and most scientific users, also turned to it, but the imperial system, based on the foot, the pound and the second, adopted in England in 1824, remained in use in many English-speaking countries. In Britain, Parliament enacted in 1965 that the metric system should be adopted but some imperial measures, such as the pint, the mile and the gallon are still in use today and a mixed bag of units are also used in the USA where the SI system has not been adopted.

LENGTH

The metre is the SI unit of length; it is defined as the length travelled in 1/299792458th of a second by light in a vacuum. It is a far cry from the earliest measures of length such as the cubit – the length from the elbow to the finger tips; the yard – once defined as the distance from the tip of Henry I's outstretched arm to his nose; and the foot.

The vernier
This device, invented by Pierre Vernier in 1631, enables a length to be measured with increased accuracy by using a movable auxiliary scale alongside the main one. In a typical example, the auxiliary scale is graduated in units 9/10ths of the units on the main scale.

The micrometer
This is used for the accurate measurement of the size or thickness of small objects. It depends on the fact that an accurately cut screw moves the same distance, forwards or backwards, for each turn of the screw.

Such a screw, calibrated along its length, is loosely tightened against the object to be measured. It is then finely tightened by turning a thimble surrounding the screw. This has a circular scale which enables fractions of a turn to be recorded.

The odometer
This consists of a wheel which is rolled along the distance to be measured. Its

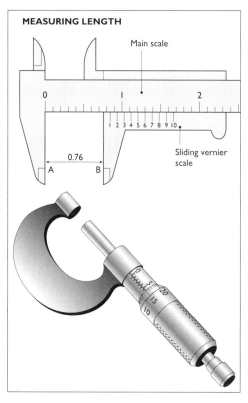

MEASURING LENGTH

Above: *The principle of the vernier. The distance A to B measured on the main scale is clearly between 0.7 and 0.8 units. It is, in fact, 0.76 units because it is the sixth gradation on the vernier scale which matches with a gradation on the main scale*

Below: *A micrometer screw gauge. The reading on the main screw is between 5.5 and 6.0 units. The thimble reading is 15, so that the measured distance is 5.65 units*

length is then calculated from the diameter of the wheel and number of rotations. The mileage recorder, linked to the speedometer of a car, operates on the same principle.

Range-finding

Long distances are generally obtained by directing a radar (⇒p. 149) or laser (⇒p. 160) beam on to the object under investigation and measuring the time taken for the beam to be reflected back. For underwater distances, such as the depths of submarines, shoals of fish or the ocean floor, Sonar or Asdic sytems (⇒p. 172) are used.

MASS AND WEIGHT

The mass of an object measures the amount of material it contains and the SI unit is the kilogram. It is defined as the mass of the international prototype kilogram, a cylinder of platinum-iridium alloy kept at Sèvres in France. The weight of an object is the force exerted on it by gravity; the SI unit is the newton.

The mass of an object never changes, but its weight depends on where it is measured because the gravitational force acting on it can change. The weight of a mass of 1 kg on Earth, for example, is nearly 10 newtons, but it is about one-sixth of that on the Moon where the gravitational force is much reduced.

Beam balances

These consist of a horizontal beam suspended from above by a string, or pivoted from below, at the mid-point. Two pans are suspended from the ends of the beam and the object in one pan is balanced against standard weights in the other. Such balances indicate the same measure of weight for an object whether they are used on Earth or on the Moon, because both the object being weighed and the 'standard' weights against which it is being balanced are always subjected to the same gravitational force.

Simple beam balances used around 5000 BC for weighing gold were improved over the years until it was possible, for example, to weigh objects up to 30 g with a sensitivity of 0.01 mg. This involved using light rider weights, which could be moved along the beam;

knife-edge pivots made of very hard materials; draughtproof cases and remote control; and dampers to limit the swing of the beam.

A Frenchman, Joseph Béranger, patented a less accurate type of beam balance, which was more useful in everyday life, in 1849. He used two pans which were supported from below by a system of levers and the arrangement was very popular in shop and kitchen scales for many years. Similar lever arrangements are used in many bathroom scales.

The steelyard

This is a variation of the beam balance which originated in Roman times. The horizontal beam is suspended, or pivoted, but not at its mid-point. An object to be weighed is suspended from the shorter arm of the beam and it is balanced by moving weights along the longer arm which is calibrated. The scales commonly used in a doctor's surgery rely on the same principle

The spring balance

Robert Hooke, an English physicist, discovered in 1676 that the extension of a spring or an elastic material was directly proportional to the force applied to it so long as the force was not big enough to overstretch it. This led to the invention of the spring balance in which the extension of a spring, supported at its upper end, is measured when an object to be weighed is hung from its lower end.

Because the spring balance is actually measuring force it is sometimes called a newton meter. It gives a different reading for the weight of an object on the Moon than on Earth.

Other methods

In a torsion balance, weights are measured by the extent to which they will twist a wire, and, in an electronic balance, the current generated in a piece of piezoelectric (⇒p. 176) material when it is stressed by a weight is used. Strain gauges may also be used. They consist of a zigzagged wire fixed firmly to a backing sheet. A weight can be measured by observing the change in current passing through the wire when it is stretched by

❛Science is measurement. ❜

ANON

having the weight put on it. In a weighbridge for heavy lorries, levers underneath a platform, or hydraulic or pneumatic systems, are used.

TEMPERATURE

The degree of hotness or coldness of a body is measured by a thermometer. An early type, designed by Galileo, depended on the expansion of air when it was heated but modern thermometers make use of the expansion of liquids. One made in 1701 by a German physicist, Daniel Gabriel Fahrenheit, a Polish-born physicist who worked in Holland, had alcohol in a bulb at one end of a thin uniform tube which was evacuated and sealed at the other end. The alcohol level moved up and down the tube as the temperature changed. Fahrenheit replaced the alcohol with mercury in 1714, and the Swedish astronomer, Anders Celsius, made a similar thermometer in 1742.

The thermometers were graduated with different scales which became known as the Fahrenheit and Centigrade, or Celsius, scales. Celsius took his zero (0°C) as the freezing point of water and chose the boiling point of water as an upper fixed point, at 100°C. In order to avoid negative readings of air temperatures, Fahrenheit had earlier taken his zero (0°F) as the temperature of a mixture of salt with ice, and his upper fixed point (100°F) as an approximation to normal body temperature. This meant that the freezing point of water was 32°F on his scale and the boiling point was 180° higher at 212°F. The SI unit of temperature is the Kelvin (⇒p. 95).

Clinical thermometer

This was invented by an English doctor, Sir Clifford Allbutt, in 1867. It has a short tube calibrated only over the range 95 to 110°F or 35 to 45°C, and there is a kink just above the bulb which contains mercury. The mercury is forced through the kink as it warms up and expands, but there is nothing to force it back as it cools down so that the thermometer can be read at leisure, and reset by shaking the mercury back down into the bulb.

Maximum and minimum thermometer

This type of thermometer was invented by James Six who lived in Colchester, England in 1782; it records the maximum and minimum temperatures reached over a period of time. It is U-shaped and the two limbs both contain mercury in the lower halves. The right hand limb is totally filled with alcohol above the mercury, and the left-hand limb partially filled. The thermometer is set by moving spring-loaded steel indicators, within the alcohol, by an external magnet, so that they rest on top of the mercury columns. The left-hand indicator moves upwards as the temperature rises, and the right-hand one as it falls. The indicators are not free to move downwards, so their lower points record the maximum temperature reached (on the left) and the minimum (on the right).

Wet and dry bulb thermometers

These thermometers are used to measure the relative humidity of the atmosphere. Two separate thermometers are placed side by side and the bulb of one of them is kept wet by being covered with a muslin dipping into water. Because the water evaporates, the 'wet bulb' thermometer records a lower temperature than the dry one. The difference between the two readings depends on the rate of evaporation of the water which, in turn, depends on the relative humidity. Tables are available relating the temperature difference to the relative humidity (⇒p. 45).

Electrical methods

An electrical resistance thermometer depends on the fact that the resistance of a metal changes with temperature. The current flowing through a coil of thin platinum wire can therefore be used to measure the temperature of the coil. The Seebeck or electrothermal effect can also be used. Two wires of different metals joined at their ends will form a loop made up of two thermocouples, one at each end, and a current will flow in it if there is a temperature difference between the two. The higher the temperature difference, the greater the current.

The Lyon thermometer made in 1743

Other methods

Because liquid crystals (⇒p. 80) vary in colour at different temperatures, strips containing them can be used as a thermometer; they are particularly useful for taking the temperature of small children but are not very accurate. Bimetallic strips, consisting of two different metals pressed together and wound into a spiral, can also be used. As the temperature rises, the two metals expand differently so that the spiral unwinds if the more expansible metal is on the inside. That can be made to turn a pointer over a scale. In digital thermometers the temperature is displayed as a number.

Very high temperatures, as in furnaces, can be measured with fair accuracy by using Seger cones which are made of clay mixed with metallic oxides. They soften and bend at specific temperatures depending on their composition. Alternatively, a pyrometer can be used. In an optical pyrometer, the light from a hot source is matched against that from a filament whose temperature can be changed by passing more or less current through it. In a radiation pyrometer, the radiation from a hot source is focused on to a thermocouple.

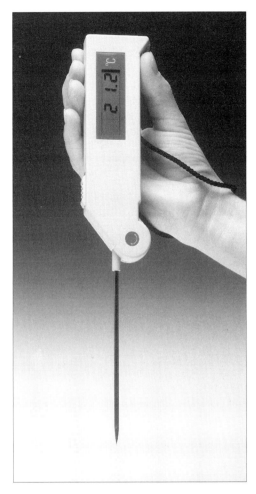

A modern digital thermometer. The stainless steel probe can be immersed up to 30 mm and the thermometer instantly displays temperatures between -50° and 150°C. It is accurate to 0.5°C between -20° and 100°C

Thermostats

These are devices which switch on or off at a pre-set temperature; they are used, for example, to control central heating systems, cookers and irons. One of the first, invented by Scotsman Andrew Ure in 1830 to control temperature during distillation, was operated by a bimetallic strip, and this method is still quite commonly used. Alternatively, the expansion and contraction of any solid, liquid or gas can be used.

PRESSURE

Because atmospheric pressure can neither be seen nor easily felt, its existence only came to light around 1640 when miners in Italy noticed that they could not pump water up from a depth of more than 34 ft (10.34 m). Even Galileo could not account for this but the reason was found by his pupil, Evangelista Torricelli, in 1644, using a tube about one-metre long, which was closed at one end and full of mercury. With his finger over the open end, he inserted it into a dish of mercury and inverted the tube. When he removed his finger, he found that the column of mercury in the tube was only 76 mm (29.9 in) high. He interpreted this as meaning that the atmospheric pressure at the bottom of the tube was only high enough to support that length of a column of mercury. And, because mercury is 13.6 times as dense as water, that corresponds to a column of water 10.34 m (33.9 ft) high.

Torricelli's tube was the first simple mercury barometer because it gives a measurement of atmospheric pressure. When the pressure falls, the column length is shorter; when it rises, it is longer. It fluctuates around 0.76 m which represents a pressure of about 1.01×10^5 pascals (Pa), 10^5 newton/sq m or 14.4 lb per sq in. Important modifications to Torricelli's simple barometer were introduced by Robert

> **6** *...the greatest difficulties have arisen for not being able to ascertain the heat to which the experimental pieces have been exposed.* **9**
>
> JOSIAH WEDGWOOD *(1730–95), English potter*

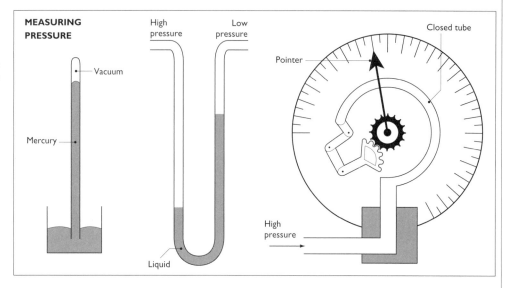

A simple barometer (left), a manometer (centre) and a Bourdon gauge (right)

Hooke (⇒p. 41) in 1665; by Jean Fortin, a French instrument-maker, in 1797; and by the English Admiral, Robert Fitzroy, the former captain of Darwin's ship, *The Beagle*, in 1858.

Aneroid (not wet) barometers

These were invented by a Frenchman, Lucien Vidie, in 1844. They are less accurate but more compact and portable than mercury barometers. They contain an evacuated capsule with thin, springy metal walls which are held apart by an external spring but which move in or out as the atmospheric pressure rises or falls, respectively. This small movement is transmitted through a system of levers and a chain or gear wheels to a pointer which moves around a clock-like dial from which the pressure can be read. Alternatively, in a barograph, the movement operates a pen which traces a continuous record of the atmospheric pressure on a piece of paper on a rotating drum.

Aneroid barometers came to be known as weather glasses. They are commonly graduated in inches with 29.9 corresponding to a pressure of 76 cm of mercury. But the unit of pressure most commonly used in meteorology is the bar, with 1 bar being equivalent to 750.07 mm of mercury, or 76 cm of mercury to 1.01325 bar or 1013.25 millibars.

Pressure gauges

A U-tube containing a liquid, such as water, mercury or an oil, is commonly used to measure the pressure of a gas or liquid; it is called a manometer. When both arms of the tube are open to the atmosphere, the two liquid levels are equal, but a difference arises when one arm is connected to a different pressure. This can be read visually, as a distance or, alternatively, the change in levels can be made to operate a float or a diaphragm so that it can be recorded by a pointer.

Gas or liquid pressures can also be measured by a Bourdon gauge invented in 1849 by a French manufacturer of model steam engines, Eugène Bourdon. The gauge contains a length of flexible metal tubing, closed at one end and bent into a C-shape. The tube straightens out slightly when the pressure of a gas or liquid within it increases, and this movement can be used to move a pointer over a circular scale so that the existing pressure can be measured. The oil pressure in a motor car engine, the pressure inside cylinders of compressed gas, and that in a car tyre are commonly measured in this way.

METEOROLOGICAL MEASUREMENTS

Pressure

Torricelli realized that the pressure measured on his simple barometer changed slightly from day to day and he related this to changes in the weather. Amongst others, Robert Fitzroy

6 We live submerged at the bottom of an ocean of air. 9

EVANGELISTA TORRICELLI (1608–47), Italian physicist

Labels in figure

MEASURING PRESSURE

Vacuum

Mercury

High pressure

Low pressure

Liquid

Pointer

Closed tube

High pressure

GALILEO GALILEI
(1564–1642)

GALILEO was born in Pisa, Italy, the son of a musician. He was a short, energetic man with red hair, and his original work in mathematics, physics and astronomy has led to him being widely regarded as the founder of modern science.

Tradition has it that he was only 17 years old when he timed a swinging chandelier in Pisa cathedral against his pulse beat and began to realize that the time of swing of a pendulum depended only on its length and not on how far it swung from side to side. In 1592, he made an early thermometer, known as a thermoscope, which depended on the expansion of air pushing liquid along a tube. In 1609, he improved Lippershey's first telescope (⇒p. 154) and observed mountains on the Moon and the four satellites of Jupiter. It is probable that he first suggested the crucial experiment with mercury in a glass tube (⇒p. 43) which Torricelli carried out a year after his death.

His astronomical work convinced him that Copernicus's view that the Earth circled the Sun was correct and that Ptolemy's view that the Earth was the centre of the universe was wrong. He expressed these thoughts in a book – *Dialogue on the Two Chief World Systems* – which he wrote in 1632. The text brought him into conflict with the Roman Catholic Church; he was brought before the Inquisition and found guilty; he recanted but was kept under house arrest for the last eight years of his life of which he was totally blind for the last five.

> ❛...there is no greater hatred in the whole world than that of ignorance for knowledge. ❜
>
> *GALILEO GALILEI (1564–1642), Italian mathematician and astronomer*

(⇒p. 44) developed that theme when he was appointed to the meteorological branch of the Board of Trade in 1854. He equipped every port with a barometer in 1858, and instituted storm warnings for shipping.

Similarly, in 1855 the director of the French Observatory, Urbain Le Verrier, recommended that a chain of weather stations be set up, and the first weather bureau was established in the USA in 1871.

All this led to the introduction of daily weather forecasts. They depend, in the main, on the collection of data from around the world on pressure, temperature, wind speed and humidity values, and its rapid circulation, first by telegraphy and now by radio. The information and the predictions made from it are summarized on weather charts or maps.

Wind speed

A common type of anemometer, used for measuring wind speeds, has three or four hemispherical cups situated at the end of radial arms so that they can rotate in a horizontal plane. The speed of rotation which measures the wind speed is read on a dial or recorded continuously by a pen on a piece of paper on a rotating drum in an anemograph.

Sir Francis Beaufort, a British naval officer, devised the Beaufort scale of wind speeds in 1805. It ranges from 0 for dead calm to 12 for hurricane winds of over 118 km/h (74 mph) and it is still in use today.

Humidity

Humidity, the amount of water vapour in the atmosphere, was originally measured on a hair hygrometer invented by a Swiss, H. de Saussure, in 1783. It contained a taut human hair connected to a pointer and relied on its change in length with change in humidity. Today it is generally measured on a wet and dry bulb thermometer (⇒p. 42).

Collecting data

The more information that is available, the easier it is to forecast the weather. To that end, A. Wilson sent thermometers up into the atmosphere on kites as early as 1749, and in 1848 the English newspaper, the *Daily News*, commissioned a well-known hot-air balloonist, James Glaisher, to collect meteorological data. In making one flight up to 8848 m (9666 yd) he was almost asphyxiated.

A more reliable source evolved in the 1930s with the invention of the radiosonde. It consists of a helium-filled balloon which carries radio equipment capable of transmitting signals back to a receiving station on Earth indicating the pressure, temperature and humidity at various altitudes as it rises. It may also carry a reflector so that its upward path can be followed by radar which collects information about the winds at different altitudes.

A radio sonde apparatus in flight carried by a helium-filled balloon

Similar information is collected from meteorological rockets and from aeroplanes.

This is all now greatly augmented by the use of meteorological satellites (⇒p. 188) which can view the Earth's weather from a greater height. The first, *Tiros I*, was launched in 1960. *Nimbus I* followed in 1964, and there are now five Meteostat satellites in orbits which monitor the weather for almost all the world.

The first of these satellites was launched in 1977 and the last in 1990; they relay a constant flow of information down to ground stations.

MEASURING TIME

❝What then is time? If no one asks me, I know what it is. If I wish to explain it to him who asks me I do not know.❞

ST AUGUSTINE,
5th century AD

Time, nowadays, can be measured with quite remarkable accuracy (⇒p. 50) but it was originally done, very roughly using sundials, water-clocks, hour-glasses and Alfred the Great's candle-clocks. The sundial came first – around 2500 BC in China – with the other methods following in turn.

All that is needed for a sundial is some

projection, or gnomon, which will cast a shadow on to a surface. The shadow moves, as the Sun does, and its position indicates the time; the surface can be calibrated accordingly. Water-clocks and hour-glasses rely on the rate of flow of water or sand through small holes, and the candle-clock on the rate of burning of wax.

WEIGHT-OPERATED CLOCK

The first weight-operated clocks, originating in Europe at the end of the 13th century, were probably inspired by a special type of water-clock invented in China in which the incoming water was used to fill buckets on a paddle-wheel. When one bucket was full, its weight operated a lever which allowed the paddle-wheel to turn a little and to bring the next bucket into place. The paddle-wheel was connected through gears to a moving pointer which indicated the time. This was the first simple use of what came to be called an escapement – a device for ensuring that a rotatory

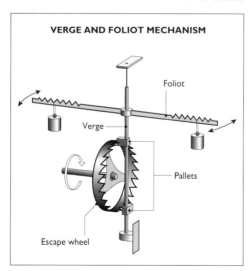

VERGE AND FOLIOT MECHANISM

Foliot

Verge

Pallets

Escape wheel

movement takes place in controlled stages. It was to be at the heart of clock design for many years.

The first weight-operated clocks were driven by a weight attached to one end of a cord wrapped round an axle. As the weight fell, the axle turned, and, through gears, turned the hands of the clock. The turning was controlled by an escapement mechanism, known as a verge and foliot, which operated on a toothed crown-wheel or escape-wheel. The verge consisted of a rod which was fitted with two pallets, projecting at right-angles to each other. They moved in and out of the teeth of the crown- or escape-wheel as the foliot, a bar carrrying two weights, swung to and fro. The wheel could, therefore, only turn in steps, and as it did so it moved a pointer. The rate at which the wheel turned could be adjusted by moving the weights on the foliot in or out – out for a slower swing and in for a faster one. It was the engagement of the pallets with the crown-wheel or escape-wheel that gave a clock its 'tick-tock' noise.

SPRING-OPERATED CLOCK

The operation of clocks by falling weights began to be replaced in the middle of the 15th century by the use of helical springs (⇒p. 48) coiled round an axle. As the spring unwound, the axle rotated but, because the tension in the spring decreased as it unwound, the rate of rotation slowed down. To compensate for this, it was necessary to introduce a fusee, which consisted of a conical drum

with a spiral groove cut into it. A cord or chain from the spring was wrapped round the groove so that the pull from the spring moved from the narrow to the wide end of the cone as it unwound. It therefore became easier to turn the fusee as the pull of the spring weakened. Spring-driven clocks were more portable than those driven by weights, so that it became possible to make the first watches at the start of the 16th century.

PENDULUM CLOCK

In 1641, Galileo (⇒p. 45) suggested to his son, Vincenzio, that he should try to make a clock which was controlled by a swinging pendulum. Vincenzio made some progress but died before the project was completed, and it was Christiaan Huygens who made the first practical pendulum clock in 1656. He came from a wealthy Dutch family and turned to science after studying law. In 1655, he observed Saturn's rings through a telescope he had made; in 1678, he expounded the wave theory of light; and he was second only to Newton (⇒p. 159) as the most influential physicist of the 17th century. His success in using a swinging pendulum instead of an oscillating foliot to control a horizontal verge led to greatly improved accuracy.

Escapements
Still greater accuracy came with the invention of the anchor escapement to replace the verge, between 1656 and 1660. There are competing claims as to

❛Has time a beginning?❜

ANON

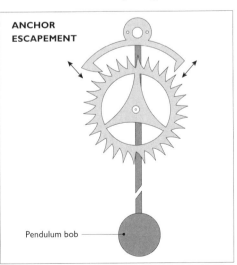

FUSEE

Chain to spring

ANCHOR ESCAPEMENT

Pendulum bob

the originator; Sir Robert Hooke, Joseph Knibb, or perhaps William Clement. The new mechanism involved a C-shaped piece of metal with a projecting pallet at both ends of the C. As it was rocked to and fro by the swinging pendulum, at first one pallet and then the other engaged with a toothed escape-wheel to control its rotation. One tooth 'escaped' at each swing of the pendulum and in the process an impulse was given to the pendulum to maintain its swing. Further inventions such as those of the dead-beat escapement by George Graham in 1715, and of the lever escapement by Thomas Mudge in 1770, were particularly significant.

Compensated pendulums

The time of swing of a pendulum depends on its length. It is one second when it is 0.9936 m long, which is why that length is commonly chosen for the pendulums in grandfather clocks; but a metal pendulum will expand or contract as the temperature changes. If it is made of steel, for example, a rise in temperature of 10°F causes a time loss of about $2\frac{1}{2}$ seconds in a day.

Great ingenuity was exhibited in designing compensated pendulums which kept the same length despite changes in temperature. George Graham (1721) used a steel pendulum rod and a glass or steel container with mercury in it as the pendulum bob. Mercury has a higher coefficient of expansion than steel and its upwards expansion in its container compensated for the downwards expansion of the pendulum

rod. John Harrison invented the grid-iron pendulum in 1726. Brass and steel rods were arranged so that the expansion of the brass rods raised the pendulum bob whilst the expansion of the steel rods lowered it. Later (1899) pendulums were made of Invar (⇒p. 16), an alloy with a negligible coefficient of expansion.

HAIR-SPRING CLOCK

In 1674, Huygens invented clocks dependent on a spiral, hair-spring and balance wheel. The spring was fixed at one end and then wound round the axle of the balance wheel before being attached to it. As the wheel oscillated to and fro under the control of the hair-spring it rocked a lever with two projecting pallets which engaged and disengaged alternately with a toothed wheel. This new arrangement had many advantages over the pendulum. It was very compact; it did not depend on gravity so that it would function in any position; and it was not greatly affected by external buffeting.

This made possible the manufacture of portable pocket watches and of chronometers which would operate satisfactorily on ships and enable seamen to fix their longitude (⇒p. 147). The problems of making them were overcome by the patient work of John Harrison between 1728 and 1762. What he started was carried on by Pierre Le Roy and Ferdinand Berthoud in France, and by Thomas Mudge, John Arnold and Thomas Earnshaw in England. Their simpler chronometers made possible in due course the charting of the world's oceans and an enormous increase in world trade.

THE 19TH CENTURY

This was a period of evolutionary rather than revolutionary change. In 1840, the Scot Alexander Bain used an electromagnetic arrangement to maintain the swing of a pendulum, and four years later the first stop watch was invented. In 1859, the Great Clock at the Houses of Parliament in England, commissioned by Sir Benjamin Hall, was set in motion. It is commonly known as Big Ben, though

> **❛He shares with Galileo a noble unsurpassable, and complete uprightness. ❜**
>
> ERNST MACH (1838–1916), Austrian physicist, on Huygens

(Left) *George Graham's compensated pendulum (1721).* (Right) *John Harrison's grid-iron pendulum (1726)*

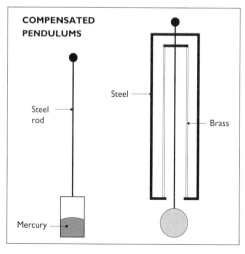

COMPENSATED PENDULUMS

Steel rod

Mercury

Steel

Brass

JOHN HARRISON
(1693–1776)

HARRISON, born near Pontefract in Yorkshire, England, began his working life in his father's trade as a carpenter. But, after moving to Lincoln, he taught himself the art of clock-making and set about trying to win a prize of £20,000 (equivalent to £1 million today) offered in 1714 by and Act of Parliament. It was to go to 'such person or persons as shall discover the longitude at sea' to an accuracy of 30 miles (48 km) after a voyage of six weeks.

He began his work in 1728 by designing a chronometer with two balance wheels which always oscillated in opposite directions so that the effect of a ship's movement on one would be counteracted by its effect on the other. He also incorporated a bimetallic strip (⇒p. 43) arrangement which changed the lengths of the balance springs as the temperature changed; and he invented a device for 'maintaining power', i.e. for keeping the clock going whilst it was being rewound. He also used the better-quality steels which were available to him, and he developed the use of jewels, such as diamonds, in making his bearings and pallets. Above all, he built his timekeepers with extreme care and precision, completing only four in 33 years.

His No. 4 chronometer was tested by his son William on a 64-day voyage of HMS Deptford from Portsmouth, England to Jamaica. On arrival on 21 January 1762, it had lost only five seconds and the longitude measurement was within 11/2 miles (2.4 km). No wonder that contemporary commentators called what looked like nothing more than a large silver watch, just over 5 in (127 mm) in diameter, 'the most famous timekeeper which ever has been or ever will be made'. No navigator of the day would have argued with that but, alas, Harrison and his son had difficulties when they came to claim their prize money. It was only after petitioning King George III, whose reaction was 'My God, I will see you righted', that they were paid in full in 1773 only three years before John died. He is buried in Hampstead churchyard.

John Harrison's chronometer which won him a £20,000 prize in 1762

strictly speaking that is the name of the bell that strikes the hours. Water-resistant watch cases were patented in 1872; Greenwich Mean Time (⇒p.149) was adopted as the standard time for the UK in 1880; the first automatic 'clocking-in' machines were used in the USA, around 1890; and wrist watches came at the end of the century.

THE 20TH CENTURY

This period has seen the introduction of radio time signals, of particular value to mariners, first from the Navy Yard in Boston, USA in 1905; then from the Eiffel Tower in Paris in 1910; and from the British Broadcasting Corporation in 1922. Summer time was adopted in

Great Britain in 1916. In 1921, a British engineer, William H. Shortt, invented the Shortt pendulum in which the pendulum that actually operates the clock is electrically controlled by a separate, free pendulum oscillating in a low-pressure environment. The self-winding wrist-watch was invented by John Harwood in 1924; the Post Office speaking clock began in Great Britain in 1936; and the first digital display clock came in 1967. But, more importantly, three basically new types of clock – the electric clock, the quartz-crystal clock, and the atomic clock – have been invented.

Electric clock

The electric clock was introduced in 1918 by Henry Warren in the USA. It was operated by a synchronous electric motor ($\Rightarrow$p. 74) designed to keep in step with the frequency of the alternating current supplied to it. Normally, this is 50 Hz in most of Europe and 60 Hz in the USA. If the AC frequency faltered, so did the clock. Nowadays, electric supply companies ensure that any variations in the frequency of the AC are averaged out over a period of time, and cheap, accurate battery-operated clocks are readily available.

Quartz-crystal clock

In the late 1920s, an American, J.W. Horton and a Canadian-born American, W.A. Marrison, working in the Bell Laboratories, developed a quartz-crystal clock. It relied on the fact that quartz is piezoelectricity ($\Rightarrow$p. 76) which means that it will vibrate under the influence of an alternating current. In practice, a piece of quartz, cut in an appropriate way, is caused to oscillate by passing an alternating current through it via electrodes attached to its surfaces. The resulting very high frequency of vibration, generally 32,768 Hz ($\Rightarrow$p. 186), is recorded electronically in such a way that an electrical pulse, produced each second, is used to activate either a mechanical or digital display of time. The frequency of vibration is so constant that a high-quality quartz-crystal clock, kept at a fixed temperature, has an accuracy of about 0.1 millisecond per day or one part in a billion. Relatively inexpensive quartz operated clocks and wrist-watches became readily available in 1969.

Atomic clock

The atomic clock, developed by Dr L. Essen and J.V.L. Parry at the National Physical Laboratory, Teddington, England, and by J.R. Zacharias at the Massachusetts Institute of Technology in the USA, in the mid-1950s, was even more accurate than the quartz-crystal clock. Its timekeeping was controlled by an oscillating energy change which can take place within a particular type of caesium atom, Cs-133 ($\Rightarrow$p. 89). It has a frequency of 9, 192, 631, 770 Hz, and the duration of that number of vibrations is, nowadays, used to define the second as the SI unit of time. In a caesium clock, that huge number is counted electronically and one second is recorded every time its value is reached.

Older caesium clocks have an accuracy of about one second in 300,000 years or about one part in 10^{13}. They use magnetic fields to control the vibrating caesium atoms. In newer versions, known as optically pumped atomic clocks, the magnetic fields are replaced by laser beams ($\Rightarrow$p. 160). Such a clock at the National Institute of Standards and Technology in Boulder, Colorado, the NIST-7, has recently been adopted as the time standard for the USA. Its estimated accuracy is one second in about one million years. Optically pumped clocks based on rubidium rather than caesium are also available commercially; they are cheaper and more compact but less accurate.

Vibrations within ammonia molecules and hydrogen atoms can also be used for measuring time with great accuracy. In the so-called ammonia maser ($\Rightarrow$p. 161), pioneered by the American C.H. Townes in 1953, the pyramidal ammonia molecule, NH_3 turns itself inside-out – like an umbrella – when stimulated by the appropriate radiation. The regular frequency with which it does this has been used in clocks, but they have been largely superceded by others which use atomic hydrogen masers first developed in 1960 by the American Norman F. Ramsey and others. They depend on the fixed frequency of radiation that can be emitted by electronic changes between different energy levels within free hydrogen atoms. Today, such clocks have an estimated possible accuracy of about one part in 10^{15}.

CHAPTER

4

TOOLS *and* DEVICES

'If a man write a better book, preach a better sermon, or make a better
mouse-trap than his neighbour, tho' he build his house in the woods,
the world will make a beaten path to his door.'

RALPH WALDO EMERSON (1803–82), American poet

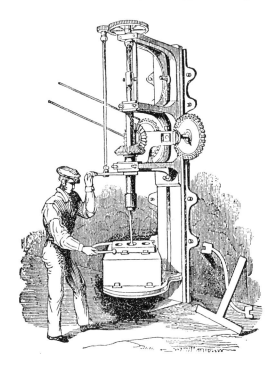

TOOLS AND DEVICES

THE MODERN CRY OF 'give us the tools and we will finish the job' would have sounded very hollow to our early ancestors because they had to make their own tools before they could even start the job. For example, they made primitive axes, hammers, chisels, saws and needles, first out of stone, wood and bone, and later out of brass, bronze and iron. The Seven Wonders of the World are a constant reminder of what they achieved. However, latterly, during the 17th and 18th century the makers of clocks and scientific instruments demanded much greater accuracy than could ever be achieved by hand tools. This need led to the invention of a few, small machine tools and later, particularly between 1800 and 1850, a much wider range of industrial tools.

MACHINE TOOLS

❝The bow-lathe is one of the classical schemes for turning linear into rotary motion.❞

J. BRONOWSKI (1908–74), Polish-born, British scientist

John Wilkinson set the ball rolling when he invented a boring machine in 1775. It used a 4.6 m (15 ft) long boring-bar, with a cutter at one end, which was held horizontally and rotated. The original intention was to make better gun barrels, but the machine was equally important in making cylinders for steam engines. It could bore a cylinder with a diameter of 1.3 m (4.3 ft) to an accuracy of about 1 mm (0.04 in).

The lathe

Ancient lathes were primitive contraptions made of wood in which one man twisted the piece to be turned by pulling on a rope wrapped around a shaft whilst a second man held the cutting tool against the piece by hand. Later, the rope was attached at one end to a springy pole or a bow and at the other to a foot-pedal so that the lathe could be operated by one man using both hands and feet.

Lathes were slowly developed into more accurate tools during the 18th century, and in 1797 the ideas of a number of inventors, notably two Frenchmen, de Vaucanson (1751) and Senot (1795), were brought together by English engineer Henry Maudslay (1771–1831) in a lathe made of metal which was large enough for industrial use. The piece to be worked was held at both ends and rotated mechanically, whilst the cutting tool was carried in a holder the movement of which, alongside the piece, was controlled by turning a

screw. This enabled the lathe to be used for cutting accurate screw threads.

Maudslay began work in the Royal Arsenal at Woolwich when he was 12 and left six years later to start an apprenticeship with Joseph Bramah. He gave that up in 1797 when he was refused an increase in wage and in 1802 began work on designing the 43 tools which were needed to implement Brunel's new method of making pulley-blocks (⇒p. 59). The success of his products and the high standards of accuracy he set established his reputation, and he exerted a lasting influence because so many future inventors trained under him. His advice to them, still of value, was to 'get a clear notion of what you desire to accomplish, and then in all probability you will succeed in doing it'.

The turret or capstan lathe, in which a number of different tools are mounted in the tool holder, was developed by the American firm of Pratt and Whitney in the 1840s.

Milling machine

Eli Whitney, the inventor of the cotton gin (⇒p. 115) made one of the first milling machines in 1818 to help in his new role as a manufacturer of firearms for the American government. It was a significant event because he adopted the newly tried method of making a gun out of a number of replaceable parts. It came to be known as the 'American System'; it played a large part in the development of mass production; and it made a fortune for Whitney.

JOSEPH BRAMAH
(1748–1814)

BRAMAH was born in Yorkshire and worked on his father's farm until, following a leg injury at the age of 16, he was apprenticed to a local carpenter. His skill with tools encouraged him to set up his own business as a cabinet-maker in London where he became a versatile inventor.

His 18 patents include a water-closet, a beer pump, a machine for numbering bank notes, and a wood-planing machine. He gained much publicity in 1784 by offering a reward of 200 guineas to anyone who could open a lock he had made. The money was not won until 67 years later when an American mechanic opened it, but only after working at it for 50 hours over a period of 16 days.

Bramah is best remembered, now, for his hydraulic press invented in 1795. It consisted of a narrow cylinder connected through a tube to a wider one; both contained water and were fitted with pistons. A force exerted on the small piston moved it a long way, whilst the larger piston moved less but applied a larger force. It was much more powerful than the existing screw presses and the principle is widely adopted today, though the water has been replaced by special oils.

Hydraulic press systems are used in car and aeroplane brakes (see below), in the raising and lowering of the undercarriages of aeroplanes, and in the operation of lock gates, lifts or elevators, swing bridges, cranes, bulldozers and many tractor implements.

Bramah died from pneumonia caught whilst supervising the use of one of his presses in uprooting some forest trees.

Joseph Bramah's famous challenge lock, made in 1784, remained unopened until 1851

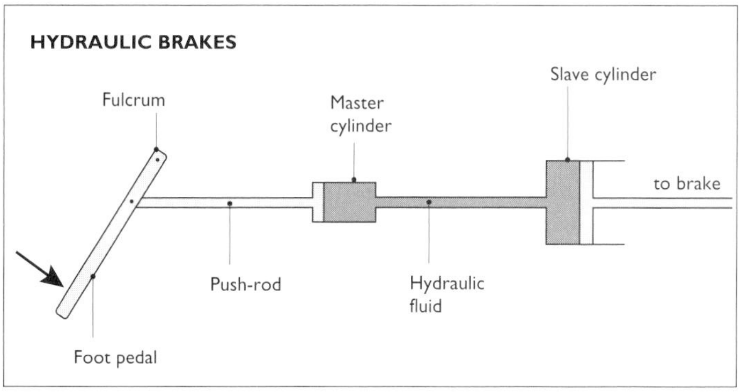

HYDRAULIC BRAKES

Fulcrum
Master cylinder
Slave cylinder
to brake
Push-rod
Hydraulic fluid
Foot pedal

The principle of the Bramah press is applied in the hydraulic brakes on a car. The force exerted on the foot by the brake pedal is multiplied first by leverage, and then by using a master cylinder with a smaller diameter than the slave cylinders which operate the brakes on each wheel (⇒p.137)

> **Man is a tool-using animal... Without tools he is nothing, with tools he is all.**

THOMAS CARLYLE (1795–1881), Scottish essayist

A universal milling machine, which could undertake many different jobs, including the cutting of drills, was invented by Joseph R. Brown in 1862.

The steam hammer
A Scottish engineer, James Nasmyth, the son of a landscape painter who had worked for Maudslay, built the first steam hammer in 1839. It consisted of a piston in a vertical cylinder which could move a heavy hammer attached to it up or down by passing steam into the cylinder either below or above the piston.

It could forge very large beams, plates and shafts, and was an excellent pile-driver when the hammer was lowered quickly, but it was also capable of cracking an egg safely!

Planing machines

The first planing machine for metals, similar to a wood planer, was invented by a French mechanic, Nicolas Focq, in 1751, but a much-improved version came in 1835 from Joseph Whitworth (1803-87). He was born in Stockport where his father was first a schoolmaster and then a non-conformist minister. After working with Maudslay for eight years, Whitworth set up on his own in Manchester and became the major British manufacturer of machine tools, eventually employing over 600 men. By building a machine capable of measuring to one millionth of an inch, he set new standards of accuracy, and his 23 exhibits at the Great Exhibition in London in 1851 stole the show. The firm which he founded is now part of Vickers but his name lives on in the British Standard Whitworth (BSW) specification for screws which he introduced in 1841, in the Whitworth engineering scholarships which he founded in 1868, and in the Whitworth Art Gallery in Manchester, England.

Automatic control

In recent years, machine tools have been operated by numerical control from data recorded on punched cards or magnetic or punched tape and, later, by computerized systems. Thomas Carlyle's description of man as a tool-using animal

is even truer today than when he wrote it more than 100 years ago.

PISTONS

Pistons are circular discs or short cylindrical pieces which can move within a hollow cylinder with a slightly larger diameter. They were probably first used by Ctesibius (⇒p. 55) in the early pumps he made which were not unlike today's syringe or bicycle pump. The function of the piston was to suck in or push out air or water as it was moved within the cylinder. For this purpose, it had to be a good fit and this was achieved by using leather washers or by wrapping rope around the circumference of the piston. Later, the piston was all-important in the design of steam and petrol engines. Here, the piston was moved by the pressure of steam or burning gas mixtures and, in order to achieve any reasonable efficiency, it was even more important that it should be a good fit (⇒p. 105).

In modern engines, a good fit is obtained by using a piston ring which is made of spring steel with a rectangular cross-section. The ring is cut through at one point so that it can be opened up slightly for fitting into grooves around the circumference at the top of a piston in order for it to spring open or shut. It was invented by an Englishman, John Barton, in 1816.

VALVES

Valves are used for controlling the passage of gases or liquids along a pipe. They function very much like a door in a corridor and they can be either one-way or two-way. That is, the door can be opened only one way or it can open both ways. Valves can be operated manually, as in a water tap, or automatically.

Ctesibius was probably the first person to use valves. Today, there are many types. A simple flap-valve consists of a flap of, say, leather which fits over a hole; pressure in one direction opens it up whilst an opposite pressure keeps it closed. A motor car tyre valve allows air into the tyre when it is being blown up but will not let the air out. A float valve, as in a carburettor (⇒p. 105), moves up and down in petrol in a valve chamber,

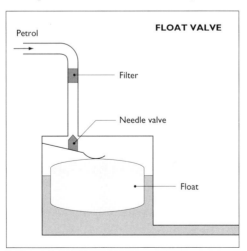

FLOAT VALVE

Petrol

Filter

Needle valve

Float

Float valve as used in the carburettor of a car engine

CTESIBIUS

CTESIBIUS was a Greek engineer who was born around 250 BC, the son of a barber. He lived and worked in Alexandria and was one of the most prolific inventors of his day. He has some quite remarkable achievements to his name, many of them dependent on the fact that he was the first to realize the uses to which pistons, valves and gear mechanisms could be put.

He built a 19-pipe musical organ operated by bellows, a particularly accurate water-clock (*clepsydra*), an early type of thermometer, a blow-pipe operated by compressed air, a simple pump, and a catapult which used leaf-springs made of bronze.

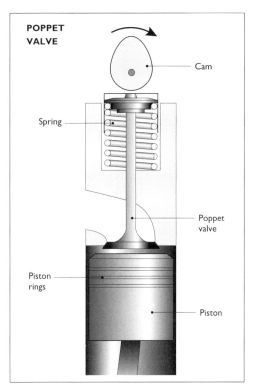

POPPET VALVE

Cam

Spring

Poppet valve

Piston rings

Piston

The spring-loaded valve is opened and shut by the rotating cam

Below: *A piston-operated lift pump. As the piston is moved up* (left), *the upper valve shuts and water is lifted out of the outlet pipe; at the same time, the lower valve opens and more water is sucked through it into the pump. As the piston moves down* (right), *the lower valve closes and the upper one opens*

stopping the inflow when at its height. Poppet valves, made of heat-resistant steel, are used to control the inlet of fuel and the outlet of exhaust gases in a petrol engine. They are shaped like a mushroom with the head machined into a conical shape which fits into the seat of the valve, and they are kept tightly shut by springs. Safety valves, fitted to boilers or other pressurized vessels, allow the pressure to be automatically released when it exceeds a safe level.

LIQUID PUMPS

These were probably invented by Ctesibius and their first use was in lifting water from wells and moving it along pipes for irrigation, distribution and drainage purposes. They are also needed today for pumping other liquids such as crude oil, petrol and blood.

Reciprocating pumps

These operate by moving a piston, a plunger or a diaphragm, with the aid of valves, to suck a fluid into a container and then push it out in bursts. The old lift pump still commonly seen on village greens is typical.

In a modern version the piston is replaced by a flexible diaphragm which is moved up and down by a lever, a cam or an electromagnet. The petrol pump in a motor car is typical.

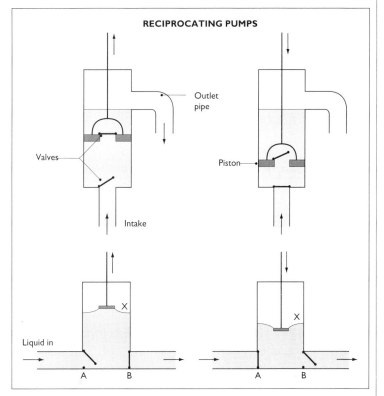

RECIPROCATING PUMPS

Outlet pipe

Valves

Intake

Piston

Liquid in

A   B

X

A   B

X

Above: *A diaphragm-operated force pump. A flexible diaphragm, X, is moved up and down either mechanically or electrically. When moving up* (left), *valve A opens and valve B shuts, drawing liquid into the pump. When moving down* (right), *valve A shuts and liquid is forced out through valve B which opens*

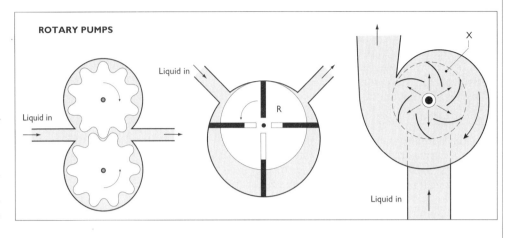

ROTARY PUMPS

Liquid in

Liquid in

R

Liquid in

X

Left: *A gear pump.* Centre: *A sliding vane pump. The eccentrically mounted rotor, R, is fitted with spring-loaded vanes which slide in or out of their casings.* Right: *A centrifugal pump. The liquid is moved through the pump by a rotating impeller, X. It is fed in through a pipe along the axis of the impeller*

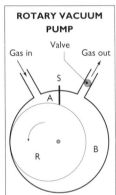

ROTARY VACUUM PUMP

Valve

Gas in   Gas out

S

A

R   B

S is a spring-loaded valve separating space A from space B. As the eccentrically mounted rotor, R, rotates, gas is sucked into space A through the inlet pipe. It is then carried round into space B and forced out through the outlet pipe, which is fitted with a non-return valve

6*A vacuum is nothing, and what is nothing cannot exist.***9**

THOMAS HOBBES *(1588–1679), English philosopher*

Rotary pumps

A variety of rotary pumps, which need no valves, and give a a steady flow of liquid, began to replace reciprocating piston pumps during the 19th century. In a gear pump, the liquid is moved by two gears rotating in a close-fitting container; in a sliding-vane pump, by spring-loaded vanes moving in and out of an eccentrically mounted rotor; in a centrifugal pump, by a twirling impeller; and in an axial-flow pump, by a central propeller.

Peristaltic pumps

These are used for pumping blood in a heart-lung machine (⇒p. 228). The blood is moved along a flexible tube by rotating external rollers which squeeze the tube in succession to replicate the way that the alimentary canal and other organs move their contents within the human body.

COMPRESSORS AND VACUUM PUMPS

Compressor pumps

These pumps are used to increase the pressure on a gas as, for example, in inflating tyres, in compressing gases into cylinders for storage, in many chemical processes, in liquefying gases, in pneumatic drills and other tools, and in gas turbines. The bicycle pump provides a simple example. Similar reciprocating piston types can be used on a larger scale, but rotary compressors, similar to those used for liquids, are more compact and effective for most purposes.

Vacuum pumps

These pumps are used to lower the pressure of a gas and to create a vacuum. The first air pump was invented by a German engineer and physicist, Otto von Guericke, who was made Burgomaster of Magdeburg for his services to the town during its siege in the Thirty Years War. His pump was a modified form of a lift pump for water but he used it in 1654 to evacuate much of the air from within a sphere of about 50 cm (19.7 in) in diameter made up of two close-fitting hemispheres. His subsequent discovery that two teams of eight horses could not pull the hemispheres apart revolutionized man's ideas of pressure and vacua.

Some 200 years later, improved air-pumps, notably those invented by the Germans, Heinrich Geissler (1855) and Hermann Sprengel (1865), gave much better vacua. They led to the discovery of X-rays and electrons, and made possible inventions such as the electric light bulb, the thermionic valve and the cathode ray tube.

The commonest type of pump which will give a good vacuum consists of a rotor which is divided into two sections, A and B (see diagram), by a spring-loaded valve, S. As the rotor turns, it first draws gas into A through the inlet, then compresses it into B, and finally ejects it through an outlet valve. To avoid gas leakage and provide lubrication, the whole casing is immersed in oil.

A vacuum can also be obtained by using a water aspirator in which water passing through a jet under pressure is used to sweep a gas along with it. There is, however, a limit to the vacuum that can be achieved in this way because of the vapour pressure exerted by water. This is avoided in a diffusion pump, sometimes known as a Gaede pump, which works on the same principle but uses mercury or a low vapour pressure oil instead of water. The mercury or oil is condensed by a cooling jacket and is reused.

THE LEVER

No one knows who invented the lever but it is a remarkably simple and effective way of 'magnifying' the effect of a force. A long crowbar, for example, can be used to lift a heavy load by pivoting it about a point known as the fulcrum. The force applied is 'magnified', but only because it moves through a greater distance than the load.

The numerical relationship (the law of moments) that the force multiplied by its distance from the fulcrum is equal to the load multiplied by its distance was probably first enunciated by Archimedes (⇒p. 58) who said to King Hieron: 'Give me a lever long enough and a place to stand, and I can move the earth'. When the King asked for a demonstration, Archimedes dragged a fully laden merchant ship out of the sea on to the beach using a connected system of levers.

Similar methods were used more fruitfully in building the pyramids. The Great Pyramid of Giza, where Cheops is buried, was built around 2500 BC, from almost $2\frac{1}{2}$ million blocks of granite, each weighing about $2\frac{1}{2}$ tonnes. Wedges,

chisels, mallets, levers, sledges, rafts and ropes were used in the construction – but it did take 100,000 men 20 years to complete.

THE WEDGE

Wedges made of stone, wood or metal have been used for many years for splitting wood or stone, holding axe- and hammer-heads firmly in place, and in lifting heavy objects so that a lever could be placed beneath them.

The effect of a wooden wedge could be magnified by soaking it in water to make it swell, once it had been hammered into position.

THE WHEEL

The wheel must rank as one of the greatest inventions, and it is also one of the oldest. The documented evidence available, today, suggests that it was probably first used on a cart and in a simple form of potter's wheel around 3500 BC in Sumeria and Mesopotamia. But it may well have existed long before that.

The particular usefulness of the circular shape may have originated from the observation that round stones roll more effectively than others, and from the practice of using tree trunks as rollers for moving heavy objects.

However that may be, the first

> ❝In time small wedges cleave the hardest oak. ❞
>
> THOMAS KYD (1558–94), English dramatist

> ❝Nature has never invented a wheel. ❞
>
> SIR CHARLES SHERRINGTON (1857–1952), English physiologist

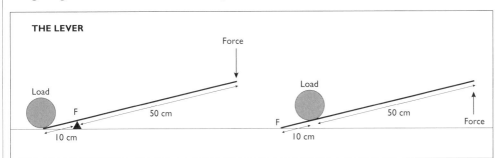

THE LEVER

Load · Force · F · 50 cm · 10 cm

Load · Force · F · 50 cm · 10 cm

Two ways of using a lever to lift a load. F is the fulcrum. In the example on the left, the force required is five times less than the load. On the right it is six times less

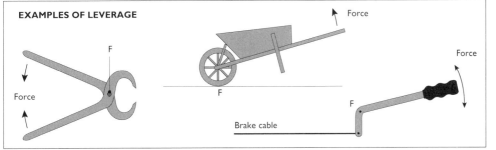

EXAMPLES OF LEVERAGE

F · Force · Force

Force · F

Force · F · Brake cable

Pincers (left), wheelbarrow (centre) and car handbrake lever (right)

ARCHIMEDES

ARCHIMEDES, perhaps the greatest of the ancient Greek scientists, was born in Syracuse, probably in 287 BC. He was predominantly a mathematician and, like many of his contemporaries, was scornful of inventors, claiming that the discovery of anything that made life easier was ignoble and vulgar compared with extending the boundaries of knowledge. It is a viewpoint, still held by some individuals today, that has tended to lower people's concept of the status of inventors which has prevailed throughout the centuries.

Archimedes did, nevertheless, leave behind some important inventions. The best known is the Archimedean screw (⇒p. 212) which can be used for lifting water by using a rotary hand action. He also devised a number of systems for lifting heavy objects by the use of pulleys and levers. To repel attacks by the Romans on his city, he invented a number of military machines and suggested that large concave mirrors might be used to concentrate the Sun's rays on to enemy ships to set them on fire.

His efforts did not keep the Romans at bay and he was killed when they stormed Syracuse in 212 BC. It is said that he was solving a mathematical problem when he was slain. But that may well be apocryphal, like the better-known tale that he leapt out of his bath and ran naked through the streets shouting 'Eureka, eureka' when he discovered, by experiment, that a crown made for King Niero was not made of pure gold.

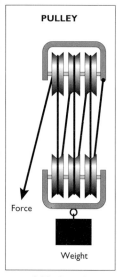

PULLEY

Force

Weight

A block and tackle arrangement of six pulleys giving a mechanical advantage of six

---

cartwheels of which any records exist were made of three shaped planks of wood pinned together by two cross-struts. The spoked wheel originated in Egypt around 2000 BC. It initially had four spokes, then six and eight and even more.

PULLEYS

A pulley consists of a wheel on a shaft which is grooved for carrying a rope or a chain, or shaped to carry an endless belt; it is commonly supported in a framework known as a block. Pulleys were used for lifting weights as early as the 4th century BC and, later, for transmitting power from one rotating shaft to another.

Different speeds of rotation between two shafts can be achieved by connecting a pulley of one size on one shaft to a pulley of a different size on another. In the early days of steam engines, the engine was used to rotate one long shaft fitted with a number of pulleys of different sizes which were connected by leather belts to pulleys on the shafts of different individual machines. A modern example is provided by the V-shaped rubber fan-belt arrangement in many motor cars. In other cases, for example the bicycle and motorcycle, the transmission linkage is provided by an endless chain running over two sprocket wheels. Its common use dates from the invention of the bush roller chain by Hans Renold in 1880.

When used for lifting, pulley systems enable the direction of a force to be changed. A rope passing over a single pulley, for example, can be pulled downwards to lift a weight up. By using compound systems with more than one pulley, it is also possible to obtain a mechanical advantage. Two pulleys, for example, enable a weight to be lifted by a force equal to only half the weight. But that lower force has to be exerted through twice the distance that the weight moves. Using four pulleys, a force will lift a weight four times greater but only for one-quarter of the distance.

Pulley blocks were of particular importance in rigging the sails, yards and masts, and manoeuvring the guns in early ships. A 74-gun ship needed almost 1500 blocks of different sizes, and the British Navy required 100,000 each year. So it was a big step forward in 1808 when Henry Maudslay (⇒p. 52) developed a new method of making them, based on an invention of Marc Isambard Brunel, the father of Brunel of ship and railway fame (⇒p. 125). A total of 43 machines was involved in making the complicated block shapes from elm logs. The mass-production operation, well ahead of the times, was completely successful, and the Admiralty made great financial savings.

Cranes, first described by the Roman architect Vitruvius, around 10 BC, provide another use of pulleys for lifting.

THE CRANK

The simplest use of a crank is as a simple winding handle to obtain levered rotation, as in turning a grindstone or a windlass; it dates from around 200 BC. However, the combination of the crank with a connecting rod was of much greater importance because it enabled rotary motion to be converted into reciprocating motion and vice versa. This was achieved by linking a rod (the connecting rod) to a crank handle so that it could swivel freely. If the rod was moved in-and-out or up-and-down, in a straight line, the crank rotated. Alternatively, rotating the crank moved the rod linearly.

An early application, during the 14th century, was to convert the rotary motion of a water-wheel into a reciprocating motion which could operate a saw, and much later it enabled the reciprocating motion of the piston in a steam engine to provide rotary motion which could turn a wheel. This development was pioneered by James Watt in 1799 but the idea was stolen and patented by Matthew Washborough and James Pickard. They tried to sell it to Watt but he refused the offer and pefected his sun-and-planet gear instead (⇒p. 100).

In a modern internal combustion engine, the piston in each cylinder is connected to its own crank on a crankshaft (⇒p. 105).

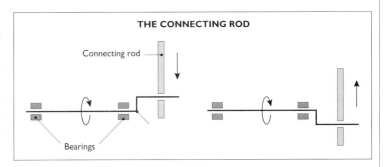

THE CONNECTING ROD

Connecting rod

Bearings

An up-and-down (reciprocating) movement of a connecting rod is turned into a rotation by a crank

CAMS

A cam is a projection on a cylindrical shaft, which imparts a linear movement to a neighbouring component when the shaft is rotated. One of the earliest uses was in trip-hammers. Projections from a shaft, which was turned by a water-wheel, first raised the hammer head by pressing down on its other end and then allowing it to fall. The idea probably originated in China and was used in the West from around AD 1000 in, for example, forging metals, beating (fulling) cloth (⇒p. 116) and pressing paper.

Today, a typical use of the cam, is in opening and closing the spring-loaded valves of an internal combustion engine (⇒p. 55).

THE GOVERNOR

A governor is a device for controlling the fuel supply to an engine or regulating the speed of rotation of a machine. James Watt is commonly regarded as the inventor because he made such good use of governors in his steam engines (⇒p. 100). They had, however, been used long before that for regulating the distance between the millstones in a grinding mill.

A governor has two or three balls, held in position around a central shaft by springs. As the shaft rotates more quickly, the balls are thrown outwards by centrifugal force. This movement is made to close a valve so as to cut down the fuel supply to (and hence slow down) the engine driving the shaft. Alternatively, the movement is used to operate a brake to slow down the shaft rotation. If the shaft begins to rotate too slowly, the inwards movement of the balls releases the brake mechanism or opens a fuel valve. The required control is achieved by using balls of the right weights.

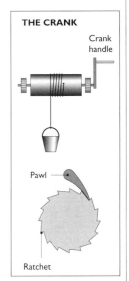

THE CRANK

Crank handle

Pawl

Ratchet

A crank handle used for turning a windlass at the top of a well. The axle is also fitted with a ratchet and an adjacent pawl (below). The pawl is swept aside when the axle is turned clockwise to raise a bucket of water. If the axle should turn anti-clockwise, it prevents the bucket dropping into the well by catching in the teeth of the ratchet

Far right: *Lubricated balls rolling round between two races reduce the friction. In a smaller bearing, as on bicycle wheels, there is only one ring of balls*

Below – Top left: *A simple spur gear train. If the larger gear has twice as many teeth as the smaller one, it will turn twice as slowly and exert twice the torque.* Top right: *Helical gears.* Centre left: *A worm gear.* Centre right: *Double helical or herring-bone gears.* Bottom left: *Rack and pinion gears.* Bottom right: *Bevel or mitre gears*

BEARINGS

Bearings are used in machines to minimize the wear and heat caused by friction between moving parts, particularly where a rotating shaft is supported. This is achieved by using journal bearings, ball bearings, or roller bearings, together with good lubrication, or by an air bearing.

In a journal bearing, the shaft fits closely in a smooth cylindrical sleeve which is coated with a low-friction material such as a plastic, brass or a special alloy. An American goldsmith, Isaac Babbitt, invented such an alloy (90 per cent tin, 7 per cent antimony and 3 per cent copper) in 1839.

Ball bearings became popular in the 1860s for use in bicycles. They consist of an outer and inner race (groove) with hard alloy-steel balls between them. In roller bearings, which can support much larger loads, the balls are replaced by cylindrical or tapered rollers.

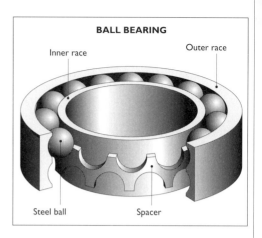

BALL BEARING

Inner race — Outer race

Steel ball — Spacer

In some dental drills and centrifuges, which are operated by compressed air, the air provides the bearing for the moving parts. Hard gemstones have been used as bearings in clocks and watches since 1704.

GEARS

Gear wheels are used to transmit power and are at the heart of almost everything that moves from motor cars to clocks to kitchen whisks. Initially, during the 1st century BC, they consisted of wooden discs with pegs projecting at right angles around the circumference or positioned between two parallel discs for greater strength. They were known as lantern pinions and they were used for many years, mainly in water-wheels and windmills, until replaced by metal, toothed wheels or gears, originally made from brass or bronze or from cast iron poured into a brass mould. Today, some small gears are made from plastic but larger ones are usually made from steel.

The simplest gears – spur gears – have teeth with straight sides and two coupled together change the direction of rotation. If they are different sizes, they will also change the speed and the torque (the turning force). The larger wheel will turn more slowly than the smaller one and exert a larger torque. A smoother transmission is generally obtained with involute gears, which have curved sides to the teeth, and the invention by Robert Willis of the odontograph, for defining the shape of the curves, was typical of the progress in design made during the first half of the 19th century. At the same time, James White patented gears with the teeth cut in

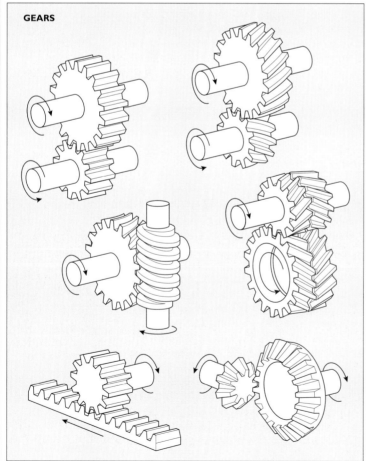

GEARS

a helical or double-helical (herring-bone) pattern. Cone-shaped (bevel or mitre) gears can drive shafts at right angles to each other; a rack and pinion system converts rotational into linear motion, or vice versa; and a worm-and-wheel arrangement causes a reduction or increase in speed and a change of direction.

Epicyclic gears transmit power from one shaft to another co-linear one. In a differential gear system a single drive shaft is connected to two other shafts by bevel gears in such a way that the two can rotate at slightly different speeds enabling, for instance, the opposite wheels on a car to move differentially when cornering.

THE RATCHET AND PAWL

This is a device which allows movement only in one direction. (⇒p. 59) A spring-loaded or free-falling catch, or pawl, is situated alongside a wheel or rack with saw-teeth. Movement of the wheel or rack in one direction brushes the pawl aside, but movement in the opposite direction is prevented by the pawl catching in the teeth. It is not known when the device was invented. It is used in windlasses or winches, in the free-wheeling mechanism of a bicycle, in ratchet screwdrivers, in rack railways and in lifts.

RIVETS

Rivets, first used in the Bronze Age, are mushroom-shaped pieces which are used for joining two overlapping sheets of metal by fitting them through holes in the sheets and hammering the protruding end flat. They were widely used during the 19th century, as steel girders and plates became available. The Forth bridge (1882–89) in Scotland, for example, needed seven million. That it is still there shows how effective riveting was, but it was also very labour-intensive. Each steel rivet was made red-hot by a boy using a portable forge. A man then held it in position in its hole for two riveters to flatten it into place with alternate hammer blows. Riveting machines were invented as early as 1838 but they were not much used until later.

Welding has largely replaced riveting for steelwork, but it is still used for joining aluminium. If access to both sides is awkward, as in some aircraft panels, the rivet might be fixed by a small explosive charge at one end. In pop-riveting, a tubular rivet is used; it is common in leather work.

❛...and from the tents The armourers, accomplishing the knights, With busy hammers closing rivets up, Give dreadful note of preparation.❜

King Henry V,
WILLIAM SHAKESPEARE
(1564–1616)

The Forth Bridge, built in Scotland between 1882 and 1889, contains seven million rivets

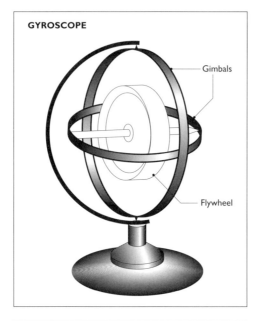

GYROSCOPE

Gimbals

Flywheel

A three-frame gyroscope. The pivoted gimbals allow the flywheel to rotate in any orientation in space

> *The mystery of mysteries is to view machines making machines.*
> BENJAMIN DISRAELI (1804–81), British statesman

THE SCREW

The invention of the screw thread, cut in wood, is commonly associated with Archimedes, and its first use was in screw-presses for squeezing oil out of olives or juice out of grapes. Later, in medieval times, it was used in screw-jacks, for lifting, as in a simple car-jack, and in vices.

Nuts and bolts and wood screws, made of metal, originated in the 16th century but the threads had to be cut on a manually operated lathe or by filing, so they were expensive and irregular in shape. When screw-cutting machines were invented, as by Maudslay in 1797 (⇒p. 52), the more accurate screws they made could be used to control the movement of a part on a machine tool or a scientific instrument.

The earliest screws had shaped, ungrooved heads and were tightened by keys (spanners). Heads with a transverse groove, which needed a screwdriver to turn them, appeared in the middle of the 18th century. A cross-shaped depression in the screw head, turned by an appropriately shaped screwdriver, is popular today, and provides a firmer grip.

THE GYROSCOPE

This consists of a balanced flywheel mounted in a framework of three gimbals, pivoted in planes at right angles to each other, so that it can be spun in any orientation in space. Once spinning, its inertia enables it to maintain its original orientation, as was first demonstrated by a French physicist, Léon Foucault. In 1851 he had proved that the Earth rotated by observing the swing of a 67 m (220 ft) pendulum, with a 28 kg (62 lb) ball, hanging from the dome of the Panthéon in Paris. A pointer attached to the ball made a mark in sand, and this mark moved as the Earth rotated about the plane of the pendulum's swing.

Today, an electrically driven gyroscope which keeps the flywheel rotating is used in gyro-compasses (⇒p. 148), as a ship's stabilizer and in many navigational aids. It can stabilize a ship by detecting any movement and by causing external fins on the ship to be adjusted accordingly. In navigation, it is used to maintain a platform within a vehicle in a fixed position. Changes in position of the vehicle in relation to this platform are monitored and the information is fed into a computer which changes the position as necessary to keep the vehicle on a predetermined course. In this way, the gyroscope acts as an automatic pilot for ships, aircraft, spacecraft and guided missiles (⇒p. 238). Much of the development work on these systems was done by an American engineer and inventor, Elmer Sperry, from 1911.

THE CENTRIFUGE

A centrifuge is used to separate components of different densities in a fluid mixture. It does this by subjecting the mixture to forces much higher than those of gravity by whirling it round in a container. A simple centrifuge will rapidly clarify muddy water, for example by propelling the small, solid particles of mud to the bottom end of the container. To separate components with very small differences of density, an ultracentrifuge, as invented by the Swede, Theodor Svedberg in 1925, has to be used. A modern version gives forces 750,000 times those of gravity.

Industrial uses include the production of cream and powdered milk, and separation of water from fuels, or swarf from oils. Gases, for example $U^{238}F_6$ and $U^{235}F_6$, can also be separated in a centrifuge.

THE SPIRIT-LEVEL

Builders, in particular, need to know when something is vertical or horizontal, and the Egyptians, perhaps when constructing the pyramids almost 5000 years ago, used what is now known as a plumb-line. It is a long string, holding a heavy weight, which when hung freely will always hang vertically. If hung from the apex of an A-frame, the line will pass through the centre of the cross-piece if the frame is standing on a horizontal surface.

Spirit-levels, first recorded in 1661, serve the same purpose. They consist of a sealed glass tube, with a slight upwards curve, mounted in a rectangular wooden or metal frame. The tube contains alcohol and a small bubble of air so that when the frame is placed on a horizontal surface or against a vertical one the bubble comes to rest between two marks on the tube at the highest point in its curve.

LOCKS

These are fastening devices which can be shut or opened by a key or by some other method. They have been used for many years and today there are many ingenious varieties designed to make life difficult for criminals. The first modern type was pioneered by Robert Barron in 1778 and Jeremiah Chubb in 1818. It is known as a lever lock because the key is used to position one or more spring-loaded levers, or tumblers, so that it can also move a bolt to make or unmake the closure. The lock is more secure, the greater the number of levers.

In 1851, Linus Yale invented the cylinder lock which was improved by his son in 1865. It was based on a design first found in wooden locks used in ancient Egypt. The key is used to rotate a cylinder within the lock which is prevented from turning without the key by five two-part pins fitting into holes drilled in the cylinder and its casing. They are held in position by springs at the casing end and the two parts of each pin are of different lengths. Inserting the correct key aligns the junctions between the two parts of the five pins in such a way that the cylinder can be rotated. It is linked by a lever to a spring-loaded bolt.

Mortise locks, fitted into the edge of a door, are more secure than those fitted externally. All types of lock can also be made more secure by shaping the key-hole so that only a key correctly grooved on each side will fit. The various grooves and projections required to achieve this are known as wards. Still greater security can be achieved by doing away with the key and operating a lock by a numerical combination or by electronic signals. A further precaution can be provided by fitting a timing mechanism so that the lock will only operate within certain hours.

RAZORS

Shaving only became relatively easy at the end of the 17th century when steel cut-throat razors were first made in Sheffield, England. It became still easier with the invention of the safety razor by King Camp Gillette in 1895. His idea was to use a holder containing a small double-edged steel blade so that that its edge was only slightly exposed. It could not, therefore, cause any deep cut and it could be replaced as it became blunt. However, it was only with the help of

⁶If I had been technically trained I would probably have quit or probably would never have begun.⁹

KING CAMP GILLETTE (1855–1932), American inventor

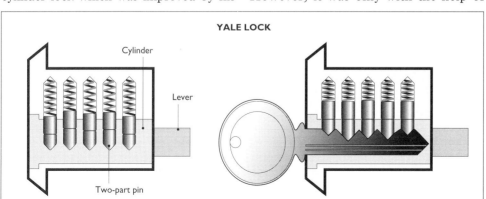

YALE LOCK

Cylinder

Lever

Two-part pin

The cylinder in the lock is prevented from turning by the five two-part spring-loaded pins. Right: The key aligns the pins so that the cylinder can be turned

William Nickerson, who solved the problem of making satisfactory blades in 1901, that the razors were first marketed in 1904. Sales in the first year were disappointing, but the razor has gone from strength to strength, significantly reduced the number of bearded men, and spawned many imitations. In the early 1970s it was made with a plastic holder and an in-built blade, and was so cheap that it could be thrown away when blunt.

Gillette (1855–1932) was born in Wisconsin, USA and began his working life as a travelling salesman before going to work at the Baltimore Seal Co., which was making the crown caps for bottles. He was an ardent socialist who wrote books on social issues and set up a 'World Corporation' in Arizona in 1910 to promote new economic planning ideas. He used to claim that he had done more than anyone else to 'change the face of mankind'.

The first successful electric razor was invented by an American, Joseph Schick, in 1928, and a battery-operated model was marketed by the Remington Rand Corporation in 1960.

SPRINGS

Springs are devices for absorbing or releasing energy. They are used, for example, to fire a gun, to power a watch, to keep two surfaces pressed together or apart, to open or shut a valve, and to provide a suspension in many forms of transport, in mattresses and in chairs. Many natural materials, such as wood and horn, are flexible so that they can be used as a type of spring as, from the very early days, in making simple hand-bows, crossbows and various siege engines.

Ctesibius (⇒p. 55) first suggested the use of metal springs. He envisaged the use of bronze, but today specially tempered steel (⇒p. 16) springs are generally preferred. There are two main types: in helical springs, the metal is wound into a helix around the surface of a cylinder; in leaf springs, a number of slightly curved, thin strips of metal of varying lengths are strapped together. Helical springs were first used in making clocks in the middle of the 15th century, and this explains why, even today, many

spring-driven mechanisms are referred to as clockwork. Leaf springs were first used to provide a suspension for road carriages as early as 1600 but did not become commonplace until around 1750.

Alternatives to metal springs are provided by rubber, first used by an Englishman, Thomas Hancock, around 1820, and by the compression of a gas in a cylinder, first suggested by Ctesibius.

AEROSOL SPRAYS

These are cylindrical metal cans which contain a gas or vapour under slight pressure together with a liquid or solution such as an insecticide, furniture polish, shaving cream, cleansing agent, oil, deodorant, paint or glue. The can is fitted with a plastic valve, operated by a push-button, and the liquid is propelled as an aerosol, a dispersion of very fine droplets, when it is opened.

The idea, deriving from the operation of a scent spray, was first tried out by a Norwegian, Erik Rotheim, in 1926, and brought to fruition in 1941 by two Americans, L.D. Goodhue, a chemist, and W.N. Sullivan, an entomologist. They were working for the US Department of Agriculture when they designed an aerosol which dispensed an insecticide. Their invention was timely because it was used in very large numbers, under the name of a bug bomb, to control insects in the Pacific area during World War II. In that form it was heavy and costly, but a cheaper, lighter version was developed after the war.

For many years, the internal pressure in aerosol sprays was provided by propellants consisting of chloro-fluorocarbons (CFCs) such as di-chlorodifluoromethane, CF_2Cl_2. These have, however, been banned by international agreement since 1987 because it was discovered that they decomposed into chlorine atoms, by ultraviolet radiation from the sun, when they reached the upper atmosphere. The chlorine atoms then broke down the ozone layer allowing too much radiation to impinge on the Earth's surface. So-called ozone-friendly propellants, such as carbon dioxide, propane and dimethyl ether are now being used, together with synthetic substitutes.

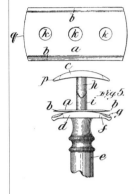

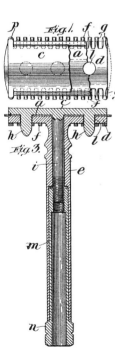

Drawings from Patent application No. 28,763 (1902) for a Gillette razor

ELECTRICITY

'But not only does a moving electric charge produce a magnetic force: a moving magnetic pole produces an electric force, which can cause a current to flow in any circuit of wires in the neighbourhood.'

E. N. DA C. ANDRADE (1887–1971),
English physicist

ELECTRICITY

IN 1800, THE INVENTION OF BATTERIES first provided a supply of electric current which is now known to consist of a flow of tiny electrons along certain materials, particularly metals such as copper and aluminium, known as conductors. Other materials such as glass, rubber and air which resist the passage of electrons are known as insulators. A battery or any other source of current can be regarded as an 'electron pump' and, other things being equal, the higher the voltage of the supply the larger the current. A current of 1 amp represents a flow of approximately 6.25×10^{18} electrons per second. The flow can be turned on or off by a switch, just as a flow of water can be controlled by a tap.

A second sort of electricity – static electricity – is less useful but has a much longer history. It can be demonstrated for example, by rubbing a plastic pen with a woollen cloth. The pen becomes charged with static electricity and will attract small pieces of dry paper or deflect a slow stream of falling water. Static electricity can cause dry hair to stand on end when it is combed, the slight crackling sometimes heard when a jumper is pulled off, a tingling feeling if you put your hand close to a switched-on television screen, and, of course, lightning.

> ❛*Why, Sir, you may soon be able to tax it.*❜
>
> *MICHAEL FARADAY (1791–1867) to GLADSTONE, then Chancellor of the Exchequer, when asked what the use of electricity was*

STATIC ELECTRICITY

The word 'electric' was coined from the Greek word for amber – *elektron* – by William Gilbert (1540–1603) in his book *De Magnete*. It had been known for a long time that amber rubbed with fur will attract small pieces of paper, and Gilbert reported that many other substances, such as sulphur and glass, behaved in the same way.

Friction machines

Otto von Guericke (⇒p. 56) invented the first machine for making electricity by friction in 1660. It consisted of a sphere of sulphur which could be spun around an axis. When he rubbed the spinning sulphur with his hand, it attracted small objects, glowed in the dark and emitted small sparks. Thereafter, much ingenuity was displayed in inventing other friction machines, such as the Italian Alessandro Volta's electrophorus (1755) and the Wimshurst machine (1878) made by an Englishman, James Wimshurst. In 1931, an American, Robert van de Graaff, invented an electrostatic generator which could produce very high voltages and produce lightning-like sparks.

Positive and negative charge

Shortly after the invention of von Guericke's friction machine, it was discovered that two pieces of amber rubbed with fur would repel each other, as would two pieces of silk rubbed with glass, but that the pieces of amber and glass would attract each other – thus the idea was born that two different types of electricity existed. The electricity associated with amber was called resinous; that with glass vitreous. Later, Benjamin Franklin (⇒p. 68) called the resinous sort negative and the vitreous sort positive. This choice was quite arbitrary but, once made, it has persisted. Like charges repel each other; unlike ones attract.

Static electricity was at first considered to be the result of a mysterious 'effluvium' but it is now known how the electrical charges arise. The atoms of which all matter is made, contain an equal number of negatively charged electrons and positively charged protons. When amber is rubbed by fur, it picks up some electrons from the fur so that it becomes negatively charged. Silk rubs some electrons off glass leaving the glass with a positive charge.

The Leyden jar

This device for storing static electricity was invented by Pieter van Musschenbroek in the town of Leyden in the Netherlands in 1746. It consisted of a glass jar coated on its lower half with tin foil on both the inside and outside. A metal chain made contact with the inner foil, and the outer foil was connected to the earth. Charging the inner foil negatively by connecting the chain to a friction machine caused the outer tin foil to become positively charged as electrons were expelled from it into the earth. A spark was produced when a wire from the outer positive foil was brought close to the inner negative foil.

Demonstrating the spark, which could be quite impressive if generated from a large jar, became something of a party piece – which could give a nasty shock to a careless operator. Musschenbroek himself once suffered so badly that he is reported as saying 'I thought it was all up with me.' At the time, the jar did not seem to have any practical application. It was, however, the forerunner of the capacitor (formerly the condenser) which is now an essential part of many electrical appliances. Modern capacitors are made from metallic conducting plates separated by an insulator such as air or oil, or from two sheets of metallic foil separated by waxed paper and rolled into a cylinder.

The lightning conductor

Flashes of lightning are caused by the build up of static electricity within clouds which produces huge sparks either within the clouds or between them and the Earth. They were investigated by Benjamin Franklin when in 1752 he flew a metal-tipped kite up into the clouds during a thunderstorm, and found that he got an electric shock when he tried to touch a metal key dangling from the end of the kite string. He was lucky because others attempting to do the same were electrocuted. It is now known that lightning flashes involve enormous charges and that is why they can be so destructive if they strike a person or building.

Damage has, however, been limited by Franklin's invention of the lightning conductor or rod, a metal strip attached to the outside of a building. It passes into the earth at its lower end, and terminates in one or more sharp points at its upper end above the highest point of the building where the lightning is most likely to strike. The conductor provides an easy path through which an electrical charge can pass to the earth.

The gold-leaf electroscope

This was invented by Englishman Abraham Bennet in 1787 and has been widely used for detecting and measuring static electricity. It consists of a metal rod with a cap at the top and two gold leaves

Franklin flies a kite into the storm clouds at Philadelphia in 1752

BENJAMIN FRANKLIN
(1706–90)

FRANKLIN was born in Boston, Massachusetts, the son of a soapmaker and one of 13 children. He began his working life at the age of 12 as a printer with his brother and then set up on his own in Philadelphia. His success in this field, together with his purchase of the *Pennsylvania Gazette* and the publication of a very popular journal, *Poor Richard's Almanac*, gave him a good income so that he was able to follow his other interests in science and public service.

He began his research into the nature of electrical charge, which led to the invention of the lightning conductor in 1746, and his book *Experiments and Observations on Electricity,* published in 1751, did much to clarify the contemporary views. In other areas, he invented the Franklin stove which had an underfloor draught; tested the designs of ships by using models;

charted the Gulf Stream and developed a way of navigating it by using thermometers; and invented bifocal lenses for spectacles. He founded the American Philosophical Society in 1743; a college that later became the University of Pennsylvania in 1749; and he was elected to the Royal Society in England in 1756.

In public life he was for many years associated with the Pennsylvania Assembly, first as Clerk from 1736; then as a member from 1751; and as its agent in England between 1757 and 1775. In 1776, he was one of the signatories of the Declaration of Independence, which he had helped to draft, and shortly after independence was granted in 1783 he was elected President of Pennsylvania. He retired from public life at the age of 82. Few have achieved so much in so many different fields.

> *His theory is therefore this, that God made the thunder, but that the lightning made itself.*
>
> THOMAS BABINGTON MACAULAY *(1800–59), English author*

at the bottom which is placed in, but insulated from, a wooden case with a glass front. If the cap is touched by a negatively charged object the charge will be shared with the rod and the leaves, and because the leaves will both be negative they will repel each other and diverge. If a positively charged object is brought up close to the cap (but not touching), it will attract electrons into the cap. This will give the cap a negative charge and the positively charged leaves will diverge.

Charged negatively (left); *charged positively* (right)

BATTERIES

Batteries provide a portable supply of electric current. The first was made by an Italian, Alessandro Volta, following the discovery by his compatriot, Luigi Galvani in 1786, that the legs of a dead frog twitched when two different metals were inserted. Galvani attributed this to some special kind of animal electricity but Volta showed that any two metals dipped into a number of different solutions will produce an electric current. He originally found which pairs of metals were most effective by feeling the sensation they caused when he put them side by side on his tongue.

His first practical battery was made in 1799 from plates of zinc and copper separated by paper soaked in brine. Each pair provided what came to be known as an electromotive force of 1.1 V or volts (the unit being named after Volta) which gave a measure of the ability of the pair to maintain a flow of electrons in a circuit. It was possible to multiply the voltage over and over again by linking one pair to another in what came to be called a voltaic pile. Traditionally, the

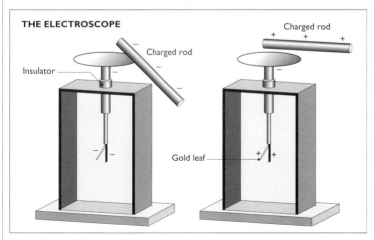

THE ELECTROSCOPE

Insulator

Charged rod

Charged rod

Gold leaf

zinc was known as the positive pole of the cell and the copper the negative. The current was regarded as flowing out of the positive pole and into the negative, but once it became known that the current consisted of a flow of negatively-charged electrons, it was realized that the electrons were being repelled by the negative pole and attracted by the positive.

Galvani (1737–98) was professor of anatomy and gynaecology at Bologna University until he lost the job in 1797 when he refused to swear allegiance to Napoleon as head of the new Cisalpine Republic. His name lives on in the words 'galvanization' (a process of rust-proofing iron or steel by coating it with zinc), 'galvanometer' (an instrument for measuring current), and 'galvanize' (meaning stimulate into activity). Volta (1745–1827) was a professor of physics first at Como and then at Pavia. Unlike Galvani, he welcomed Napoleon's arrival and was made a Count by him.

Primary cells

Voltaic piles were not entirely reliable and in the search for something better hundreds of alternatives were tried. Two that succeeded were the inventions of an Englishman, J. F. Daniell in 1836, and a Frenchman, Georges Leclanché in 1868.

In the Daniell cell, a porous pot, containing a zinc rod immersed in dilute sulphuric acid, stands in a solution of copper sulphate in a copper container. The cell has a voltage of about 1.1, but it has to be assembled just before use and cannot be left set up.

The Leclanché cell consists of a zinc rod and a porous pot, both of which are immersed separately in an ammonium chloride solution in a glass container. The porous pot contains a mixture of powdered carbon and manganese dioxide surrounding a central, carbon rod. The zinc and carbon rods provide the terminals, and the voltage is about 1.5.

The electricity provided by both cells originates from irreversible chemical reactions within the cells, and as they take place the cells run down and become useless. Because they can only be used once, and cannnot be recharged, they are called primary cells.

Volta demonstrates his pile to Napoleon

Dry cells

Dry cells are not really dry but they are unspillable and, therefore, suitable for use in torches and portable radios. The first dry cell was invented by Leclanché in 1877 and is still in use today. An outer cylindrical casing made of zinc is lined with absorbent material, and a central carbon rod, surrounded by a mixture of powdered carbon and manganese dioxide, is packed in. All the contents are moistened with an ammonium chloride solution, and the cell is sealed to prevent drying out. This type of dry cell is still widely used, but it has been supplemented by cells in which the ammonium chloride is replaced by zinc chloride or potassium hydroxide.

There are also a number of so-called button cells made in the shape of a flat disc. They have a long life and can be made in minute sizes so that they are particularly useful in hearing aids, watches, and heart pacemakers. Typical cells consist of a sealed nickel container holding a paste of graphite and mercury(II) or silver oxide separated from a paste of zinc by a porous material soaked in potassium hydroxide solution. Alternatively, a lithium battery contains an iodine compound separated from lithium by a layer of lithium iodide, all contained in a stainless-steel case.

Secondary cells

Secondary cells, or accumulators, rely on chemical reactions which are reversible. Once the chemicals in the cell have been used up, they can be reformed by recharging the cell. There are two common types – the lead-acid and the Ni-Fe.

The lead-acid accumulator is made up of cells containing a plate of lead and one of lead(IV) oxide immersed in sulphuric acid in a glass or plastic container. It was invented by the Frenchman Gaston Planté in 1859, but is nowadays made by an improved method invented by his compatriot, Camille Faure, in 1880. The voltage of the cell is about 2, but three or six cells can be linked to give the common 6 V or 12 V batteries. These can provide the very high current that is required in starting a car engine. They are, however, very heavy; they run down quickly if high currents are extracted continuously; and they can only be re-charged rather slowly. For these reasons, their use in propelling electric vehicles is limited.

The Ni-Fe accumulator was invented by Thomas Edison ($\Rightarrow$p. 8) in 1900. Each cell consists of plates of nickel and iron (or cadmium) immersed in potassium hydroxide solution, and gives a voltage of about 1.3. It cannot provide a high enough current to start a car engine, but it is lighter than a lead-acid accumulator, and very robust, so it is useful for driving electric vehicles. It is also available in small sizes suitable for use in toys, portable radios and computers.

FUEL CELLS

A fuel cell uses a reaction between a fuel and oxygen to provide electricity. The hydrogen/oxygen cell is typical. In principle, when hydrogen reacts with oxygen to form water it could produce a voltage of about 1.3 V. But whereas the energy from this reaction can be obtained as heat, simply by burning hydrogen in oxygen, it is difficult to generate the energy as electricity.

The first attempt was made by Sir William Grove in 1839, but what he called his 'voltaic gas battery' was no more than a curiosity and not much progress was made until an English engineer, Tom Bacon, began to work on the project in the 1930s. By 1959 he had made a 5 kW cell in which hydrogen and oxygen gas were passed over specially designed electrodes immersed in potassium hydroxide solution. Further progress was made, mainly in the USA, which enabled a fuel cell to be chosen to provide both power and drinking water in the *Apollo* spacecraft ($\Rightarrow$p. 249) which took Neil Armstrong to the moon on 21 July 1969. He said that 'the journey would not have been possible without Tom Bacon's work'.

When Bacon retired in 1973, research on fuel cells was more or less abandoned in Britain but it has continued in Germany, Japan and the USA. There are, however, formidable problems to be solved before a commercially viable product, perhaps using fuels such as hydrocarbons, methanol, and even carbon, can be made.

ELECTROMAGNETISM

Electromagnetism is the study of the relationship between electricity and magnetism which was first observed by a Danish professor of physics, Hans Christian Oersted. During a routine lecture to his students in 1820 he demonstrated that passing a current along a wire caused a compass needle placed just below the wire to turn. The discovery caused a surge of activity and led to many of the early electrical inventions.

A Frenchman, André Marie Ampère (1775–1836), who was largely self-taught, soon found that two parallel wires carrying current in the same direction attracted each other but that they repelled each other when the currents

❛In the 1930s I saw the fuel cell as the perfect power source for a vehicle: clean, silent, compact and highly efficient. ❜

TOM BACON (1904–92), *English inventor*

MICHAEL FARADAY
(1791–1867)

Michael Faraday was born at Newington Butts, near London, the third son of an ailing blacksmith. He was apprenticed to a bookseller and bookbinder when he was 13 and he quickly became interested in the scientific books in the shop. By chance, a customer who knew of this interest gave him a ticket to attend a course of lectures at the Royal Institution in England given by the President, Sir Humphry Davy. The young Faraday took full advantage of this opportunity, sending Davy an illustrated version of notes he had taken on the lectures and asking for a job. It was 1813, and Faraday spent the next 45 years at the Royal Institution eventually succeeding Davy as President in 1827.

He invented a method of liquefying gases such as chlorine, but is best remembered as the world's greatest experimental physicist; one contemporary said of him that 'he smells the truth'. His work on the relationship between electricity and magnetism was behind almost all the contemporary inventions. His memory lives on, too, in the Christmas Lectures, still given at the Royal Institution, which he started in 1826.

His family belonged to a small, strict religious sect known as the Sandemanians and he married the daughter of a fellow member when he was 30. The marriage was happy, but his beliefs limited his social life and led him to reject all opportunities of wealth and honour that came his way.

He was buried in a simple grave with only his relations and nearest friends present.

> *"Sir H. Davy's greatest discovery was Michael Faraday."*
>
> *Anon*

were in opposite directions. He also demonstrated that a coil of wire carrying a current acted like a bar magnet, and he put forward the first mathematical theory of electromagnetism.

Ampère was also active as a mathematician, chemist and philosopher, and his name is commemorated in the amp, the SI unit of current.

Despite his success, his private life was beset with misfortune. His father, regarded as an aristocrat, was guillotined in 1793 when André was 18 years old; ten years later his wife died; and his second marriage was a disaster. He chose '*Tandem felix*' (Happy at last) as his epitaph.

Electromagnets

Electromagnets, invented by an Englishman, William Sturgeon, in 1823, and improved by an American, Joseph Henry, in 1829, are made by wrapping a coil of insulated wire round an iron core. When a current is passed through the wire, the assembly acts as a strong magnet; when the current is stopped, most of the magnetism is lost. Electromagnets are, therefore, different from permanent magnets because they can, in effect, be 'switched' on and off. Electromagnets are used in many electrical appliances, and for handling scrap iron.

The same principle is used in a solenoid switch, which consists of a coil of wire (the solenoid) surrounding an iron plunger. When a small current is passed through the coil, the plunger is drawn into the coil and this movement can be used to control a much larger current. When the driver of a car, for example, turns the starter key, a small current operates a solenoid switch which allows a much larger current to pass from the battery to the starter motor.

Electromagnetic induction

Ampère's work in France was supplemented by that of Michael Faraday in England. He knew that a current would produce a magnetic effect so he tried, from 1824, to produce a current by means of a magnet. He succeeded in 1831 when he demonstrated that moving a magnet towards a wire caused a current to flow in the wire in one direction, whilst moving it away produced a current in the opposite direction. He also found that a current was generated in a copper disc when it was rotated between the poles of a magnet. The currents were said to be induced and the phenomenon was called electromagnetic induction. It had in fact been discovered, independently, by Joseph Henry in 1830, but he only published his findings after Faraday's had been made known.

THE DYNAMO

A dynamo converts mechanical energy into electrical energy and the first was made by a Frenchman, Hippolyte Pixii, in 1832. It produced electricity by rotating a horseshoe magnet, by hand, underneath two coils of wire but was little more than a toy and it had to be developed in a number of ways before it became of practical use.

First, it was found to be more efficient to use a rotating coil and a stationary magnet. Then, the voltage available from a single coil, which rose to a maximum and fell to a minimum as it was rotated, was evened out by winding a number of coils in an assembly which came to be known as an armature or rotor. At first, the solid armatures overheated, but this problem was solved by winding the coils on to a laminated core made from thin steel plates. The early work was done by an Italian, Antonio Pacinotti, in 1860, and a Belgian, Zénobe Gramme, in 1870.

The first dynamos used permanent magnets, and these are still found in some small generators known as magnetos. In most cases, however, they were replaced around 1825 by electromagnets operated by external batteries. Then, in 1855, a Danish engineer, Soren Hjorth, suggested that the electromagnets could be powered by using some of the electricity from the dynamo itself. Dynamos made in this way were completely self-contained. All that was required was for the rotor to be driven by a steam engine or a water-wheel. It was the beginning of industrial power generation.

AC or DC

As the coils rotate within the field of an external magnet, their wires pass through it first in one direction and then in another. As a result, the direction of the current in the wires keeps changing so that such a dynamo produces alternating current. It is commonly called an alternator.

In order to make use of the induced current, some method of feeding it out of the rotating coils had to be devised, and this involved what are now called slip-rings. They consist of two separate rings

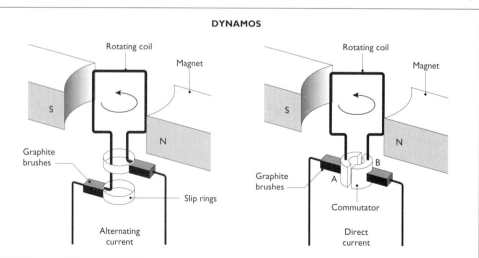

DYNAMOS

The principle of (left) *an AC dynamo, with slip-rings, and* (right) *a DC dynamo, with a commutator*

mounted alongside each other on the shaft of the rotor. One end of the wire from the coils is attached to the first ring and the other end to the second.

Originally, each of the rotating rings brushed against stationary pieces of metal which carried the current to the external circuit but this caused sparking. Improvement was achieved by the use of graphite brushes, held against the rings by springs, which were invented by an American, Charles J. Van de Poele, in 1888.

The commutator

In a direct current dynamo, the slip-rings used in an alternator are replaced by a commutator of a type first used by Ampère. For a single coil, it consists of a copper ring, mounted on the shaft of the rotor, which is split into two unconnected half-rings, A and B (see diagram). One end of the wire from the coil is linked to A and the other to B, and both A and B are connected to the external circuit through separate brushes.

As both the coil and the commutator rotate, the current in the coil changes direction, but this is counteracted because the current in the external circuit flows first from A to B and then from B to A. When, as in practice, more than one coil is involved, the commutator has to be split into more than two segments so that there is a pair for each coil.

Power stations

The first practical use of dynamos was to provide power for arc lamps in localized situations such as lighthouses, shops, railway stations and theatres. But it was the widespread adoption of the much more convenient incandescent lamp (⇒p. 75) in the 1880s that led to the building of the first big power stations.

Thomas Edison built the Pearl Street station in New York, in 1882; R.E.B. Crompton started the Kensington and Knightsbridge Electric Supply Co. in 1886; and Sebastian de Ferranti founded the London Electricity Supply Co., with a power station at Deptford in 1889. They were all driven by coal-fired steam-engines, but George Westinghouse (⇒p. 128) built the first major hydroelectric station at Niagara Falls in 1893.

Some controversy ensued as to whether it was better to transmit electricity by using direct or alternating current. In the end, alternating current, favoured and developed by de Ferranti and Westinghouse but opposed by Edison, won the day. It can be generated more easily within a power station, and its voltage can be easily stepped up or down by using transformers (⇒p. 74). It is most economical to transmit the power at a high voltage and a low amperage, and on the main British grid system voltages of 270,000 or, for some longer distances, 400,000 are used. Transformers are required, at power stations, to step up the voltage to these levels and, at various substations along the way, to step it down in stages to 132,000, 33,000, 11,000 and, eventually, to 240 V for use in domestic properties.

The alternators in modern power stations are driven by turbines fuelled by coal, oil, gas or nuclear power and there are many huge hydroelectric schemes using water power (⇒p. 87). In the combined-cycle gas turbine (CCGT) process, which is particularly efficient and causes relatively low atmospheric pollution, the hot exhaust gases from a gas turbine are used to raise steam to drive a steam turbine. In the combined heat and power (CHP) process, electricity is produced along with heat for local industrial use or area heating.

It may have started in order to provide light for arc lamps, but nowadays the list of electrical appliances which the industries and citizens of an advanced country take for granted is extensive. When the 'lights go out' almost everything comes to a grinding halt.

ELECTRIC MOTORS

Dynamos (⇒p. 72) convert rotary motion into electricity; electric motors do the opposite. The principles on which motors operate were demonstrated in models made by Michael Faraday in 1821 and by Joseph Henry in 1831. In 1837 an American, Thomas Davenport, made a more useful motor but its application was limited by the fact that it had to be powered by batteries. It was only when electricity became more widely available from dynamos that the use of motors increased.

❝I weigh my words when I say that if a nation could purchase a potential Watt, or Davy, or Faraday, at the cost of £100,000 down, he would be dirt cheap. ❞

T.H. HUXLEY (1825–95), English biologist

The first motor was made in 1873 by Zénobe Gramme (⇒p. 72) when he found that a DC dynamo would function as a motor if it was supplied with direct current. The motor could also easily be modified so that it would operate on both direct and alternating current. It is now called a universal motor, and small horse-power motors of this type are widely used in domestic appliances such as vacuum cleaners, food processors, lawn mowers and hand tools.

Induction motors

Induction motors were invented by Nikola Tesla in 1888. He was born in Croatia but emigrated to the USA and worked with Thomas Edison (⇒p. 7) until they quarrelled, when he began to collaborate with George Westinghouse (⇒p. 128). The motor consists of a special type of rotor known as a squirrel-cage armature, which is surrounded by a cylindrical array of electromagnets. The armature is made up of an iron core carrying a number of copper bars, arranged cylindrically and held in position by copper rings at each end.

An alternating current is passed into each electromagnet, in turn, which produces a circulating magnetic field. This induces currents in the copper bars of the armature which cause it to become magnetic. In effect, the field moving round the outer cylinder then 'pulls' the rotor around with it. There are no brushes involved, and induction motors can be made with much greater power than universal motors. They are widely used industrially.

This common type of induction motor is called a rotary induction motor. In a linear induction motor, the outer electromagnets are laid out, not in a cylinder, but in a flat straight line. As alternating current is passed in turn into the electromagnets, a magnetic field passes along the line and this will 'roll' a nearby rotor along with it.

Synchronous motors

If an ordinary rotary induction motor is run off alternating current from a mains supply, which is at a constant frequency, the circulating magnetic field will rotate at a constant speed but the rotor 'slips' behind, depending on its load, so that its speed is not constant. In synchronous motors, any 'slip' is avoided by using a magnetic armature in the rotor. They were invented by a Swede, Ernst Danielson, in 1902, and are used, for example, in clocks, record-players, and tape or video-recorders where constant speed must be maintained.

INDUCTION COIL

An induction coil produces pulses of high voltage electricity from a low voltage supply. It consists of about 100 turns of thick, insulated copper wire wound around a cylinder of iron wires, which is known as the primary coil. This is surrounded by, but not connected to, a secondary coil made up of thousands of turns of miles of very fine insulated wire. When an intermittent, low-voltage direct current is fed into the primary coil, pulses of high voltage are induced in the secondary one. It is not a matter of getting 'something for nothing'; the low-voltage current in the primary coil has a high amperage whereas the high voltage current in the secondary is of low amperage. The intermittent current in the primary was originally obtained from batteries via a make-and-break switch similar to that used in an electric bell. Later, a mercury interrupter was used.

The induction coil was invented by an Irish priest, Father Nicholas Callan, around 1840 and one of his coils could produce a 40 cm (15.7 in) spark through air. It was then popularized by a German physicist, Heinrich Daniel Rühmkorff, and it played an important role in the discovery of cathode rays (⇒p. 77) and X-rays (⇒p. 77). The main modern use is to provide the high-voltage current to fire the sparking plug in internal combustion engines. The coil-ignition system in a typical motor-car engine will step up the 6 V or 12 V to around 30,000 V.

Transformers

If an alternating current is fed into the primary of an induction coil, an alternating current with a higher voltage is induced in the secondary coil. Conversely, feeding an alternating current into the secondary coil gives one of lower voltage in the primary.

Induction coils used in this way are generally known as transformers. The principle was demonstrated by Michael Faraday (⇒p. 71) in 1831, but the first useful transformers were made by an American, William Stanley in 1885.

Large transformers are important in the transmission of electric power from power stations to the end user (⇒p. 73), and within some homes there may be a requirement for a 4 V or 12 V direct current supply to operate a bell system or a model railway train, respectively. This can be met by using a small, portable transformer to step down the voltage and an associated rectifier to convert it from alternating to direct current. Transformers cannot transform direct current and that is the main reason why alternating current is so widely used.

ELECTRIC LIGHTING

Oil lamps, candles and gas-lighting were slowly replaced by electric lighting in the second half of the 19th century, beginning with carbon arc-lamps which rely on the vivid white light emitted when a spark is struck between the nearby tips of two carbon rods. They were invented by an Englishman, W.E. Staite, in 1846 and were tried in a few lighthouses around 1860 but they were not more widely used because they required high currents, were bulky, and needed some arrangement to keep the gap between the two carbon rods constant as their ends burnt away. In the 1870s, dynamos gave better supplies of current and two more compact forms of arc-lamp invented by Paul Jablockhoff, a Russian living in Paris, and by an Englishman, R.E.B. Crompton, were installed in some department stores and public places but were soon superseded by incandescent filament lamps.

Filament lamps

Staite demonstrated a lamp in 1847 using a filament made of a platinum-iridium alloy with a high melting point. The filament got hot enough to emit a reasonable amount of light when a current was passed through, but it soon broke because it reacted with the air in the container. Another inventor, the American J.W. Starr, encountered the same problem when he used a carbon filament.

J.W. Swan in England and Thomas Edison in the USA had more success around 1880. They were able to use the superior pumps (⇒p. 56) which had been developed in the 1860s to remove more air from the containers of their bulbs, and they were both lucky enough to have assistants who were excellent glass blowers. They both opted for carbon filaments and did much research, largely by trial and error, to find the best source. Edison, for instance, tested 6000 different fibrous materials, collected from all corners of the world, before picking on bamboo which he then carbonized by baking.

Swan announced his invention in 1879, ten months before Edison, but did not begin manufacture until 1881, a few months after Edison. As legal complications over patent rights loomed, the two decided to co-operate and their carbon filament bulbs, sold under the trade name of Ediswan, dominated the market. They were safer and more convenient than anything with a naked flame but their light was yellowish and less than 1 per cent of the electrical energy they used was converted into light, with the rest being dissipated as heat. This was because the filament temperature had to be kept below about 1750°C to prevent a deposit of carbon forming on the inside of the container. Eventually, they were replaced in 1910 when an American, W.D. Coolidge, used powder technology (⇒p. 17) to make tungsten filaments which could be heated well above 2000°C. Tungsten filament bulbs, therefore, gave whiter light and were two to three times more efficient.

The efficiency and life of the tungsten filament bulb was increased still further in 1913 when an American chemist, Irving Langmuir, working in the General Electric research laboratories at Schenectady, coiled the filament and filled the bulbs with an inert gas. In 1934, the coiled filament was itself recoiled. The quartz-halogen bulb, introduced in the 1960s for use in car headlights and cine projectors, was even more efficient because the addition of a halogen to the inert gas, together with the replacement of glass by quartz, enabled the filament temperature to be raised still higher.

❛When all candles bee out, all cats bee gray.❜

JOHN HEYWOOD (c. 1497–1580), English playwright

Discharge lamps

Even today, the standard domestic filament bulb, known in the trade as a GLS (general lighting system) bulb, only converts about 10 per cent of the electrical energy it uses into light so that it is being challenged by discharge lamps in which a current is passed through a gas at a low pressure. The colour of the light depends on the gas involved. Neon gas gives a bright orange-red light, and was first used in advertising signs in Paris in 1910. Mercury or sodium vapour gives a bluish-green or yellow light, respectively, and both have been used in street lighting since the 1930s.

Similar discharge lamps, which are three or four times more efficient than filament lamps, have became popular in what is now known as fluorescent or strip-lighting. The familar long cylindrical tubes, containing mercury vapour at a low pressure, are coated on the inside with chemicals, known as phosphors, which fluoresce and emit 'white' light under the influence of the ultra-violet light emanating from the mercury. More compact fluorescent bulbs, using new phosphors, have recently been made as an alternative to the GLS bulb which still predominates in the home. Initially, they are more expensive than filament bulbs, but their running costs are lower as they are more efficient and have a longer life. A high-intensity discharge (HID) bulb used in shop windows is even more efficent but has a still higher initial cost.

An alternative kind of discharge lamp is provided by induction lighting. In this system a gas in a container is made to luminesce by being subjected to powerful radio waves from an adjacent source. Such a system would be expected to have a long life but it is, at present, extremely expensive to localize the effect of the radio waves so as to prevent them from causing massive interference with other nearby electrical equipment such as television sets. However, induction lights have been made since 1991 for use on sites such as tunnels where bulb replacement is very expensive.

PIEZOELECTRICITY

The Frenchman Pierre Curie and his brother, Jacques Paul, discovered what came to be known as piezoelectricity in 1883 when they found that some crystals, such as quartz, which were normally non-conductors of electricity became slightly conducting when they were stressed in a particular direction by hanging a weight from them. For a given voltage, the bigger the weight, the larger the current which would pass. The opposite effect was also observed – when an electric field was applied to the crystal it underwent mechanical deformation.

Pierre Curie used the effect in his invention of the piezoelectric quartz electrometer. It could measure very small currents of the order of 10^{-11} amperes and it was used by Manya (later Marie) Sklodowska, who married Pierre in 1885, in her investigation of the radioactivity of a sample of a uranium ore, called pitchblende, which led to the discovery of polonium and radium in 1898.

Later, piezoelectric crystals found a number of other uses. In microphones and pick-ups for gramophone discs they converted vibrational movements into electric currents. Conversely, they were caused to vibrate by electrical energy in loudspeakers, quartz crystal clocks and ultra-sound generators. In boiler igniters, they produced a spark when they were stressed.

THE ELECTRON

Electrons were discovered by an investigation into the effect of passing an electric current through a gas contained in a cylindrical discharge tube. The current from a high voltage supply was fed in at one end through an electrode (the cathode) and out at the other end via another electrode (the anode). As the pressure was reduced by pumping out more and more of the gas, a remarkable series of colourful changes took place until, at a very low pressure, the tube was occupied by a dark space whilst the glass fluoresced. There was much argument as to the nature of the dark space until it became clear, towards the end of the 19th century, that it consisted of a stream of electrons. These are now known to be minute, negatively charged particles which are a component part of all matter. Their discovery led to many very important inventions.

Cathode ray tubes

The stream of electrons emanating from the cathode came to be known as cathode rays and they were investigated by an English physicist, Sir J.J. Thomson, in 1897. His apparatus, similar to that used by a German contemporary, Ferdinand Braun, has developed into today's cathode ray tube (CRT) seen, most commonly, in a television tube. It consists of a discharge tube, containing a gas under reduced pressure, fitted internally with a perforated anode and a slit. This provides a narrow beam of cathode rays (electrons) which causes fluorescence when it impinges on the coating of phosphors at the end of the tube. The intensity of the fluorescence depends on the intensity of the beam. The beam can be deflected in opposite directions by magnetic and/or electric fields suitably placed outside the tube so that the end of the beam can be directed at will over the phosphors.

The oscilloscope

This is a CRT designed to display the way in which a current changes with time. The electron beam in a CRT is deflected by two plates. One is used to keep moving the beam sideways and then back again to provide a time-axis which can be in tenths, hundredths or thousandths of a second. The other, which moves the beam up and down, is connected to the current under investigation. They are used to study alternating currents, heart beats in electrocardiography (⇒p. 230), and the electrical activity in the brain in electroencephalography (⇒p. 230).

X-ray tubes

Wilhelm Röntgen, a German professor of physics, discovered in 1895 that wrapped photographic plates became fogged when left near a discharge tube and this is now known to be due to the emission of a very penetrating radiation, known as X-rays, from solids when they are bombarded by cathode rays.

Röntgen made the first X-ray tube and used the X-rays for taking photographs (radiography, ⇒p. 225). They are also used, nowadays, in treating cancer (radiotherapy, ⇒p. 226), and in X-ray crystallography, a method of investigating

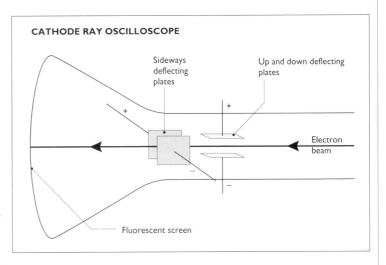

CATHODE RAY OSCILLOSCOPE

Sideways deflecting plates

Up and down deflecting plates

Electron beam

Fluorescent screen

the internal structure of crystals pioneered by an Australian-born British physicist, Sir William Henry Bragg, and his son, Sir William Laurence Bragg, in 1914.

A modern X-ray tube consists of a CRT containing a high vacuum. Electrons from a white-hot tungsten filament are accelerated by passing through a high voltage before being directed at an angle on to a water-cooled tungsten anode.

Valves or tubes

In 1883, Edison (⇒p. 7), discovered that a current would flow between an incandescent filament and a nearby wire if the wire was connected to the positive end of the filament but not if it was connected to the negative end. This became known as the Edison effect and was explained by assuming that the hot filament emitted electrons which were attracted by the wire when it was positively charged but repelled when it was negative.

It led to the invention of what came to be known as valves in Britain or tubes in the USA. The first, a thermionic diode valve, was patented by an English professor of electrical engineering, John Ambrose Fleming, in 1904. It acted as a one-way switch so that it was able to rectify AC into DC in a radio circuit. This had previously been attempted by the highly unreliable method of tickling a crystal with a flexible wire known as a cat's whisker. Fleming's valve was therefore a great step forward, but it was soon superseded by the invention in 1906 of a vacuum tube triode by an American,

A beam of electrons in an evacuated tube is deflected sideways or up and down by deflecting plates

❝I had no idea what the rays were so I simply called them X-rays – X being the mathematical symbol for an unknown quantity.❞

WILHELM RÖNTGEN (1845–1923), German physicist

THERMIONIC VALVES OR TUBES

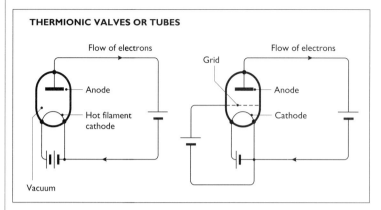

Flow of electrons

Anode

Hot filament cathode

Vacuum

Grid

Flow of electrons

Anode

Cathode

Simple circuits for (left) a thermionic diode and (right) a thermionic triode

Lee de Forest. It acted as a rectifier, like Fleming's valve, but also as an amplifier. This was achieved by fitting a perforated grid as a third electrode between the cathode and anode of a diode valve but closer to the cathode. The grid could be used to control the flow of electrons, and hence the current, between the cathode and anode. When the grid was negatively charged in relation to the cathode, it repelled the electrons from the cathode and lowered the current; when it was positively charged it attracted the electrons and increased it.

In this way, a small grid current could control a larger current flowing in the cathode–anode circuit. Two-stage amplification could be achieved by feeding the output from one valve into

the grid circuit of a second. This type of valve was used in radio and other circuits for over 40 years before being replaced by the transistor (⇒p. 80).

Photocells

Devices for converting light energy into electricity were first made in 1904 and are now known as photoemissive cells. They are used as light meters, for the automatic switching of lights when it gets dark or light, in burglar alarms, in automatic door-opening systems, and in the transmission of pictures by photo-telegraphy. They depend on the fact that some metals, such as caesium, will emit electrons when light of the correct wavelength falls on them. A simple cell contains such a metal as the cathode alongside an anode in an evacuated glass container. The cathode is connected to the negative pole of a battery and the anode to the positive pole. When light falls on the cathode, the electrons released are attracted by the anode so that a current passes.

Another type of photocell, the photoconductive cell, depends on the decrease in the resistance of materials, such as selenium, when light falls on them.

A third kind of photocell – the photovoltaic cell – depends on the fact,

A Kia solar-powered car made in South Korea in 1993

which has been known for over a hundred years, that a voltage can be produced when light falls on the junction of some pairs of different materials. However, it is only recently, with the advent of semiconductors (see below), that the effect has been used in making photovoltaic or solar cells which convert the sun's energy directly into electricity. The development work began in 1954 and was undertaken by G.M. Chapin, C.S. Fuller and G.L. Peterson in the Bell Telephone Laboratories in the USA. By linking many cells together to provide higher voltages they can be used to power cars, or even aeroplanes for short journeys, but despite much research they remain expensive and give only a low output. Their use in spacecraft has been particularly important; indeed, space travel might not have been possible without them. They are also used to provide power in many pocket calculators.

SEMICONDUCTORS

An electrical conductor has to be able to allow the flow of negatively charged electrons which constitute the current. Within a pure metal such a flow is possible because the electrons from the individual atoms in the metal crystal interact to occupy bands with different energy levels within the crystal. The electrons can move within any one band unless it is full, or they can move from one full band to another unfilled one of similar energy. The conductivity of a pure metal generally decreases as the temperature rises because the increased thermal vibration upsets the regular array of atoms within the crystal. This makes it more difficult for electrons to move through the crystal, just as it is more difficult for a person to move through a jostling mass of people than through a rank of soldiers on parade.

However, some pure and impure metals, known as semiconductors, have low conductivities which increase with temperature. In intrinsic semiconductors, such as germanium, the energy difference between the highest full band and the next higher, empty one is very small so that electrons might flow from one to the other, particularly if the energy of the

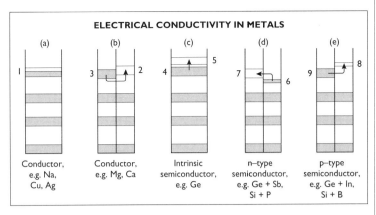

ELECTRICAL CONDUCTIVITY IN METALS

(a) Conductor, e.g. Na, Cu, Ag — (b) Conductor, e.g. Mg, Ca — (c) Intrinsic semiconductor, e.g. Ge — (d) n–type semiconductor, e.g. Ge + Sb, Si + P — (e) p–type semiconductor, e.g. Ge + In, Si + B

electrons is raised by increasing the temperature.

In extrinsic semiconductors, additional energy levels similar to those available in a pure metal are provided by adding an impurity. The pure metal is said to be doped. Addition of phosphorus to silicon, for example, provides a full band just below an empty one in the silicon. Movement of electrons into the silicon causes it to become negatively charged. It is called an n-type semiconductor. On the other hand, addition of boron to silicon gives an empty band just above a full one in the silicon. Movement of electrons out of the silicon leaves it with positively charged holes. It is called a p-type semiconductor.

Junction diodes

Junction diodes have the same characteristics as thermionic diodes (⇒p. 77) and eventually came to replace them because they are smaller and use less power. They are made from an n-type semiconductor and an adjacent p-type. When the n-type is connected to the positive pole of a cell and the p-type to the negative pole, the n-type electrons are drawn towards the positive pole and the p-type holes to the negative pole. As they both move away from the n–p junction, an uncharged (depletion) layer builds up at the junction and this prevents the passage of current. The diode is said to be reverse biased. But, when the poles are reversed, both the n-type electrons and the p-type holes are drawn across the junction, so that there is no depletion layer and current can flow through the diode; it is said to be forward biased. Diodes will, therefore, function as switches or as rectifiers for converting

Full bands are shaded. Left to right - Conductivity due to: (a) a partially filled band, 1; (b) overlap of empty band, 2, with full band, 3; (c) narrow gap between full band, 4, and empty band, 5; (d) full band, 6, in impurity just below empty band, 7, in pure metal (e) empty band, 8, in impurity just above full band in pure metal

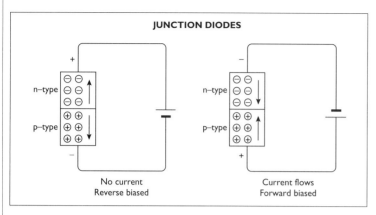

JUNCTION DIODES

n–type

p-type

No current
Reverse biased

n–type

p-type

Current flows
Forward biased

Reverse biased - no current flows (left) and forward biased - current flows (right)

alternating into direct current. They can also be used to prevent a current supply being misconnected.

Light-emitting diodes
Diodes made from suitable materials, such as gallium arsenide phosphide, will emit light when a current is passed through them. Light-emitting diodes (LEDs) were first made by General Electric, in the USA in 1962, and used as indicator or warning lights and in the display units of calculators and digital watches. For such a display, seven diodes are grouped together so that they can show the numbers from 0 to 9 and some letters of the alphabet. LEDs are also used to indicate sound levels. As the sound increases, more diodes, or ones with different colours, light up on an indicator.

For some of these purposes, particularly those which involve portable, battery-operated equipment, liquid crystals provide an alternative because they require much less power. They are crystals of complex molecules whose structure changes when a voltage is applied. In a liquid-crystal display, as first made by the Swiss Hoffman La Roche company in 1971, the crystals are

Representation of numbers and letters by using seven small light-emitting diodes or liquid crystals

sandwiched in groups of seven, as in an LED display, between two sheets of glass rendered conducting by a surface treatment. Passing a current through some of the crystals but not through others causes colour changes which show up as numbers or letters.

TRANSISTORS

Junction or bipolar transistors were invented in 1948 by William Shockley, Walter Brattain and John Bardeen, working in the Bell Telephone Laboratories in the USA. Their first commercial application was in hearing aids, in 1952, but they are now used by the million in almost all electronic equipment. They have replaced the thermionic valve or tube because they need much less power to operate and because they are much smaller, cheaper, cooler, more reliable, more robust and quicker to react. Their invention revolutionized many industries and enabled new ones to be founded.

A typical n–p–n junction transistor consists of a very thin slice of p-type semiconductor, known as the base, sandwiched between two pieces of n-type, one of which is called the collector and the other the emitter. Passing a small current through the base-emitter circuit, which makes that p–n junction forward biased, allows a current to pass between the collector and emitter but only in one direction. The transistor can therefore be used both as a switch and a rectifier. It also functions as an amplifier because the collector current might be a hundred times greater than the base current. Further, staged amplification can be achieved by using the output from one transistor as the input for another. In a p–n–p transistor, a thin slice of n-type semiconductor is sandwiched between two pieces of p-type.

Field effect transistors
Field effect transistors, which are much smaller than junction or bipolar ones, were developed in the 1960s. In a typical example, known as a MOSFET (metallic oxide semiconductor field effect transistor) depletion type, a channel of n-type material passes through p-type. The surface is covered with a thin insulating

0123456789

ACEFHIJLPU

layer of silicon dioxide. Electrons will flow along the n-type channel if one end (the source) is negative and the other (the drain) is positive. However, that flow can be controlled by making a so-called gate, between the source and the drain, negative. This expels electrons from the channel below it and builds up an uncharged depletion layer.

In an enhancement type of transistor, the source and the drain are separated regions of n-type material so that no current will pass between them. But making the gate positive draws electrons into the region below it which allows current to flow from source to drain.

INTEGRATED CIRCUITS

In printed cicuits, introduced in the late 1940s, an insulating board has copper strips on its surface which replace the wires used in older electrical circuits. The printed circuit board is made either by coating all the surface with copper and etching away the unneeded portions or by depositing the strips electrolytically. The individual components of the circuit are fitted into pre-drilled holes in the copper strips and soldered in position.

The printed circuit was more compact than a wired circuit but the integrated circuit or silicon chip, first made in the late 1950s, is even more so. It is only a few millimetres square and very thin but it has all the necessary components of a circuit – transistors, diodes, resistors and capacitors – embedded in it. There may be thousands of them in one chip. The idea was developed in the USA in the 1950s. It was first mooted by Geoffrey Dummer in 1952, but the first prototype chip was designed in 1958 by Jack Kilby of Texas Instruments. A year later, Robert Noyce of Fairchild Semiconductors independently invented a method of manufacture.

The chip is made from a cylindrical crystal of pure silicon about 1 m (39.4 in) long and 15 cm (5.9 in) in diameter which is sliced into thin circular wafers from which over 500 chips can be made. The circuit to be implanted into each chip is drawn many times larger than the size of the chip and copied many times over by photographic reduction on to the wafer. Different areas of each chip are treated in different ways by masking off those requiring no treatment, and by subjecting the others to heat, light or various chemicals. In this way, different components are implanted in the chip. They are built up, layer by layer, and connected internally, where necessary, by fine strips of gold or aluminium which also make links to external metal-pin connectors. As many as 50 different processes may be involved, and the work is so delicate that robots (⇒p. 205) are employed. At the end, the wafer is cut and the separate, small chips are then cased in a larger protective layer of plastic or ceramic material from which the connector pins protrude.

SUPERCONDUCTORS

When an electric current passes along a wire under normal circumstances the resistance of the wire causes some of the electrical energy to be converted into unwanted heat. This means that some of the energy is wasted and that care has to be taken to design electrical appliances so that they do not overheat when working. A possible way of avoiding such problems came to light when a Dutch physicist,

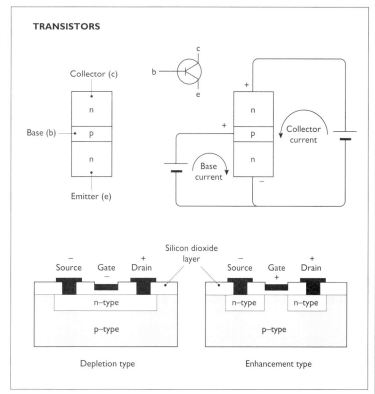

TRANSISTORS

Collector (c)
Base (b)
Emitter (e)

Collector current
Base current

Silicon dioxide layer
Source Gate Drain
Source Gate Drain
n–type
p–type
n–type   n–type
p–type

Depletion type   Enhancement type

Above: *An n-p-n junction or bipolar transistor. Current will only flow through the transistor from collector to emitter if the lower junction is forward biased by a small base current.*
Below: *MOSFET transistors. The flow of current between the source and the drain is controlled by making the gate negative or positive*

Heike Kamerlingh Onnes, discovered in 1911 that some metals exhibited no electrical resistance if they were cooled to temperatures close to absolute zero (0 K or −273.16°C, ⇒p. 95). At such temperatures, a current will pass along a wire with no loss of power and no heat will be produced. The phenomenon is called superconductivity.

At the time it had only a very limited, specialized use because expensive liquid helium, at −269°C, was required to reach the necessary low temperatures. But in 1986 a Swiss, K. Alex Müller, and a German, J. Georg Bednorz, working for IBM in Zürich, Switzerland, made a new ceramic material (⇒p. 22) which became superconducting below the higher temperature of −243°C. This breakthrough led to other materials that exhibited superconductivity when cooled by the relatively cheap liquid nitrogen at −196°C. They are brittle compounds and, at the moment, difficult to make into wires but if the technical problems can be overcome, their use in the transmission of electricity, in making extremely powerful electromagnets or speedier computers and in other ways, could well lead to many revolutionary inventions.

DOMESTIC APPLIANCES

The increasing availability of electricity and cheap, reliable electric motors during the past hundred years has led to the invention of many labour-saving domestic appliances which have revolutionized everyday life.

Electric heaters

The first electric heaters were invented in the 1890s by Dr W. Leigh Burton in the USA and by Colonel R.E. Bell Crompton, in partnership with H.J. Dowsing, in England. Current was passed through iron wires, which were covered by clay or enamel, set into cast-iron casings. A major breakthrough came with the invention of nichrome, an alloy of nickel, chromium and iron, by an American, Albert Marsh, in 1906. Passing an electric current through wire made of this alloy makes it red hot but does not melt it and an Englishman, C.R. Belling, used the wire in fires he designed in 1912. He wound the wire round a frame or bar made of fire-clay and began to manufacture 'Standard' fires in a shed in his garden. More modern inventions include fan heaters, night storage-heaters and infra-red heaters.

Hand tools

Electric drills were invented by a German, Wilhelm Fein, in 1895, but they only became popular when redesigned by two American inventors, S. Duncan Black and Alonso G. Decker, in 1917. Modern drills are lighter and more powerful, and have an on-off switch in a pistol-type grip. They are generally fitted with gears so that the drill can be rotated at different speeds, and with a hammer mechanism to assist in drilling into masonry.

The electric motors used in hand drills have also been applied in making handsaws, planes, screwdrivers and hedge cutters. Nowadays, many of the appliances are also available in fully portable form operated by rechargeable batteries.

Carpet cleaners

The first carpet sweeper was made in 1876 when M.R. Bissell of Grand Rapids in Michigan, USA, adapted the idea, from an earlier road sweeper, of using two brushes which rotated as his machine was pushed over a carpet. His first model caught on and spawned a competitor, the Ewbank Royal.

The first electrical vacuum-cleaning system was patented by an English civil engineer, H.C Booth, in 1901. He had the idea when he saw how much dust was blown out of a carpet by a jet of compressed air. His system used an electric pump to remove the dust from a carpet by sucking air along a tube and through a cloth filter. The pump was mounted on a horse-drawn cart and the electricity came from a dynamo driven by a petrol engine. Booth's British Vacuum Cleaner Co. had some success, particularly after it was chosen to clean the Westminster Abbey carpet for the coronation of Edward VII in 1901, but the equipment was bulky, noisy and heavy.

The first portable unit was designed in 1907 by an American janitor, J.M. Spangler, who suffered from asthma and

But you weren't considered a good housewife unless you took your mats down to the yard, put them on the washing line and beat the life out of them.

19th-century recollection

thought that keeping the dust down would help him. He used an electric motor to rotate a horizontal, cylindrical brush at the front of his machine and a fan behind it to suck the dirt into a collecting bag which was, in the prototype, a pillow case. His machine worked well enough and was patented in the USA in 1907, and in Britain in 1908, but he did not have the resources to promote the invention so he sold the rights to a relative, William H. 'Boss' Hoover, who was a harness maker. Hoover developed the machine into the Hoover Model 'O', which was launched in 1908. In 1926, he added a beater to the rotating brush so that the new machine could 'beat as it swept as it cleaned' which was widely used as an advertising slogan.

Washing machines

Typical early electric washing machines, such as the models made between 1900 and 1910 by A.J. Fisher and the Hurley Machine Co. in the USA, were simply fitted with an electrically operated agitator in a tub. They were an improvement on the older manual use of dollies, possers and washboards, and on the many machines patented in the latter half of the 19th century which had tried to automate such operations by hand-operated crank mechanisms, but the water still had to be pre-heated, the tub filled and emptied by hand, and the clothes still had to be wrung dry.

Later developments, which began around 1920 in the USA, introduced automatic control of the water supply to the tub and heating to the required temperature within it; automatic draining via an electrically driven pump; some control of washing programmes by time-switches; and the attachment of an electrically operated mangle on the top of the machine. Then, in the 1950s, came the twin-tub, with the washing carried out in one tub and the drying in another which was perforated so that water was ejected from the wet clothes when it was spun at high speed.

Today's modern machine is generally both a washer and a spin drier. It has a perforated steel drum, placed inside a watertight casing, which can be rotated slowly for washing and rinsing cycles,

A French advertisement for household electrical appliances, 1913

and at higher speed for spin drying. It can be a top- or front-loader and, by using a microprocessor (⇒p. 201), it can automatically undertake many different programmes. The washing can be also be aided by the automatic and timely addition of a vast choice of detergents (⇒p. 31) and fabric conditioners. Separate spin-driers or hot-air driers are also available.

Microwave ovens

Microwaves have wavelengths between 1 mm and 30 cm, or frequencies between 300 and 1 gigahertz. Used in cooking, they cause water molecules to rotate or vibrate, and this raises the temperature until, eventually, the water boils. The cooking, therefore, takes place within the food, and because the waves are very penetrating it takes place quickly.

R.E.B. CROMPTON
(1845–1940)

Rookes Evelyn Bell Crompton was born near Thirsk in Yorkshire and was educated at Elstree and Harrow school. During his holidays he built a full-sized steam road locomotive and he worked on this project whilst serving in the Indian Army after he left school. His vehicles worked well enough but the time was not ripe for their exploitation.

On his return home, and retirement from the Army, he went to work for the family-owned Stanton Iron Works in Derbyshire, where he introduced electric lighting which was powered by French dynamos. This led him to found his own companies to make electrical equipment and appliances, generating systems, many electrical instruments, and lead-acid accumulators. They were merged in 1927 into Crompton Parkinson Ltd.

During the Boer War, he was commandant, as a colonel, of the unit which eventually became the Royal Corps of Electrical and Mechanical Engineers (REME). In World War I, he was appointed by Winston Churchill as an adviser on tanks.

He was always a strong supporter of standardization and was involved in the setting-up of the National Physical Laboratory, the British Standards Institution and the Royal Automobile Club. He was awarded many engineering honours and elected a Fellow of the Royal Society in 1933.

Microwaves were first used in radar (⇒p. 149) and it was an American engineer, Percy LeBaron Spencer working for the Raytheon company, who patented the idea of a microwave oven in 1945 after noticing that chocolate in his pocket softened when he was close to radar equipment. The first practical ovens were marketed by Raytheon in 1947, but they did not become popular for domestic use until cheaper, more powerful and more compact designs emerged in the 1970s.

They suffer from the disadvantage that they do not 'brown' the surface of food as they cook it.

Electric ovens
The Bernina Hotel in Samaden, Switzerland used a home-made electric oven for cooking in 1889, and commercial ovens made by the Carpenter Electric Heating Co. in the USA, and by Crompton and Company in England, appeared shortly afterwards but they were not popular because electricity was not widely available. They were expensive and slow to heat or cook anything. As electricity supplies improved and cookers became cheaper and better, their efficiency and cleanliness came to be appreciated. A thermostatic control was fitted into a Creda cooker in 1931.

Dishwashers
A number of dishwashers were marketed in the latter part of the 19th century but they were mainly used in large commercial establishments. A rack, full of crockery, was rotated by hand in a cylinder full of water, or sprayed with water from a hand-operated pump. Electrically operated machines first appeared in 1906, but they only became popular for domestic use in the 1960s, by which time they had been fully automated, were leak-proof, and efficient detergents were available.

Food processors
Today's food processors grew out of very simple electric stirrers or whisks made in the early years of this century. They were originally intended for chemical use, but their wider potential became clear when they were found to be ideal for mixing milkshakes. By the 1930s they were being manufactured with an integral motor to which a number of accessories could be attached so that they could be used for mixing, mincing, slicing and other operations. The Mixmaster, made by the Sunbeam Corporation of Chicago, and The Kenwood Chef, designed by Kenneth Wood in England, were typical. Modern versions are more powerful and more sophisticated.

CHAPTER

6

ENERGY *and* POWER

'There is in a body in movement an effort or *énergie*
which is not at all in a body at rest.'

From a French encyclopedia, 1785

ENERGY AND POWER

OUR ANCESTORS HAD TO RELY ON THEIR OWN ENERGY AND POWER and that of their animals. Throughout history, however, there has been a constant search for other sources and for new ways of putting them to useful work.

UNITS

Energy is a measure of the capacity to do work whereas power is a measure of the rate at which the work is done. Thus, a man uses energy and does work when he lifts a suitcase. If he lifts it twice as quickly he uses the same energy but needs twice the power. The SI unit of energy is the joule, with 1 J being the work required to move a force of 1 newton over a distance of 1 metre. This is equivalent to lifting a small apple, of mass 102 g (3.6 oz) by 1 m (3.3 ft). The unit of power is the watt with 1 W equivalent to 1 J per second. The older unit of horse power, based by James Watt (⇒p. 102) on an estimate that an average horse could lift a weight of 51 kg (112 lb) to a height of 60 m (197 ft) in one minute and could go on doing it for a whole shift, is now taken as 745.70 W.

WATER WHEELS

An undershot wheel (left), a breast wheel (centre) and an overshot wheel (right)

WATER POWER

Water power was first used around the 1st century BC in Greece in what is now known as a Greek or Norse mill. The lower end of a vertical shaft was fitted with vanes or paddles on to one side of which a jet from a fast moving stream was directed. At the top, the shaft passed through a lower millstone and rotated an upper one so that corn or olives could be ground between the two.

Water-wheels

The idea was developed, particularly by the Roman architect and military engineer, Vitruvius, who, in the 1st century AD, used a vertical paddle-wheel with a horizontal shaft. The paddles were flat and were immersed in a stream flowing below the wheel which was said to be undershot. The rotating wheel operated a horizontal millstone through a system of gears. However, it had to rely on a satisfactory flow of water in the stream, and it was eventually superseded by overshot wheels. In these, water was fed on to the top of a wheel with bucket-shaped paddles. The buckets filled with water, one after another, and it was their weight which rotated the wheel. They were commonly fed from an artificially made dam or mill-pond, and were more controllable and more efficient than undershot wheels. In a breast wheel, the water fell on to the wheel at its midpoint.

Water-wheels provided the main source of power until well into the 19th century. The *Domesday Book* (1086) records 5624 in England, south of the River Trent, and it has been estimated that there were 500,000 in Europe by 1800. They were used for turning millstones for grinding, for pumping water for storage and irrigation purposes, for driving machinery, and, with cams (⇒p. 59) fitted on to their shafts, for operating hammer-mills and bellows.

Floating mills

Floating mills were invented by a Byzantine general, Belisarius, who, having occupied Rome in AD 537, was besieged there by the Ostrogoths. He set up a series of floating mills in which a number of water-wheels were mounted on the same horizontal shaft on both sides of a boat, or between two boats, anchored in a fast flowing part of a river. Similar mills came to be used on many European rivers, and some lasted into the 19th century.

Water turbines

Even the simplest, wooden water-wheel could work steadily day and night and, unlike animals, it did not need feeding, but it did not rotate rapidly so that the average output was only about 6 kW with an efficiency of about 20 per cent. Later, metal wheels could produce more power, and when the wheel was developed into a turbine (Latin *turbo* = a whirl or spinning top), which could rotate much more rapidly, still larger amounts of power became available.

The first water turbine was designed by Benoît Fourneyron in 1827. A rapid flow of water down a vertical pipe was given a swirling motion by passing through stationary vanes inside the pipe. They directed the flow on to an inner set of vanes, mounted in a rotor around a vertical axle. In an early model built in 1838 and operated by a 107 m (351 ft) head of water, the rotor turned at 2300 rpm and provided 50 kW of power. An English-born American, James Francis, who was the chief engineer on the Merrimack River in New Hampshire, improved the efficiency in 1852 by designing a turbine through which water could flow with less turbulence.

Alternative arrangements were patented by Lester Pelton, an American engineer in about 1870, and by an Austrian, Viktor Kaplan, in 1920. Pelton was a carpenter who joined in the Californian gold rush in 1849 and took an interest in the water-wheels he found there. Kaplan taught mechanical engineering at the Technische Hochschule in Brunn, Germany. In the Pelton wheel, a high-pressure jet of water is directed on to hemispherical cups around the rim of the wheel. In Kaplan's axial flow turbine, water is passed over a propeller in which the blade angles can change according to the water pressure. Pelton wheels are best for high heads of water; Kaplan turbines for low heads; and Francis turbines for medium heads.

Hydroelectric power

In a hydroelectric power station water is fed from a height through tunnels and pipes (penstocks) down on to the blades of a turbine which drives an alternator (⇒p.72). The water was at first taken from the top of natural waterfalls as at Niagara in the USA in 1893. Later, dams were built to provide reservoirs of water. It is expensive to do this but, once

constructed, the running costs of hydroelectric power stations are low and they provide a very reliable source of electricity with no associated atmospheric pollution problems. The Itaipu station on the Paraná river near the border of Brazil and Paraguay, opened in 1984, now produces 13,320 MW of power, and there are many other similar schemes which, taken together, provide approximately one-fifth of the world's electricity supply. There are also opportunities for further expansion.

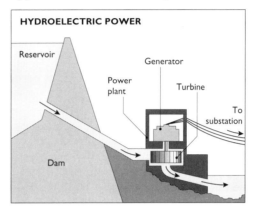

HYDROELECTRIC POWER

Reservoir · Generator · Power plant · Turbine · To substation · Dam

Water from a reservoir causes a turbine to rotate and drive an electric generator

Tidal energy

The relentless ebb and flow of the tide all over the world provides a potential source of vast energy, but it is at the moment largely untapped. Tides have been used to operate water-wheels for many years and such an arrangement at Dover, England, is mentioned in the *Domesday Book* of 1086. A tide-mill for pumping water was also built in the River Thames in 1582.

Today, the main application of tidal power is near St Malo in France. In 1966, a 750 m (2460 ft) dam was built across the estuary of the River Rance to provide a basin of water behind it. Twenty-four tunnels through the dam, fitted with sluice gates, allow water to enter the basin as the tide rises, and to flow out again as it falls. Electricity is generated by reversible Kaplan-type turbines in each tunnel which operate both when the water enters and when it leaves. The 24 generators have a total maximum output of 240 MW.

For such a tidal power station to be feasible there must be a rise and fall of tide of more than 6 m (19 ft). Similar schemes might be possible in a few places

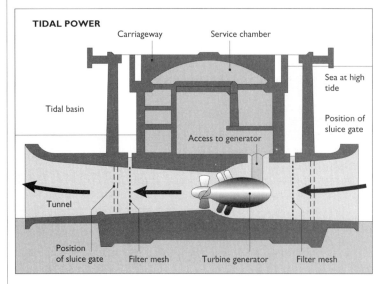

TIDAL POWER

Carriageway — Service chamber

Tidal basin

Sea at high tide

Position of sluice gate

Access to generator

Tunnel

Position of sluice gate — Filter mesh — Turbine generator — Filter mesh

Sea water, moving through tunnels, rotates Kaplan-type turbines which drive electric generators

elsewhere in the world but it is a complicated matter to know whether they could be successful and, so far, there has been more discussion than decision.

Much ingenuity has been applied in trying to make tidal waves move part of a submerged or floating object and then use that movement to produce electricity. The obvious problems have not yet been fully solved.

WIND POWER

The power of the wind is more unreliable and more difficult to harness than that of water, and no attempt was made to use it until the 7th century when windmills first appeared in Persia. They had vertical shafts, but the first European mills, dating from the end of the 12th century, had horizontal, or slightly tilted, shafts. There were two main types – wooden, post and smock mills, or tower mills with the main body built of brick or stone.

In post mills the whole structure was supported above the ground on a stout central post. It could be manually rotated by a beam so that the sails could be set to face the wind. In smock or tower mills, the main body rested on the ground and only the cap, carrying the sails and the shaft, rotated. After 1745 that rotation could be automatically controlled by fitting a fantail, invented by an Englishman, Edmund Lee. This was a miniature wind-wheel mounted on the back of the cap at right angles to the main sails. It only turned when those

sails were not facing into the wind, and when it did so it reorientated the cap correctly through a system of gears. It was the earliest example of an automatic control system.

At first, the sails – generally two or four of them – were made of wooden frameworks covered by cloth which could be furled when the wind was strong. Then, in 1772, spring sails were invented by a Scot, Andrew Meikle. They had spring-loaded wooden shutters, linked together by a bar, which could open and shut much like a Venetian blind. When the wind was too strong it opened the shutters and released the pressure. During the 16th century, a slight twist in the shape of the sails was introduced, and around 1800 ingenious devices were invented for adjusting the sails from inside the mill.

Modern windmills

Old wooden windmills, with a maximum power of about 40 kW, declined in use during the second half of the 19th century. At the same time, a need arose for smaller ones to pump water and generate electricity in rural areas. They were made of metal and had a multi-bladed, fan-like rotor, fitted with a spring-loaded tail-vane to keep the rotor facing the wind, mounted on top of a pylon.

Generation of electricity on a larger scale using a windmill with a two-bladed aeroplane-type propeller, 50 m (160 ft) across, was tried in Vermont, USA in 1941. The Smith–Putnam machine, mounted on a tower at the top of a hill, generated up to 1250 kW, but it was unreliable and one of its blades blew off in 1945. Later, the oil crisis of the 1970s, and an increasing awareness of environmental issues, brought a renewed interest.

Today, there are an increasing number of wind-turbine generators, which is the name generally given to the modern windmill systems. There are many different types with the larger individual ones having propeller blades up to 100 m (330 ft) in diameter and giving up to 4 MW of power. Smaller ones, with a typical power of 500 W, are grouped together on wind-farms, as on those springing up in Cornwall, England, and

Wales for generating electricity. Alternatives to the aeroplane propeller type are provided by machines which rotate about a vertical axis. They have the advantage of not having to face the wind, but may need a kick-start. One such, based on a design invented by a Frenchman, G.J. Darrieus in the 1920s, looks like a two-bladed egg-whisk standing on end. Another, invented in the 1970s by Dr P. Musgrave, is H-shaped with two vertical aerofoil blades at each end of a horizontal beam. The vertical blades are hinged so that they tilt outwards as the speed of rotation rises which gives good control.

NUCLEAR ENERGY

Nuclear energy is released when the nuclei of some atoms are split in nuclear fission or joined together in nuclear fusion. The first hint that it might be a possibility came in 1896 when a French physicist, Antoine Henri Becquerel, found that uranium compounds emitted penetrating radiation which passed through the supposedly impervious wrapping of a photographic plate. By 1900, a New Zealand-born British physicist, Ernest Rutherford, and an English chemist, Frederick Soddy, had discovered that all the elements with the heaviest atoms – polonium, radon, actinium, thorium, protoactinium and radium – were like uranium in exhibiting what came to be known as radioactivity. Their atoms disintegrated quite spontaneously with the emission of three different kinds of radiation which were called α-, β- and γ- rays. As considerable amounts of energy were released, they pointed out that it provided a potential new source of power. 'If it could be tapped and controlled,' Soddy wrote in 1903, 'what an agent it would be in shaping the world's destiny'.

Atomic structure
The 92 naturally occurring elements are made up of atoms of different size and mass ranging from those of hydrogen, the smallest, to those of uranium, the largest. When eventually it was found that one uranium atom was approximately 238 times heavier than one hydrogen atom it was given a relative atomic mass of 238.

Because it was the 92nd heaviest atom it was given an atomic number of 92. This was summarized in the symbol $^{238}_{92}U$ for one uranium atom. On the same basis, the hydrogen atom was ^1_1H.

For many years, atoms of elements had been regarded as the smallest particles that could possibly exist but, following the work of J.J. Thomson ($\Rightarrow$p. 77) and Ernest Rutherford, it was realized by 1914 that all atoms had their own individual structures. They consisted, it was thought, of two sub-atomic particles – positively-charged protons with the same mass as a hydrogen atom, and negatively-charged electrons almost 2000 times lighter. But in 1932, an English physicist, Sir James Chadwick, bombarded beryllium with α-rays from radium and discovered a third sub-atomic particle, the neutron. It had the same mass as the proton but no electrical charge.

Each atom contains a number of electrons, equal to its atomic number, around a central nucleus made up of protons and neutrons. The number of protons in the nucleus is equal to the number of extra-nuclear electrons, so that the atom as a whole is electrically neutral, and the nucleus also contains sufficient neutrons to make up the mass of the atom. The chemical properties of an atom depend only on the arrangement of its extra-nuclear electrons.

The uranium atom
Uranium, a dense silvery metal, was extracted from an ore called pitchblende by a German analytical chemist, Martin Heinrich Klaproth, in 1789, and it was thought to be made up entirely of $^{238}_{92}U$ atoms. In 1919, however, an English physicist, F.W. Aston, used a mass spectrograph which he had invented, to show that, in common with most other elements, it actually contained different kinds of atoms, known as isotopes. Natural uranium does, in fact, contain 140 atoms of ^{238}U for every 1 atom of ^{235}U, and minute traces of ^{234}U. The three isotopes are chemically alike, because they all have 92 extra-nuclear electrons, but they differ in mass and in the stability of their nuclei.

In any atomic nucleus there are repulsive forces between the protons and

❝Atoms are small, hard balls invented by Dr Dalton.❞

ANONYMOUS SCHOOLBOY

❝We shall never get people whose time is money to take much interest in atoms.❞

SAMUEL BUTLER (1612–80), English satirist

Below top: A chain reaction is possible if the fission of one U atom by one neutron, n, produces an amount of energy, E, and three secondary neutrons Below bottom: The chain will only be sustained if the piece of uranium bombarded by the neutrons is above the critical size, as in (b). If below that size, as in (a), too many neutrons will escape without causing fission

binding forces between the protons and neutrons. In the nucleus of $^{238}_{92}U$, containing 92 protons and 146 neutrons, the binding forces just outweigh the repulsive ones. The ^{235}U nucleus, with three fewer neutrons, is less stable, and ^{234}U even less so.

The fission of uranium

In 1934, Enrico Fermi, professor of physics at Rome University, bombarded different elements with neutrons but could not interpret the results when he used uranium. The matter was only clarified at the end of 1938 when two Germans, Otto Hahn and Fritz Strassmann, and two Austrians, Lise Meitner and her nephew Otto Frisch, suggested that the neutrons were actually splitting some of the uranium atoms in two.

The importance of this, called 'fission' by Frisch, became apparent when it was realized that it not only produced energy but, at the same time, released secondary neutrons. If they could be made to fission other uranium atoms, a self-sustaining chain reaction would build up. Practical use of nuclear energy was now in sight. If the energy could be released slowly, in a controlled way, a new source of power for peaceful purposes might be attainable. If it was released quickly, it might be possible to make an atomic bomb ($\Rightarrow$p. 242).

The first atomic pile

When neutrons are used as bombarding particles they have a different effect on

the ^{238}U nucleus than on the less stable ^{235}U one. Slow neutrons will fission ^{235}U but they are captured by ^{238}U as are most of the faster neutrons. And because ^{235}U atoms are so thinly spread, and most of the secondary neutrons are fast, it was found to be impossible to set up a chain reaction in a solid block of natural uranium.

Fermi, who had fled to the USA from the Fascist regime in Italy in 1938, solved the problem in collaboration with the Hungarian-born Leo Szilard. They built CP-1 (Chicago Pile Number 1) in a squash court at the University of Chicago in 1942. It was an assembly of blocks of graphite in which lumps of naturally occurring uranium and uranium oxide were embedded. The purpose of the graphite, known as a moderator, was to slow down the fast secondary neutrons to give them a better chance of fissioning ^{235}U nuclei. In a small pile, many neutrons might still escape from the surface, without causing any fission, so that a chain reaction would not build up, but as the pile got bigger it would eventually reach what was called the critical size at which a chain reaction would become possible. Movable sheets of cadmium, a particularly good absorber of neutrons, were incorporated to act as control rods.

The pile, built up in layers, reached its critical size when it was 25 ft (7.62 m) wide and 13 ft (3.96 m) high. But, with the control rods fully inserted, it lay dormant. On the afternoon of 2 December 1942, the rods were slowly withdrawn from the pile and it eventually emitted enough power to light a small torch bulb for about $4^1/_2$ minutes. Fermi said that the pile could be controlled 'as easily as driving a car'. One observer commented that 'he had seen a miracle', and others spoke of 'an awesome silence' and 'an eerie feeling'. It was the start of the nuclear age, but Szilard predicted that the occasion would 'go down as a black day in the history of mankind'.

There was an important spin-off. Some of the ^{238}U atoms in the pile captured neutrons and were transformed into a new element, plutonium. Its atom, $^{239}_{94}Pu$, contains 94 electrons, 94 protons and 145 neutrons. Like ^{235}U, it has a very unstable nucleus.

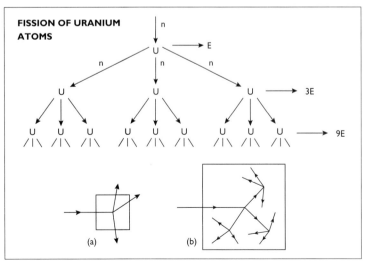

FISSION OF URANIUM ATOMS

NUCLEAR REACTORS

CP-1 (see above) was never intended to produce much power but it was the prototype for today's nuclear reactors, which are used to generate some 17 per cent of the world's electricity (in France, the figure is 75 per cent) and to propel submarines and warships.

The first nuclear reactor specifically designed for electricity generation was built at Obninsk, near Moscow, in 1954, but it was the opening of a nuclear power station at Calder Hall in Britain in 1956 that seemed to herald a new age of cheap, nuclear electricity. Alas, severe engineering problems, uncertainty about energy requirements, a series of well-publicized disasters, difficult environmental issues and much public hostility have prevented the dreams from being fulfilled.

Nevertheless, several hundred types of reactor have been tried. In the most commonly used type, called thermal reactors, there is a central core containing a fissionable material (the fuel), a moderator and some control rods. A chain reaction is allowed to build up in the core so that it gets hot but the temperature is kept within limits by using the control rods. The heat is removed from the core, by passing a coolant over it, and transferred to a heat exchanger where steam is generated to drive a turbine.

Pressurized water reactor

The pressurized water reactor (PWR) is the main type of modern reactor and is widely used all over the world. It was designed in the USA and was fitted into the submarine USS *Nautilus* in 1954, before being installed in the Shippingpoint power station near Philadelphia in 1957. The fuel consists of pellets of uranium dioxide in which the uranium has been enriched to contain 3 per cent of ^{235}U. It is held in long, thin cylinders made of a zirconium alloy.

An aerial view of the Sizewell B nuclear power station, the first pressurized water reactor (PWR) to be built in England. Situated on the Suffolk coast, it cost nearly £3 billion, has an output of 1200 megawatt, and first fed electricity into the national grid in February 1995

These cylinders, together with the control rods, are immersed in a strong welded steel vessel containing ordinary water under a pressure of about 150 bar ($\Rightarrow$p. 44) to prevent it from boiling. The water acts both as the moderator and as the coolant. The reactor is enclosed in a steel and concrete shield.

Many countries have bought PWRs from the USA, and others have designed their own. Sizewell B in Suffolk is a British version completed in 1994. The CANDU (CANadian Deuterium Uranium) reactor, designed in 1967, uses natural uranium clad in a zirconium alloy as the fuel, and heavy water at 85 bar as moderator and coolant.

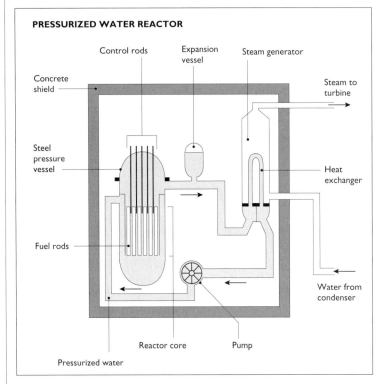

PRESSURIZED WATER REACTOR

- Control rods
- Expansion vessel
- Steam generator
- Concrete shield
- Steam to turbine
- Steel pressure vessel
- Heat exchanger
- Fuel rods
- Water from condenser
- Reactor core
- Pump
- Pressurized water

Pressurized water, passed over fissioning uranium in the fuel rods, acts as a moderator and a coolant. The heated water is used, in a heat exchanger, to convert a separate water supply into steam, which drives a turbine

Gas-cooled reactors

The Calder Hall reactor is an example of an early gas-cooled reactor which is now known as a Magnox reactor. It uses natural uranium rods, clad in a magnesium alloy (Magnox), as fuel; graphite as a moderator; and carbon dioxide gas at 19 bar as a coolant. Eighteen similar reactors were built in Britain until they were superseded in 1971 by AGR (advanced gas-cooled reactors). In these, the fuel is made of pellets of 2 per cent enriched uranium

oxide clad in stainless steel, and the coolant is carbon dioxide at 40 bar. They are more economical than Magnox reactors because they operate at a higher temperature. Many of the early Magnox and AGR plants are still operating but gas-cooling was never much used outside Britain.

A number of high temperature, gas-cooled reactors (HTGR) have also been constructed but have not, so far, got beyond the experimental stage. They use highly enriched uranium, together with thorium, as the fuel. It is embedded in a ceramic material capable of withstanding the high temperatures involved, and helium gas is used as the coolant.

Fast breeder reactors

In a typical thermal reactor, for 100 atoms of ^{235}U that are fissioned, only about 60 atoms of ^{238}U are converted into plutonium to take their place as fissionable fuel. As a result, the reactor 'runs down' and has to be refuelled when only 2 to 3 per cent of the total uranium has, in fact, been used up. Fast breeder reactors (FBRs), working on a different principle, are designed to use more than half of the uranium. They use a mixture of enriched uranium oxide and plutonium oxide as the fuel and molten sodium as the coolant. There is no moderator which is why they are called fast reactors. Some of the fast neutrons carry on a chain reaction by fissioning ^{235}U atoms and ^{239}Pu atoms, whilst others convert ^{238}U atoms into plutonium. The reactor is called a 'breeder' because more plutonium is made than is used up. The first FBRs were opened at Dounreay in Scotland in 1959 and at Idaho in the USA in 1963. Others followed, but they are all now out of favour except in Japan.

NUCLEAR FUSION

Fission of the heavy uranium nucleus into lighter nuclei releases energy, and calculations indicated that even more energy would be available if light nuclei could be fused together to give a heavier one. Two German physicists, Carl von Weizsäcker and Hans Bethe, had indeed proposed in 1938 that the energy produced in the Sun and other stars came from the fusion of four hydrogen nuclei into one helium nucleus.

It is not easy to simulate such a process on Earth because nuclei are positively charged so that they strongly repel each other. The only chance of getting them to fuse is to heat them to temperatures similar to those in the Sun. This was achieved in the hydrogen bomb ($\Rightarrow$p. 242) in 1952, but controlled nuclear fusion is still being investigated.

The research is concentrated on the two isotopes of hydrogen – deuterium (D or $^2_1$H) and tritium (T or $^3_1$H). Ordinary hydrogen, obtained from water, contains about 0.015 per cent of deuterium, but tritium, which is radioactive, does not occur naturally in significant amounts. It can, however, be made by bombarding lithium isotopes, for example ^{6}Li, with neutrons. At a high enough temperature, deuterium and tritium form helium together with some neutrons. The difficulty is in getting that high temperature and devising a container which can withstand it. The most hopeful method involves heating a mixture of deuterium and tritium until it is in the form of a plasma consisting of a mixture of charged particles. This is done in a steel doughnut-shaped vessel known as a tokamak which is surrounded by powerful electromagnets. The magnetic field which they can generate is used to hold the plasma in the centre away from the walls of the vessel. The neutrons that are released when fusion takes place will impinge on lithium compounds around the vessel to provide tritium, so that the overall reaction will be the formation of helium from deuterium and lithium-6. In 1991, workers on the JET (Joint European Torus) project at Culham, England, achieved a release of about 1 MW of energy; in 1993, the team at the Plasma Physics Laboratory at Princeton University, New Jersey, produced 5.6 MW.

An alternative approach uses powerful laser beams to heat small pellets of a mixture of deuterium and tritium.

SOLAR ENERGY

The Sun is a very hot ball of gas with an estimated diameter of 1,392,000 km (865,000 miles), and an estimated temperature of 5500°C at its surface rising to 14,000,000°C at its centre. For over 5000 million years it has been emitting a vast amount of energy and it provides, in one way or another, a major part of the Earth's energy requirements.

Nevertheless, it is difficult to use that energy directly because it is so widely and so irregularly spread over the surface of the Earth. It has long been appreciated that it is best to build houses in positions that make the most of the available sun. Because glass lets sunlight in but does not let heat out, greenhouses with all-glass windows became popular during the 19th century as glass became more readily available. In recent years, the same idea has been adopted to provide hot water for houses, particularly in sunny parts of the world, by the use of solar panels. These are generally mounted on a roof and contain an array of copper piping, through which water is pumped, sandwiched between a sheet of glass at the front and an insulator at the back. The pipes are painted black so that they will absorb the maximum amount of sunlight and modern panels use specially made transparent insulating materials to achieve improved efficiency. This system can, nevertheless, only provide water at a relatively low temperature which can be fed into a domestic hot water supply, radiators or a swimming pool.

Higher temperatures can only be obtained from sunlight by focusing it with a system of lenses and/or mirrors. Archimedes ($\Rightarrow$p. 58), it is said, reflected the Sun off mirrors to terrorize the Roman fleet which beseiged Syracuse in 215 BC, and the French chemist, Antoine Lavoisier, constructed a large burning glass in 1774 so that he could heat chemicals.

In 1981, the construction of a large modern solar furnace was begun in the Mojave Desert in California in the USA. It was called LUZ after the Israeli firm who built it, or Solar 1, and its original capacity of 10 MW has recently been expanded to 675 MW. It uses parabolic mirrors, arranged in troughs and controlled by computers, to focus the Sun's energy on to tubes through which an oil is passed to convey the energy to a steam generator. But this is an exceptional example which accounts for over 90 per cent of the world's present

❛If sunbeams were weapons of war, we would have had solar energy long ago. ❜

GEORGE PORTER (1920–), English chemist

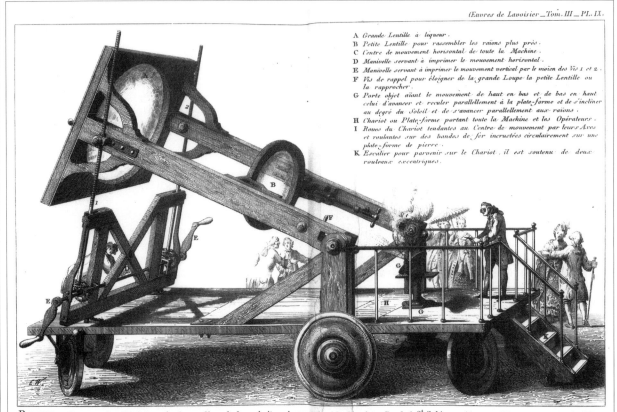

(Œuvres de Lavoisier_Tom. III_PL. IX.)

A *Grande Lentille à liqueur.*
B *Petite Lentille pour rassembler les raions plus près.*
C *Centre de mouvement horisontal de toute la Machine.*
D *Manivelle servant à imprimer le mouvement horisontal.*
E *Manivelle servant à imprimer le mouvement vertical par le moïen des Vis 1 et 2.*
F *Vis de rappel pour éloigner de la grande Loupe la petite Lentille ou la rapprocher.*
G *Porte objet aïant le mouvement de haut en bas et de bas en haut celui d'avancer et reculer parallellement à la plate-forme et de s'incliner au degré du Soleil et de s'avancer parallellement aux raions.*
H *Chariot ou Plate-forme portant toute la Machine et les Opérateurs.*
I *Roues du Chariot tendantes au Centre de mouvement par leurs Axes et roulantes sur des bandes de fer incrustées circulairement sur une plate-forme de pierre.*
K *Escalier pour parvenir sur le Chariot, il est soutenu de deux rouleaux excentriques.*

DESSEIN en Perspective d'une Grande Loupe formée par 2 Glaces de 52 po. de diam. chacune coulées à la Manufacture Royale de S.! Gobin, courbées et travaillées sur une portion de Sphère de 16 pieds de diam. par M.! de Berniere, Controlleur des Ponts et Chaussées, et ensuite opposées l'une à l'autre par la concavité. L'espace lenticulaire qu'elles laissent entr'elles a été rempli d'esprit de vin il a quatre pieds de diam. et plus de 6 pouc. d'epaisseur au centre: Cette Loupe a été construite d'après le désir de L'ACADÉMIE Roiale des Sciences, aux frais et par les soins de Monsieur DE TRUDAINE, Honoraire de cette Académie: sous les yeux de Messieurs de Montigny, Macquer, Briston, Cadet et Lavoisier, nommés Commissaires par l'Académie. La Monture a été construite d'après les idées de M.! de Berniere, perfectionnée et exécutée par M.! Charpentier, Mécanicien au Vieux Louvre.   L. Monsieur De Trudaine.   Par son très humble et très obeissant Serviteur, Charpentier.

Lavoisier's burning glass, 1774

production of solar energy. There are other schemes in the USA and in France, Israel and Australia but it is still uncertain whether they can be developed to a stage where they will be more universally adopted.

Solar cells (⇒p. 78) convert the Sun's energy directly into electricity but have only been used so far in special situations.

GEOTHERMAL ENERGY

Radioactive decay in underground rocks heats them up and the vast amount of energy which builds up in the Earth's crust is known as geothermal energy. In some places it is released dramatically, but irregularly, in volcanic eruptions. In others, where underground water is present, it escapes more steadily via hot springs and can be used. Most commonly, the temperature is relatively low and the energy is used directly for domestic, agricultural and industrial heating. In a few places, however, the temperature of the hot spring is high enough to run a steam turbine in a power station. This has been done in Lardarello, in Italy, since 1913; at Wairakei in New Zealand, since 1958; and in Iceland, Mexico, Japan and the USA.

In recent years, attempts have been made to harness more geothermal energy from dry rocks. In Cornwall, England, for example, three holes were drilled to a depth of 2 km (1.25 miles). When water was pumped down one hole it passed into the others through cracks in the ground before rising as hot water to the surface. This seemed a reasonable theoretical possibility as a viable source of energy but little practical progress was made.

PERPETUAL MOTION

Many inventors have wasted much time on trying to make perpetual motion

WILLIAM THOMSON (LORD KELVIN)
(1824–1907)

WILLIAM THOMSON, the son of a farm labourer who became professor of mathematics at Glasgow University, was educated first at Glasgow and then at Cambridge University. He was appointed professor of mathematics and natural philosophy at Glasgow in 1846 and held the position for 53 years, making a remarkable contribution to both pure and applied science. He was the first to use the word energy to mean the capacity to do work, around 1850, and was one of the founders of the science of thermo-dynamics in which the relationship between heat and other forms of energy is studied.

He invented a mirror galvanometer which was of great value in early telegraphy and he directed the laying of the first successful transatlantic submarine cable in 1857. He also devised a number of other electrical instruments which were made and marketed by his own firm, Kelvin and White. Sailing was one of his hobbies and he invented a ship's compass, a tide predictor and other aids. In 1852, he invented what is now known as a heat pump, used for a refrigerator (⇒p. 216) where an electrically driven pump extracts heat from within and releases it externally. On a larger scale, heat can be taken from a river or lake, or from the ground, and used for heating a building. This was first achieved in 1927 when T.G.N. Haldane heated his home in Scotland. More recently, the Royal Festival Hall in London was originally heated by cooling the water in the nearby River Thames.

Thomson was created 1st Baron Kelvin of Largs in 1892 and the name Kelvin lives on as the SI unit of temperature. This came out of his proposal, in 1848, of an original scale of temperature known as the absolute, Kelvin or thermodynamic scale. A temperature of $0\,K$ is equal to $-273.16\,°C$, and $0°\,C$ is $273.16\,K$.

His intellect, generosity, energy and enthusiasm made him a leading light amongst physicists in the latter half of the 19th century, and his prowess was recognized when he was buried in Westminster Abbey alongside Isaac Newton.

Lord Kelvin – a drawing by Spy, Vanity Fair, 1897

machines, which in effect seek to get energy from nowhere. Early attempts are recorded in *The Century of Inventions* written by the Marquis of Worcester in 1655 and in *Perpetuum Mobile* written by Henry Dircks in 1861. Even today, there is still some attraction in the idea of getting something for nothing, but it is no longer possible to get a patent for a perpetual motion machine.

Examples range from the bizarre to the sophisticated. The motion of a car, driven by electric motors powered by a battery, is used to drive a dynamo which constantly recharges the battery so that the car goes on for ever. A water-wheel is operated from a water supply above it and used to drive a machine; simultaneously it drives a pump which replenishes the water supply. A spinning wheel with balls inside it is made so that it appears that the balls on one side are always further from the centre than those on the other side; the wheel rotates perpetually. A magnet pulls a steel ball up an inclined plane with a hole at the top; when the ball reaches the hole it falls through on to a curved chute which delivers it back to the bottom of the plane so that it can be pulled up again. None of those ideas will work.

A radiometer, invented in 1875 by a British physicist, William Crookes, appears to achieve perpetual motion. It

❛It simply ain't possible to make something out of nothing.❜

A_NON_

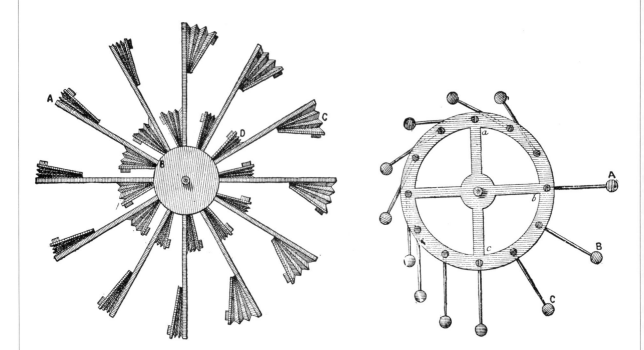

Perpetual motion – two machines, neither of which will work: Above left: A machine invented by Bernard Launy. Each hollow spoke contains enough liquid to fill the spoke and one of the weighted bellows fitted to it. Right: A machine invented by Jeremie Metz. The central wheel carries weighted bars.

❝ What would the world look like if I rode on a beam of light? ❞

ALBERT EINSTEIN *(1879–1955), German-Swiss-American physicist, at the age of 14*

consists of a paddle-wheel of lightweight vanes which is free to rotate around a vertical axis inside a partly evacuated glass globe. The wheel rotates perpetually but this only happens because the vanes are black on one side and shiny on the other. The black sides absorb radiation more effectively than the shiny sides and the difference in temperature which builds up causes the rotation. It is, of course, powered by the radiation.

Matter and energy

It only became clear in the middle of the 19th century that perpetual motion was impossible as ideas about energy, and its relation to heat and work, developed. This was mainly due to the work of the American-born Benjamin Thomson (Count Rumford), the German, J.R. Mayer, and the Briton, James Prescott Joule.

Eventually it was realized that although one form of energy could be converted into another, it could neither be created nor destroyed – a simple formulation of the law of conservation of energy. As the first law of thermodynamics, it is restated as 'the energy of an isolated system remains constant'.

Albert Einstein, a German-born American, who began his working life as an inspector in the Swiss Patent Office, predicted in 1905 that matter

and energy could be interconverted. They were related, he concluded, by the equation $E = mc^2$ where E is the energy in joules, m the mass in kilograms and c the velocity of light. Because c has such a large value ($\Rightarrow$p. 152) this means that very small amounts of matter would give very large amounts of energy if the change could be brought about completely. For example, 1 g of matter would yield about 30.55×10^6 kW of electricity, or as much energy as could be got from burning 4.2×10^6 kg of fuel oil. Therefore, matter must be regarded as a form of energy – and the law of conservation of energy must be restated as 'the sum of the quantity of matter and energy in an isolated system is constant'.

Sir James Jeans (1877–1946), an English physicist and mathematician probably best known as the author of a number of popular books on astronomy, called matter 'bottled energy'. The problem in obtaining the energy has always been in how to uncork the bottle effectively. When 16g of methane, for example, is burnt in oxygen or air to form carbon dioxide or steam, as in a natural gas fire, only a minute amount of the available mass (99×10^{-10}g) is converted into energy with the liberation of only 890 joules.

CHAPTER

ENGINES

engine *en'jin*, a mechanical contrivance, *esp* a complex piece of machinery in which power is applied to do work; a locomotive; a military machine; anything used to effect a purpose; a source of power *(fig)*; a device, contrivance or trick *(obs)*; a snare *(obs)*; an instrument of torture *(obs)*; a person used as a tool *(archaic)*

THE CHAMBERS DICTIONARY,
1993

ENGINES

FROM ABOUT 1700 ONWARDS, England was transformed from a rural to an industrial economy; it saw a massive increase in its overseas trade; and there was an explosive growth in its wealth and in its population. If one invention was responsible, it was the steam engine, which provided a means of converting the heat energy in steam into mechanical energy. Despite what had been achieved by water-wheels and windmills, it greatly 'increased the powers of man' and was at the very heart of the Industrial Revolution, before being followed, in turn, by steam turbines, internal combustion engines and jet engines which increased the power still further.

> 'Science owes more to the steam engine than the steam engine owes to science.'
>
> ANON

HERO'S AEOLIPILE

This was invented, probably during the 1st century AD, and the name is derived from *Aeolus*, god of the winds and *pilla*, ball. It consisted of a hollow sphere mounted in bearings opposite each other so that it was free to rotate about a horizontal axis. Above and below the bearings, the sphere was fitted with outlet pipes bent at their ends in opposite directions. Steam was fed into the sphere via one of the bearings and a tube leading from a boiler below it. The only exit for the steam was through the two outlet pipes, and the emergence of two jets of steam, in opposite directions, caused the sphere to rotate. The contrivance was regarded as a toy but it was, in reality, an embryonic steam-operated jet engine.

SAVERY'S FIRE-ENGINE

Savery's machine, made in England in 1698, was intended for draining mines or pumping water; he called it a fire-engine and advertised it as 'The Miner's Friend'. It needed a fire to raise the steam required to operate it, but it was not really an engine because it had no moving parts other than some valves which were opened and closed by hand.

It operated by filling a container with steam and then creating a partial vacuum within the container by pouring cold water over its outer surface to condense the steam. Water was then drawn into the container from, for example, the bottom of a mine through an inlet pipe, before being expelled through an outlet pipe by passing more steam in. The cycle could then be repeated but water could only be lifted from depths less than 34 ft (10.36 m) because it was really being pushed up by atmospheric pressure (⇒p. 43).

PAPIN'S PISTON-DRIVEN STEAM ENGINE

The first successful steam engine to use a piston was invented by a Frenchman, Denis Papin, whose name is more commonly asociated with the invention of his steam digester which lives on, today, as the pressure cooker.

He began in 1674 by making a gunpowder engine, which relied on the ignition of gunpowder inside a cylinder pushing a piston up the cylinder. When the excess gases in the cylinder escaped through a valve, and the remainder was allowed to cool, a partial vacuum was formed so that the piston was pushed downwards by atmospheric pressure.

The engine was not very successful but it led Papin on to the idea that he could replace the gunpowder by water. And so it was that he built a steam engine in 1698, the same year as Savery. Water was heated inside a vertical cylinder fitted with a piston, and the steam produced pushed the piston up the cylinder. When the steam was condensed, by cooling, the piston was moved downwards by atmospheric pressure and could be made to operate a pump via a pulley system.

NEWCOMEN'S PUMPING ENGINE

Thomas Newcomen used to visit mines in the West Country of England, where he

HERO OF ALEXANDRIA

HERO was a prolific inventor and a clever engineer who was probably born around AD 60; he lived in Alexandria. Many of his writings have survived so that much of his work is well authenticated. He designed military catapults; he built a small windmill which could operate an organ; and he contrived an arrangement of pulleys and gears, operated by the expansion of air in a container on heating, which would open the doors of a temple. His inventions include the aeolipile, surveying equipment, and a screw-press for extracting juice from grapes or oil from olives. His name has also been associated with early water-clocks, thermometers, automatic vending machines, and hodometers (instruments for measuring the distance travelled by a wheeled vehicle).

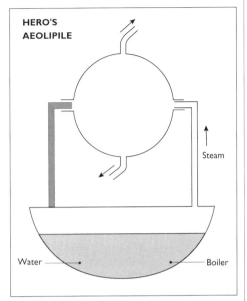

HERO'S AEOLIPILE

Steam

Water · · Boiler

The emergence of steam from the two outlet pipes causes the sphere to rotate

Hero of Alexandria demonstrating his aeolipile

6*The clock, not the steam engine, is the key-machine of the modern industrial age.*9

LEWIS MUMFORD (1895–1990), *American author*

worked as a blacksmith, so that he was well aware of the need for better pumps to prevent them from flooding. When he heard of Papin's steam engine he joined forces with John Calley, a plumber and glazier, to try to build an improved version. Their first steam engine was installed in a coal-mine in Staffordshire in 1712. It used a piston in a vertical cylinder, as in Papin's engine, but was considerably more sophisticated. To ensure a good fit between the cylinder and the piston, Newcomen fitted a flexible leather disc on top of the latter and floated some water above it.

Steam from a boiler was fed in at the base of the cylinder and forced the piston up. But, when that steam was condensed, by injecting a spray of cold water, a vacuum was created inside the cylinder so that the piston was pushed down by the external atmospheric pressure. This downward movement ejected water from the cylinder, and was converted into an upwards pull on a pump rod via a chain operated by a balance-beam which acted like a see-saw. When the piston was at the bottom of the stroke, it was raised again by readmitting steam into the cylinder and by a counter-weight on the pump rod or the balance-beam. The cycle could then be repeated.

The Newcomen engine was highly successful and was used all over Europe for more than 50 years. By 1740, an engine with a cylinder 9 ft (2.74 m) long and 30 in (76 cm) in diameter could do in one day the work previously done by shifts of 25 men and 10 horses in one week. In 1775, a still larger engine, built by John Smeaton, the creator of the Eddystone lighthouse (⇒p. 25), emptied a dry dock in Kronstad, Russia, in two weeks. It had previously taken a year using high windmills.

Steam enters the cylinder above the piston through valve A, and below it through valve B. The steam is forced out into a separate water-cooled condenser through valve C on the up-stroke or valve D on the down-stroke

Newcomen's engine was, nevertheless, far from perfect. It converted only about one per cent of the available heat energy into mechanical energy and, as a result, used vast amounts of fuel. This did not matter too much when it was used in coal-mines, and Newcomen engines played a large part in keeping the coal industry alive by bringing many flooded mines back into production.

WATT'S STEAM ENGINE

James Watt (⇒p. 102) was responsible for converting Newcomen's basic and inefficient engine, which was only really suitable for pumping water, into a reliable and flexible source of power for a wide range of industries. He saw that the main inefficiency of the Newcomen engine was caused by the repeated heating and cooling of its cylinder. How could this be avoided? The answer came to him one Sunday in spring 1765 when he was walking on the Green of Glasgow. The cylinder, he realized, could be kept permanently hot if the steam was passed into a separate vessel, through a valved pipe, before it was condensed. Furthermore, the cylinder could be kept hot, and the condensing vessel cold, by external lagging. However, it was not until 1776 that he built his first successful engine.

Thereafter, he improved it in many ways. In particular, he patented a double-acting steam engine in 1782 to replace the previous single-acting versions. A cover on the top of the cylinder was fitted with a newly invented stuffing-box which prevented any escape of steam whilst allowing free up-and-down movement of the piston rod. When operating, the piston was moved downwards to the bottom of its stroke by feeding steam in above it, and this movement forced exhaust steam (from the previous stroke) out into a separate condenser. The supply of steam was then redirected, through a valve, so as to enter the cylinder below the piston. This pushed it to the top of the stroke and, once again, ejected exhaust steam into the condenser. And so on.

Because the piston rod both pulled and pushed in this double-acting engine, the balance-beam, operated by chains in a single-acting engine, which only reacted

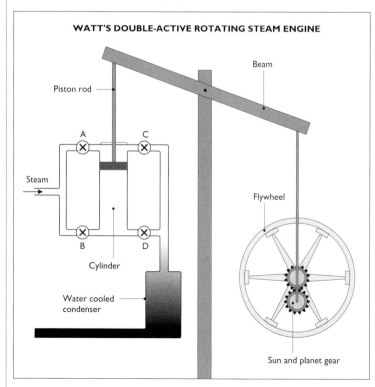

WATT'S DOUBLE-ACTIVE ROTATING STEAM ENGINE

Beam
Piston rod
A C
Steam
B D
Cylinder
Water cooled condenser
Flywheel
Sun and planet gear

James Watt with a model of his engine, after a painting by Marcus Stone

to a pull, had to be modified. Watt devised a system of linked rods to cope with this, and he also incorporated a sun-and-planet gear mechanism for converting the reciprocating motion of the piston rod into rotary motion; a heavy flywheel; a centrifugal governor (⇒p. 59); a newly designed poppet valve (⇒p. 55); and an indicator for measuring steam pressure. The newly patented 'rotative steam engine' was used to drive machinery, first in spinning and weaving mills, and later in a wide variety of other factories. It was the key invention which opened the door to the Industrial Revolution.

One of the first Watt engines was installed in the Samuel Whitbread brewery in London in 1785 to grind malt. The cylinder was 25 in (63 cm) in diameter; the stroke of the piston 6 ft (1.83 m); and the flywheel was 14 ft (4.27 m) across. The engine did the work of 24 horses and it can still be seen in operation in the Powerhouse Museum in Sydney, Australia.

HIGH-PRESSURE ENGINES

Watt used steam at a pressure of about 2 to 3 lb/m^2 (0.14 to 0.21 kg/cm^2) in his engines but he realized that higher pressure would produce more power. The reason for this is that the temperature of steam increases with pressure, as in a pressure cooker, and the higher the temperature inside an engine the greater the energy it will provide. Watt was, however, reluctant to use higher pressures because he thought that his engines, though well built for their day, might not stand up to the increased stresses. This next step forward was, therefore, pioneered by Oliver Evans (1755–1819) in America and by Richard Trevithick (1771–1833) in England.

Oliver Evans was born on a farm in Newport, Delaware and, after leaving school at 14, he was apprenticed to a wagonmaker. He took out a US patent for a steam-driven carriage as early as 1789 but he had no financial support and when his idea was ridiculed by the authorities in Pennsylvania and Maryland he concentrated on designing stationary engines. He built some 50 engines, operating at pressures up to 200 lb/in^2 (14.06 kg/cm^2) before he died in 1819, shortly after his main factory had been destroyed by a fire started by one of his employees who bore a grudge.

Trevithick was born in Redruth, Cornwall, where his father managed a local coal mine. He served an engineering apprenticeship with William Murdoch, one of Watt's assistants, and was familiar with the Newcomen engine used in his father's mine, so it was not surprising that he turned his attention, around 1800, to designing his own double-acting engine.

❝He traces the steam engine back to the tea-kettle.❞

BENJAMIN DISRAELI, British statesman, in a speech in the House of Commons, 11 April 1845

The steam he used was at a pressure of 60 lb/in² (4.22 kg/cm²) and a temperature of 145°C. As safety valves he incorporated, first, weights placed on top of discs covering openings in the boiler, and, later, a plug of lead just below the water line. The cylinder, positioned horizontally within the boiler to keep it hot was connected directly to a crankshaft (⇒p. 59) to provide rotary motion. Trevithick discarded Watt's separate condensing vessel and ejected the exhaust steam directly from the cylinder into the atmosphere. This made his engines noisy so that they came to be known as 'puffers'.

They were, however, much lighter and more powerful than previous designs and Trevithick was able to adapt them to drive a road vehicle in 1803, and, a year later, the first steam locomotive ever made. However, nothing that he did was commercially successful and he was considerably in debt when he died in 1833.

STEAM TURBINES

The 'snorting steam and the piston stroke' of the steam engine were not challenged as the best source of energy until the internal combustion engine and electrical power began to compete towards the end of the 19th century. However, even then, the invention of the steam turbine in 1882 meant that steam still had a big role to play.

A turbine is a device in which a liquid or gas passing over blades attached to a shaft causes the shaft to rotate, for example as in the water-wheel and the windmill. Carl de Laval, a Swede, was the first to realize that it might be possible to drive a turbine by using steam. He was involved in designing a cream-separator and he needed higher rotational speeds than he could obtain from a traditional steam engine. He achieved these speeds by directing jets of very high-pressure steam against the blades of a single turbine wheel.

JAMES WATT
(1736–1819)

WATT was born in Greenock, Scotland, the son of a merchant and joiner. He learnt his early mechanical skills in his father's workshop, as an assistant to an optician, and as an instrument maker in London, before he was appointed mathematical instrument maker at the University of Glasgow. It was whilst he was mending a Newcomen engine in 1764 that he began to think of ways to improve it, and he soon left his university post to devote full attention to this new project. He made models to satisfy himself that his ideas would work, and took out a patent in 1769 for 'A New Method of Lessening the Consumption of Steam and Fuel in Fire Engines'. But building a working engine turned out to be a very frustrating experience. A partnership with John Roebuck, a Scottish industrialist, suffered a financial collapse; the mechanics involved could not achieve the accuracy required; he was not in good health; his wife died; and he had to take work as a canal surveyor to earn some money. It all led him to say that 'of all the things in life there is nothing more foolish than inventing'.

Fortunately, things improved when Watt met Matthew Boulton, the wealthy owner of a machine shop in Birmingham manned by skilled craftsmen. The firm of Boulton and Watt was established in 1775, and their first steam engine was completed a year later. Boulton's confident business approach ensured continuing sales and Watt's inventive mind introduced many technical changes.

Watt retired in 1800 when his basic patents ran out. By then, the firm of Boulton and Watt had made over 500 steam engines. He said 'My inventions are giving employment to the best part of a million people, and having added many millions to the natural riches, I have a natural right to rest in my extreme age.'

He died at the age of 83 and was buried in Westminster Abbey. The inscription on his tomb praises him as a 'benefactor of humanity'.

The speed of rotation of his turbine was, however, far too high for most uses, and the steam turbine only became successful when its design was modified by Charles Parsons. He was born in London in 1854, the fourth son of the Earl of Rosse, himself a distinguished astronomer. After private tuition at home, Parsons studied mathematics at the Universities of Dublin and Cambridge before serving an engineering apprenticeship. Whilst working on traditional steam engines, he recognized that for the successful generation of electricity, something would be required to turn a dynamo more rapidly so he turned his attention to the steam turbine.

Parsons realized that the exchange of energy between the steam and the turbine blades in the de Laval turbine took place in one stage; it was a 'head-on' collision. He hit on the idea of exchanging the energy, more smoothly and more completely, in stages. A shaft was fitted with a number of turbine wheels and supported, horizontally on bearings, within a steam-proof, cylindrical casing. Fixed blades were attached around the inside of the casing and between the turbine wheels with their blades set more or less at right angles to those on the wheels. High-pressure steam, fed into the casing, passed alternately through the fixed blades and over the turbine blades. The thrust on the latter caused the shaft to rotate. The blades fitted at the inlet were smaller than those at the outlet, because the former had to withstand a much higher pressure of steam. At the outlet, the low-pressure steam passed into a condenser and the vacuum produced helped to maintain the flow of steam.

Steam turbines are more efficient than traditional steam engines and they are extremely reliable. Parsons used them, at first, to generate electricity, and he designed a high-speed dynamo for this purpose. His earliest turbo-generator could only power seven one-kilowatt fires; those fitted in a modern power station can provide power for a city with a population of one million. Later, in 1894, he used his engine to drive an experimental 100 ft (30.48 m) ship, the SY *Turbinia*, at 34.5 knots, during a Spithead review, and this led to its adoption as a marine engine, by the Royal Navy and later by the merchant navy.

He became a Fellow of the Royal Society when he was 42; he was knighted in 1911; and he received the Order of Merit in 1927. Appropriately, perhaps, he died in his bunk on board ship off the West Indies in 1931.

The SY Turbinia *fitted by Sir Charles Parsons with his experimental turbine engine in 1894, making it the first turbine-powered vessel in the world*

INTERNAL COMBUSTION ENGINES

Internal combustion engines convert the chemical energy in a gaseous or liquid fuel into mechanical energy, generally by moving a piston inside a cylinder by burning a mixture of the fuel and air inside the cylinder.

GAS ENGINES

The first commercial gas engine, which functioned very much like Newcomen's steam engine, was invented by Étienne Lenoir in 1859. He was born in Belgium but moved to France when he was 16 years old. In his engine, a mixture of coal gas and air was drawn into a cylinder fitted with a piston, and was exploded by passing an electric spark generated by an induction coil. The explosion moved the piston in the cylinder (the power stroke), and the waste gases were pushed out from the cylinder as the piston returned to its original position. The cycle could then be repeated – thus it was called a two-stroke engine.

The engine was quite large but had a power of only 2 hp (1.5 kW). Nevertheless, it was satisfactory for operating small machines such as lathes and pumps and over 400 were made. Lenoir died in 1900 without any acclaim for his achievements.

The Otto four-stroke cycle

The first fully successful gas engine was built by a German, Nikolaus August Otto (1832–91), in 1876. It operated on the so-called Otto four-stroke cycle, which has been widely used ever since. The cylinder in an Otto engine has two valves at the top, one entry valve for the introduction of the gas–air mixture and one exhaust valve for the removal of the combustion products. The four strokes involved in the cycle are as summarized in the diagram opposite: as intake, compression, power and exhaust.

Otto was born near Schlangenbad in Germany and, though he left school at 16 without any recognized technical education, he was full of ideas and a good organizer. Like most other inventors, he was also persistent. When one of the his first engines blew up in 1861 he was left almost penniless, and it

was only a successful link-up with a compatriot, Eugen Langen, which kept him going. Later, his engines were so successful that competitors tried to attack him by claiming that he had infringed the 1862 patent rights of a Frenchman, Beau de Rochas.

Be that as it may, Otto's engines were remarkably successful and, by the time of his death, more than 30,000 had been sold. One of the first, the 'Otto Silent', produced only 3 hp (2.2 kW), but by 1917, when they reached the zenith of their popularity, engines of 5000 hp (3675 kW) were available and they were fully competitive with steam engines.

PETROL ENGINES

The first petrol engines were built by two Germans, Gottlieb Daimler in 1883, and Karl Benz in 1884. In both designs, a mixture of petrol and air was fed into a cylinder from a carburettor and ignited, but they differed in the type of carburettor and the method of ignition used. The engines functioned in much the same way as a gas engine but they had distinct advantages. First, the liquid petrol was more easily stored and transported than any gaseous fuel; and second, the petrol engine could run at a much higher speed, and had a higher power/weight ratio than any gas engine.

Daimler (1834–1900) was born in Schorndorf, the son of a baker. He served an apprenticeship with a gun-maker and, after spending some years abroad, worked with Otto and Langen from 1872 to 1882, until he left to set up on his own in Bad Cannstadt, near Stuttgart. Benz (1844–1929) was the son of an engine-driver. He spent his life in Mannheim, where he founded Benz and Company in 1883.

The carburettor

Most modern-day carburettors are based on the invention of the spray carburettor by Wilhelm Maybach, an associate of Daimler's, in 1893. Petrol is stored at a constant level inside a cylindrical chamber by using a float (⇒p. 54). As the float moves up and down, it opens or

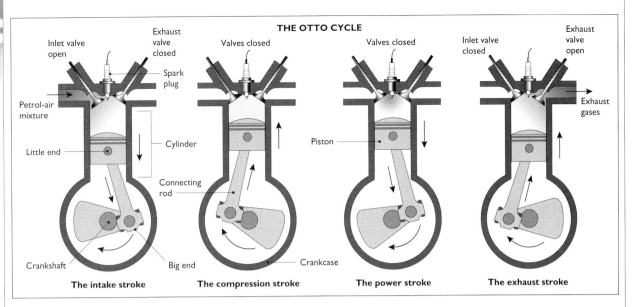

THE OTTO CYCLE

The intake stroke | The compression stroke | The power stroke | The exhaust stroke

Labels: Inlet valve open, Exhaust valve closed, Spark plug, Petrol-air mixture, Little end, Cylinder, Connecting rod, Crankshaft, Big end, Crankcase, Valves closed, Valves closed, Piston, Inlet valve closed, Exhaust valve open, Exhaust gases

shuts a needle-valve to control the petrol supply being pumped from the main tank. The petrol in the chamber can pass through a fine jet into the air intake, and the flow of air across the jet draws the petrol out in a fine spray, which ensures good mixing. The air intake is fitted with an adjustable shutter (a choke) which, when it is closed, limits the supply of air and ensures the petrol-rich mixture which is needed for starting a cold engine.

Carburettors are not needed in fuel-injection systems in which the fuel is injected directly into the cylinder.

Ignition

The fuel mixture in a cylinder was originally ignited by either hot-tube or flame ignition. In the former, there was an externally heated incandescent tube which protruded into the cylinder and which could be uncovered to fire the mixture. In the latter, a shutter was opened to expose the fuel mixture to a flame, but, as the process of ignition blew it out, a second flame was also needed to relight it.

Both methods were soon replaced by electrical ignition as used by Lenoir in his gas engine and as favoured by Benz. This was achieved by fitting a spark plug, which had been invented by Lenoir in 1883, through the cylinder head. It was operated by the voltage obtainable from a magneto ($\Rightarrow$p. 72) or from an induction coil ($\Rightarrow$p. 74) powered by a battery. Coil ignition eventually predominated and the

precise timing of the spark was controlled by a rotating contact-breaker (distributor) which was driven, through gears, by the engine. The faster the engine worked, the faster the sparks were passed.

As with carburettors, there have been many patented types of spark plug, but it is more the materials that have changed rather than the principles. Nowadays, the current necessary to operate the spark may be provided by electronic circuitry rather than a coil.

The crankshaft

Connecting rods link the lower ends of the pistons in an engine to a crankshaft which is rotated by the up and down movement of the pistons ($\Rightarrow$p. 55). Because each piston only drives the crankshaft round on one stroke out of every four, most engines have four, six or eight cylinders, so that some pistons are moving up whilst the others move down. The crankshaft is also connected to a heavy toothed flywheel at the gear box end and its momentum ensures that the shaft rotates smoothly. An engine is also started by turning this flywheel using a starter motor.

The camshaft

The inlet of fuel and the outlet of exhaust gases are controlled by poppet valves ($\Rightarrow$p. 55) made of heat-resistant steel. They are kept tightly shut by springs, but they can be opened by lifting them off

1 On the intake stroke, the piston moves down and a mixture of petrol and air from the carburettor is drawn into the cylinder through the open inlet valve. 2 On the compression stroke, the piston moves up and compresses the petrol-air mixture. 3 On the power stroke, the compressed mixture is ignited by a spark from the plug and this drives the piston down. 4 On the exhaust stroke, the piston moves up and pushes the exhaust gases out through the open exhaust valve

their seats using valve rockers or tappets. These open and close the valves at the correct moment because they are operated by cams (⇒p. 55) on a camshaft, the rotation of which is linked to that of the crankshaft. The rotating crankshaft can also be used to drive a cooling fan, an alternator for charging the car battery, and an oil pump.

Lubrication

The friction between the many moving parts in an engine would cause excessive heating and wear without the thorough system of lubrication which is part and parcel of modern design. An English engineer, F.W. Lanchester, was the first to use pressurized lubrication in 1897. He pumped oil round the engine and that has been the normal practice ever since. There have, however, been tremendous advances in the types of oil used.

Oils get thinner, i.e. less viscous, as they are heated, and this lowers their lubricating power. Yet a motor-car oil must lubricate well both below 0°C, when a car is started in winter, or well over 200°C in the centre of an engine at full throttle. It was once necessary to use a different engine oil during the winter from that used in the summer months, but multigrade oils are now available. They contain polymers (⇒p. 32) which expand as the temperature rises and this counteracts the thinning of the oil so that the overall viscosity is not changed. They also contain detergents (⇒p. 31) and dispersants, which prevent the build-up of any solid deposits on the engine surfaces.

Compression ratio

A compression ratio of 10:1, for a typical family car, means that the fuel mixture is compressed to 1/10th of its original volume in the compression stroke. The higher the ratio the more powerful the engine, but there are limitations because too much compression causes the petrol–air mixture to detonate prematurely. This results in a metallic rattle known as knocking or pinking, a loss of power, and possible damage to the engine.

An American engineer, Thomas Midgley, discovered in 1920 that such ill-effects could be lessened by adding lead tetraethyl to petrol. It was called an anti-knock agent and, as it improved the performance of an engine, it was widely used until doubts about its safety began to be expressed around 1965. As a result, lead-free petrol came to be favoured, becoming available in the USA in 1975, and in the UK in 1986.

TWO-STROKE COMPRESSION ENGINES

The four-stroke petrol engines had an advantage over the early two-stroke gas engines in so far as they compressed the fuel mixture before igniting it. This caused the mixture to burn more rapidly and produce more power. However, to achieve this, four strokes instead of two were needed for every one power stroke.

The best of both worlds was combined in an engine designed by Sir Dugald Clerk, a Scot, in 1878; it is still in use today and its operation is summarized in the diagram below.

As the movement of the cylinder is used to open and shut the various ports, the engine does not require any valves. It is, therefore, relatively light and cheap to make. However, it is not very efficient and its main use is in gas engines and in small, petrol engines as used in lawn-mowers, outboard motors and small motor cycles or cars.

DIESEL ENGINES

Rudolph Diesel (1858–1913) was born in Paris and educated in Augsburg and Munich. He began work as a refrigeration engineer, but turned his attention to designing what he called a 'rational heat

Sparking a compressed fuel-air mixture drives the piston down (left). *This rotates the crankshaft and pushes the new mixture into the top of the cylinder from the crankcase below through the transfer port. As the piston rises* (right), *the new mixture is compressed, and at the same time, the exhaust gases are expelled through the exhaust port. The two-stroke cycle is then repeated*

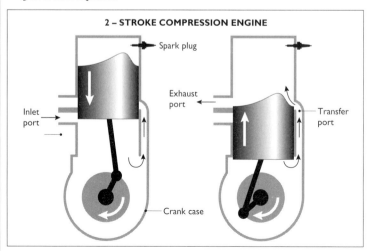

2 – STROKE COMPRESSION ENGINE

Spark plug

Exhaust port

Inlet port

Transfer port

Crank case

motor' in 1885. He had been impressed by the large amount of heat generated by ammonia compressors in refrigerator systems (⇒p. 215) and it occurred to him that he might be able to use such heat to ignite a fuel–air mixture in a cylinder.

Diesel designed an engine that works on the same four-stroke cycle as the Otto engine but without a spark plug. Air is drawn into a cylinder through an inlet valve by the downward movement of a piston. It is then compressed, to about 1/22nd of its original volume, by moving the piston upwards, and this raises the temperature. A fine spray of diesel oil is then pumped through a jet into the hot air (fuel injection). The correct timing of the injection is controlled by linking the pump to the engine. The temperature of the air is high enough to ignite the mixture in the cylinder so that the piston is forced down in the power stroke. When the piston moves up again, the exhaust gases are pushed out through an exhaust valve. The four-stroke cycle is then repeated. In summary, it is air intake, compression, power, and exhaust.

The theoretical efficiency of the diesel engine is higher than that of a petrol engine. Moreover, diesel engines need no electrical ignition and the oil they use is cheaper than petrol.

On the other hand, the high compression on which their efficiency depends can only be achieved in a strongly built and, therefore, heavy and expensive engine. Diesel patented his engine in 1892 and, by 1897, it was popular for use as a stationary engine in power plants, and for driving ships and trains. Later, in the 1920s, it was adapted for use in trucks and buses, and more recently it has been fitted into cars.

Diesel was to make a fortune from his invention but his success was ill-fated. He came close to death when one of his early engines blew up and, in later years, he lost his money in a number of rash ventures. Following a nervous breakdown, he fell overboard from an Antwerp–Harwich ferry in 1913, leaving about £1000 to his name.

THE WANKEL ROTARY ENGINE

The reciprocating action of a piston engine can only provide rotary motion via some mechanism such as a crankshaft (⇒p. 59) and it has long been an inventor's dream to design an engine which could turn a shaft directly. A German engineer, Felix Wankel, patented such a rotary engine in 1929, but the practical difficulties involved were so great that it was not commercially made until 1956.

A wide, triangular rotor, with curved, hollowed-out sides, is placed inside an approximately oval-shaped chamber. The rotor is geared, centrally, to the shaft which it drives, and the chamber contains a spark-plug positioned opposite inlet and exhaust ports. The circulation of the rotor, in turn, draws fuel mixture in, compresses and ignites it, and then expels the exhaust gases. The power stroke is applied to one face of the rotor after another.

The resulting smooth-running and powerful engine was first fitted to an NSU Spider car in 1964 and it has been tried a number of times since. However, problems encountered with the sealing have so far prevented it from competing successfully with traditional piston engines.

The circulating rotor, in turn (left to right), draws a fuel-air mixture in through the inlet port and then compresses it. The compressed mixture is then ignited by a spark to provide power to keep the rotor moving. As it rotates and drives the shaft it also expels the exhaust gases through the exhaust port. The power is applied to one face of the rotor after another

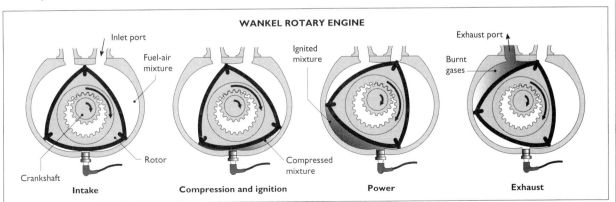

WANKEL ROTARY ENGINE

Inlet port · Fuel-air mixture · Ignited mixture · Exhaust port · Burnt gases · Rotor · Crankshaft · Compressed mixture

Intake · **Compression and ignition** · **Power** · **Exhaust**

TURBOJET ENGINES

In a turbojet engine, air is drawn in at the front of a tube and passed through compressors to combustion chambers into which paraffin is injected and burnt. The hot, compressed gases are then passed, first, through a turbine which they rotate, and then out of an exhaust nozzle. The rotating turbine drives the compressors, and the high-velocity jet of gases escaping from the exhaust nozzle provides the propulsive power of the engine.

The Heinkel 178, built in Germany in 1939, and designed by a 28-year-old German inventor, Dr Hans von Ohain, was the first aircraft to use a jet engine. However, Englishman Frank Whittle had patented the same idea, independently, in 1930.

Whittle was born on 1 June 1907 in Coventry, and he first began to think about jet engines whilst he was at the Royal Air Force College at Cranwell, but all his superiors were very scathing. It was not until 1934, when the Air Force sent him to Cambridge University, that he found enough encouragement to set up a company – Power Jets Ltd, with a capital of £10,000 – to exploit his ideas.

The company eventually built an engine for an experimental plane known as the Gloster-Whittle E28/39. This was tested successfully in 1941, but Power Jets was regarded as too small to carry the project forward so it was taken over by the government in 1944, and became part of Rolls-Royce. Whittle's small team was soon disbanded and he himself left the field at the young age of 41. He retired from the Royal Air Force as an Air Commodore; he was elected a Fellow of the Royal Society; he was knighted; and he was granted £100,000 by the Royal Commission on Awards to Inventors in 1946. He died in 1996.

Jet engines were not developed quickly enough to make a very significant contribution during World War II, and it was not until the 1950s that they came into their own. By then, considerable rivalry developed between British and American companies to build the best engines and they all turned in the 1960s to an idea which Whittle had patented 20 years earlier – the bypass engine. In this design, much of the air coming from the compressors was passed around the core of the engine, keeping the outer casing cool and providing welcome sound-proofing. Another less successful innovation was the attempt by Rolls-Royce to use carbon fibre (⇒p. 38) in its original RB 211 engine. Its failure to withstand the stresses was a disastrous setback, in 1971, but the company survived to resurrect the engine into an outstanding commercial success.

Ever since the early days, the inability of the available materials to withstand the very high temperature at the centre of a jet engine has been a limiting design factor. Special steels have been used, so far, but it may require ceramics (⇒p. 23) to stand up to the temperatures of around 2000°C expected in future engines.

Air, drawn in at the front, is compressed and heated by passing through rotating compressors before being mixed with paraffin in a combustion chamber. The ignition of that mixture produces very hot gases which propel the engine forwards as they pass out of the exhaust nozzle at the rear. First, however, they are used to rotate a turbine which drives the compressors at the front of the engine.

TURBOPROP ENGINES

The turbine in a turbojet engine can be adapted to drive a propeller, through an appropriate system of gears, as well as the compressors. The result is known as a turboprop engine; it is particularly well suited for use in aeroplanes of intermediate size and speed. Some energy remains for use in jet propulsion and the balance between propeller and jet can be varied to meet different requirements.

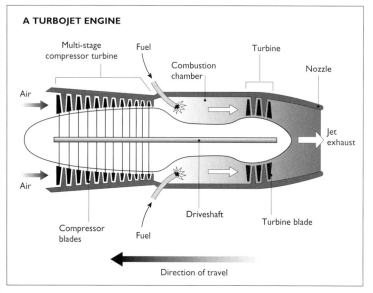

A TURBOJET ENGINE

Multi-stage compressor turbine

Fuel

Combustion chamber

Turbine

Nozzle

Air

Jet exhaust

Air

Compressor blades

Fuel

Driveshaft

Turbine blade

Direction of travel

8

TEXTILES

'Wanted immediately, two Journeymen Clock-makers, or others that understands Tooth and Pinion well: Also a Smith that can forge and file - Likewise two wood turners that has been accustomed to Wheelmaking, Spoleturning etc. Weavers residing at the Mill may have good work. There is employment at the above Place for Women, Children, etc. and good wages.'

THE DERBY MERCURY,
13 December 1771

ROVING MACHINE.—SIXTH PROCESS.

TEXTILES

THE MECHANIZATION of spinning, weaving and associated crafts, which began during the 18th century, changed the making of cloth in many parts of the world from a rural activity into a massive industry. This process played a predominant role in the Industrial Revolution.

A Saxony-type spinning wheel

SPINNING

The spinning of fibres such as flax, cotton and wool to give a spun-thread or yarn strong enough for weaving was done, long ago, entirely by hand by rolling the fibres between the fingers or between a thigh and a hand. The first improvement involved the use of a wooden spindle, notched at one end and fitted with a wooden or porcelain disc (whorl) at the other to act as a sort of flywheel. In spinning, a mass of fibres was held on a stick, known as the distaff, and a length of material drawn from this source was attached to the notched end of the spindle, which was then twirled, whilst hanging free, to spin the fibre. The spun length was then wound on to the spindle and notched in position so that the whole operation could be repeated.

Far right: The yarn is twisted before being wound on to the bobbin. It is kept taut by rotating the bobbin slightly faster than the flyer

The spinning-wheel

The spinning-wheel was invented, probably in India, around the 13th century. The spindle was fitted horizontally in bearings and was rotated by a cord passing round a large hand-driven wheel. The wheel was turned by the right hand, whilst the fibres were fed on to the spindle from a distaff with the left.

In the Saxony wheel, invented in the 15th century, the spindle had an attached flyer, and a separate, coaxial bobbin. The fibres were fed on to the flyer, which introduced the twist, before being wound on to the bobbin. The bobbin was turned slightly faster than the flyer so that the fibre was always kept taut. A spinning-wheel fitted with a treadle was introduced in the 16th century.

The spinning-jenny

By 1750, the traditional hand-spinning methods could not meet the increasing demand for yarn. To try to close the gap, in 1761 the Society for the Encouragement of Arts, Commerce and Manufactures in Britain offered a prize of £50 to the inventor of an improved spinning machine. James Hargreaves, a poor, illiterate man who lived near

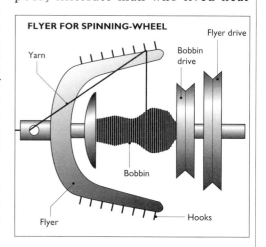

FLYER FOR SPINNING-WHEEL
Flyer drive
Yarn
Bobbin drive
Bobbin
Flyer
Hooks

SIR RICHARD ARKWRIGHT
(1732–92)

RICHARD ARKWRIGHT, the youngest of 13 children of poor parents, began his working life as a barber and wig-maker in Bolton, England. In 1771, he joined forces with Jedidiah Strutt, a stocking manufacturer from Nottingham, to set up a spinning mill at Cromford, north of Derby. Alongside, he built houses, together with a school, a church and all the other amenities necessary for a small industrial community. In 1776, he built a second factory, seven-stories high, in Cromford, and by 1782 he was employing 5000 workers. It was the beginning of the Industrial Revolution and Arkwright's methods were copied by potters in Staffordshire, iron-founders in Derbyshire, cotton manufacturers in Lancashire and wool-makers in Yorkshire. The new factories were water-powered so they had to be sited near an available source but, within a few years, they were steam-powered so that a ready supply of coal was necessary.

Many of the new factories were run paternalistically; others fell into the category of 'dark satanic mills'.

Arkwright suffered from the mob like most of his contemporaries, and one of his factories in Chorley was destroyed in 1779.

Some doubt was cast on the genuine originality of his inventions when, after much litigation, his 1775 patent was rescinded in 1785. Nevertheless, he was knighted a year later and died, wealthy and highly respected, at Cromford on 3 August 1792.

> **‘And was Jerusalem builded here Among these dark Satanic mills?’**
>
> WILLIAM BLAKE *(1757–1827), English poet*

Sir Richard Arkwright. An engraving by J. Jenkins from a painting by Joseph Wright

Blackburn in England, met the need with his spinning-jenny; 'jenny', perhaps, being a colloquialism for 'engine'. His machine, patented in 1770, had a complicated action but it enabled one operator to spin on to eight spindles at a time and, by 1766, on to 16. The invention did not commend itself to those spinners who lost their jobs and a local mob expressed its anger by gutting Hargreaves's house in 1768. He moved to Nottinghamshire where he set up a spinning mill in which he worked until his death in 1778.

Arkwright's water frame
Hargreaves's spinning-jenny was not easy to operate and did not produce yarn which was strong enough for the warp threads (⇒p. 112) in weaving. Richard Arkwright overcame those problems in 1769 by introducing four pairs of rollers into a machine which he patented. By rotating one pair faster than the preceding one, the fibres were stretched before being spun. His machine, originally intended to be driven by a horse, came to be known as the 'water-frame' because it was in fact driven by a water-wheel. In 1775, he took out a new patent covering various improvements he had made to his earlier machine.

Crompton's mule
Between 1774 and 1779, an improved spinning machine was invented by Samuel Crompton who worked as a spinner near Bolton in England. He combined Hargreaves and Arkwright's best ideas into what was called 'Crompton's mule' because it was a hybrid, but he was too poor to patent it and sold his idea for £67. It was outstandingly successful and in 1812 he was granted £5000 by Parliament as a belated payment for his discovery, but he still had to rely on a small annuity for suppport in the years before his death in 1827.

> **‘The object of my pursuit was that every thread of cotton should (as near as possible) be equally good.’**
>
> SAMUEL CROMPTON *(1753–1827), English inventor*

Ring-spinning

In 1815, the water frame began to be replaced by a very similar machine called the throstle-frame. It was driven by steam-power and made a shrill bird-like noise. Hence the name 'throstle'. It led on to the invention of ring-spinning by John Thorpe of Providence, Rhode Island in 1828. In this method, the fibres are stretched by passing through a series of rollers before they are guided down, through a C-shaped loop, on to a spindle which rotates about a vertical axis. The loop is free to rotate around the spindle on a collar, and the spindle carries a conical-shaped bobbin. The rotating loop spins the fibres which are then wound on to the bobbin. This winding takes place evenly because the collar is moved up and down along the length of the bobbin.

Ring-spinning became well established by 1850 and is still widely used. Machines fitted with 500 spindles, which each rotate 12,000 times per minute, can wind 4 miles of yarn on to each bobbin before it is full and ready to be changed automatically.

Rotor spinning

Rotor-spinning, introduced in the 1970s, is even faster than ring-spinning. The fibres are fed into a cylindrical rotor, with grooves on its inner surface, which rotates at up to 50,000 revolutions per minute. Centrifugal force pushes the fibres into the grooves where they are compacted into yarn before being peeled off.

WEAVING

Weaving is the interlacing of threads, generally at right angles to each other, as carried out in a loom. The lengthwise threads are called the warp; the crosswise ones the weft, woof or filling.

The horizontal hand loom

The commonest early looms were made from a wooden frame held in a horizontal position with the warp threads stretched between the back and front edges. The warp threads were known individually as ends; the weft threads as picks. A series of ends laid out in a loom was called a sheet. The ends in a sheet were manipulated by heddles which consisted of short lengths of cord or wire with a loop at one end attached to a stick known as a heddle-rod or shaft. In the very simplest form of weaving, every alternate end in a sheet was passed through the loop in a heddle so that all of them were raised when the heddle-rod was lifted. This was known as shedding, and the space between the two sheets as the shed. As each pick was fed in through the shed it was pushed up against its predecessor (beaten in) by the weaver's sword or comb.

In newer looms, at the end of the 13th century, the weft threads were fed across the loom in a wooden shuttle. The loops in the heddles were in the centre of a length of cord or wire so that the ends to which they were attached could be either lowered or raised. More than one rod or shaft of heddles could be used so that sheets of ends could be raised or lowered in different ways to make different patterns of cloth. The beating in was improved by using a grating of thin parallel wires known as a reed, and the heddle shafts were operated by foot treadles so that the weaver's hands were free to pass the shuttle.

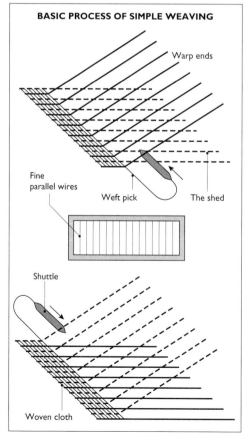

BASIC PROCESS OF SIMPLE WEAVING

Warp ends

Fine parallel wires

Weft pick

The shed

Shuttle

Woven cloth

Top: A group of warp ends is lifted by a heddle to reveal the shed through which the weft thread is passed by a shuttle moving from front to back. That thread is then beaten in by a reed (centre). Bottom: The alternate group of ends is lifted and the shuttle passed from back to front

The flying shuttle

John Kay, the son of a Lancashire farmer, invented the flying shuttle in 1733 to overcome the difficulty of passing the shuttle through the shed by hand which was very tedious and needed two people for broad pieces of cloth. Kay's shuttle was boat-shaped and contained a bobbin full of yarn. It was propelled on wheels across a horizonal batten, known as the shuttle race, and the weaver could pass it to and fro by tugging on a cord.

Kay did not reap any great benefits from his invention. His idea was stolen by employers and was highly unpopular with their employees. When his house was ransacked by a mob he felt obliged to leave the country and went to France where he died, some 25 years later, in poverty. It is not known where he was buried.

Power looms

The Revd Edmund Cartwright was born in Marnham in Nottinghamshire, England in 1743, and after an early education at Wakefield Grammar School he entered University College, Oxford at the age of 14. He became rector of Goadby Marwood in Leicestershire in 1779 and began to take an interest in agriculture and textiles.

The idea of making an automatic loom struck him on a visit to one of Arkwright's spinning factories. He wrote 'that as plain weaving involved only three movements which followed each other in succession there would be little difficulty in producing them repeatedly'. However, he did not find it at all easy, either mechanically or socially, to bring his ideas to fruition.

His first machine, patented on 4 April 1785, was not very successful, but he took out further patents in each of the following three years and in 1787 set up a factory in Doncaster with 20 looms, all driven by water-power. This, too, was an unsuccessful venture, and plans to start up a factory holding 400 looms in Manchester in 1791 had to be abandoned when rioters burnt down the building. Petitions to Parliament were also organized to try to prevent the adoption of the new looms.

The social opposition eventually declined and the mechanical drawbacks of Cartwright's loom were overcome by refinements made by, for example, Thomas Johnson, William Horrocks, Richard Roberts, William Crompton and his son, George, and Brigham Bigelow. Cartwright was granted £10,000 by the government in 1809, and by 1833 there were 85,000 power looms in use in England.

Jacquard looms

Early looms could not be fitted with more than 24 heddle-shafts and this limited the range of patterns which could be woven. The difficulty was overcome by using a special operator known as a drawboy. He sat on top of the loom and used cords to pull up whatever particular combination of ends was required by the pattern being woven. However, the system was costly in labour and any pattern could be ruined by an unskilled or careless drawboy.

Basile Bouchon, a master weaver in the French silk industry around Lyons, was the first to suggest, in 1725, that the drawboy could be replaced by a perforated roll of paper. The paper rotated round a cylinder and entered a selector box where each perforation caused one particular combination of ends to be lifted.

He could not, however, get his idea to work well in practice and it was not until 1805 that it was perfected by a fellow countryman, Joseph-Marie Jacquard, who used a continuous chain of perforated, rectangular cards instead of Bouchon's roll of paper. Each card operated one particular shedding operation and the subsequent throw of the shuttle. Up to 30,000 punched cards could be used in weaving one piece of silk so that very exotic designs could be achieved.

Jacquard was awarded the Chevalier de la Légion d'Honneur by Napoleon in 1806 and granted a state pension of 3000 francs. However, as before this innovation caused unrest and in 1810 drawboys rampaged through Lyons destroying Jacquard's looms and threatening his life. Nevertheless, his system was successful and by 1812 there were 11,000 Jacquard looms operating in France. He died in 1834.

Automatic looms

The automatic loom invented by J.H. Northrop of Massachusetts in 1895 has been described as 'the loom of the 20th century'. It incorporated a mechanism by which the bobbin in the shuttle, or sometimes the whole shuttle, was replaced automatically as and when necessary without stopping the loom. There was little left for the weaver to do other than rectify faults, with the result that one weaver could oversee 24 looms. The loom was expensive so that capital costs rose but labour costs declined.

Shuttle-free looms

The speed of operation of a traditional loom, fitted with a thread-carrying shuttle, was limited by the fact that the shuttle could only be moved to and fro relatively slowly. To overcome this, so-called shuttle-free looms have been invented. There are three main types. In 1950, Sulzer Bros, a Swiss firm of locomotive makers, marketed a loom which had been first patented in 1931. It uses a 'dummy' shuttle which does not carry its own thread. Instead, it picks up thread at the start of each run across the loom. In 1957, the first nozzle or fluid-jet loom was patented in Czechoslovakia. It uses a high-pressure jet of water or air to propel the pick through the shed. In 1963, Dornier, the German aircraft manufacturer, invented a rapier loom which uses a flexible steel tape to carry the weft thread through the shed. Later, two 'rapiers' were used, so that one could be inserted from either side of the loom. Modern looms are based on these three inventions. They can insert up to 1500 picks per minute.

SILK THROWING

China has been well known for the high quality of its silk products since time immemorial, and when the overland route to the West was opened up in the 13th century it became known as the Silk Road. So it was that silkworms were carried along that road, probably in hollowed-out bamboo poles, to set up the European silk trade which was centred in Piedmont, Italy, around the city of Lucca.

Silk differs from other fibres such as wool, cotton and flax, because the silkworm produces it in very fine, continuous filaments. Before weaving, these are wound on to a bobbin, cleaned and twisted to form so-called spun silk threads. However, as they are not very strong it is necessary, particularly for making warp thread, to subject them to a further process which is known as 'doubling' or 'throwing', which involves a second twisting of the spun silk threads.

By the beginning of the 14th century, the Lucca manufacturers had invented a successful silk-throwing machine which enabled them to monopolize the market for warp thread. In 1714, John Lombe, a partner in a silk spinning mill in Derby, decided to put an end to that. Having first learnt the language, he travelled to Italy, managed to get a job inside one of the Lucca mills, and eventually returned to England with drawings he had made of their silk-throwing machine. He could be described as one of the first industrial spies.

Lombe patented the machine in England in 1716 and, together with his half-brother, Thomas, set up a factory in Derby in 1720. It was powered by a single water-wheel and employed about 300 workers. At the time, it was mass production on a large scale; a very early start to the Industrial Revolution. But perhaps it is true that crime does not pay. The factory was not very successful and John Lombe died two years after it was built, at the age of 29. The tale is told that he was, in fact, poisoned by a woman sent from Italy to exact retribution.

THE COTTON GIN

With the increase in productivity in both spinning and weaving in the latter half of the 18th century, bottlenecks began to develop in the supply of raw materials. So far as cotton was concerned, the main source was the southern states of America, but the separation of the fibres from the seeds was a very slow business. The work was carried out manually by slaves until Eli Whitney invented the cotton gin in 1793. It used a raking process. The raw cotton was placed in a container which had slits in its lower surface through which cotton seeds could

> ❝ *The worms were hallow'd that did breed the silk.* ❞
>
> Othello, *WILLIAM SHAKESPEARE (1564–1616)*

ELI WHITNEY
(1765–1825)

WHITNEY was born in Westboro, Massachusetts, the son of a farmer. From an early age he liked nothing better than making and mending things and he spent a lot of time in a small repair shop on his father's farm. After studying law at Yale between 1789 and 1792, he went to teach in Georgia where he lived on a cotton plantation.

He got the idea for his gin, it is said, by watching cows lick stalks of corn with their rough tongues. It took him only ten days to produce the design, and manufacture began in 1794 in partnership with Phineas Miller and with the help of a $50,000 grant from the state of South Carolina. The gin could do the work of 50 slaves and its immediate success and widespread adoption revolutionized the economics of cotton growing.

However, the process was easy to copy and Whitney grew tired of fighting expensive lawsuits to protect his patent rights. So, in 1798, he was glad to accept a new challenge when he was granted a government contract to make 10,000 muskets. In a new factory in New Haven, Connecticut, he put particular emphasis on using a few skilled craftsmen and machine tools to make interchangeable parts which could be assembled by semi-skilled workers. In his day, it was a new approach which was known as the American system. It made him a fortune and is now widely adopted in most industries

Eli Whitney's gin, 1793

not pass. Fibres of cotton were drawn out through the slits by a rotating cylinder which had thin spikes protruding from its surface, and the cotton was removed from the spikes by counter-rotating brushes so that they did not get clogged up.

OTHER PROCESSES

Carding and combing
These are processes for disentangling fibres in preparation for spinning. Carding disentangles the fibres into a thin web, and combing separates the longer fibres from the shorter ones so that they can be used for making better-quality cloths.

Long ago, the processes were carried out by hand using the dried heads of thistles (Latin *carduus*) or teasels. Today, they are done by machines using wire brushes.

Felting

Felting is probably older than weaving. It converts fibres into fabrics by compressing them together under steam heat. Because of its naturally crinkly nature, wool makes particularly good felt, but today a wide variety of fibres, both natural and synthetic and either separately or mixed together, can be used.

Gigging

Gigging is the raising of a nap on the surface of a cloth to make it feel softer and warmer. In early gig mills, dating from the 15th century, the material was passed over a rotating cylinder covered with dried teasel heads. They have been replaced by surfaces covered with short steel spikes. If required, the nap is cut to a uniform height by rotary cutters in a machine similar to a lawn-mower.

Fulling

Fulling hardens a soft cloth, such as wool, in a process akin to felting. It was originally carried out by trampling the wet material underfoot with, perhaps, the addition of wood ashes or fuller's earth, a naturally occurring clay-like substance. It was mechanized as early as the 12th century when the trampling was superseded by pounding with wooden mallets operated by a water-wheel. Today, the fabric is soaked in soapy water and passed through compression rollers.

Bleaching

Before a fabric can be dyed evenly it must be bleached to remove any irregularity of colour that might be present. Before 1758 this was done by treatment with buttermilk, and after 1758 with sulphuric acid, followed by long exposure to the sun in bleach fields. It could take months in northern latitudes, so that the invention of synthetic bleaches was very important. Javel water, first made by the French chemist, Claude Louis Berthollet in 1785, and bleaching powder by a Scot, Charles Tennant in 1799, were both used. They function by releasing chlorine gas which is the actual bleaching agent and, today, it is the gas itself, obtained from cylinders of liquid chlorine, which is generally used. For milder bleaching it might be replaced by hydrogen peroxide.

Dyeing

Some dyes (⇒p. 24) can simply be applied by dipping the fabric; some will dye one type of fabric but not another; some are formed within the fibres of a material by dipping it first in one solution and then in another with which the first will react; and some require the material to be treated with a mordant, such as alum, before it can be dyed. In all cases, the aim is to ensure that the dye remains fast, i.e. is not affected by washing or light. The dyes can also be applied in different ways. In batik, for example, which originated in Indonesia, dyes are applied irregularly by treating the fabric with wax, oil or mud before dipping in the dye.

SEWING

Sewing has been the traditional method of joining fabrics ever since the first bone or ivory needles were made some 25,000 years ago. But it is a slow, painstaking process when done by hand so it is not surprising that there were many attempts at mechanization during the 19th century. A poor French tailor, Barthélemy Thimonnier, built the first successful sewing machines in 1830 and used them in a factory in Paris for making army uniforms but, within a year, other disgruntled tailors had smashed them all to pieces. He tried again in the late 1840s and set up the first French sewing machine company, but he died in 1857 disillusioned and ruined.

An American engineer, Elias Howe, patented his machine in 1846. It made use of the lock-stitch which linked two threads together. One came from a bobbin above the materials being sewn, and the other from a bobbin below. The upper thread passed through an eye in the lower end of a needle which was moved up and down through the materials by rotating a handle. As the upper thread formed a loop on the under-side of the materials, a thread from the lower bobbin was passed through it, via a shuttle, to create the stitch. However, the machine was difficult to handle and was not widely accepted.

It was another American, Isaac Merritt Singer, who overcame the problems by combining elements of Thimonnier's and

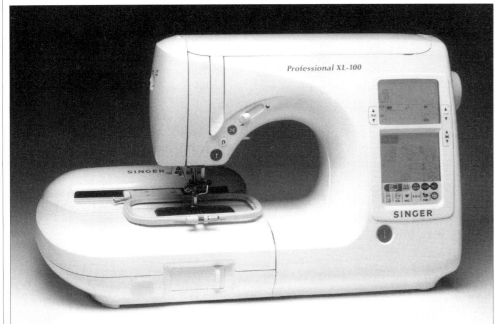

The Singer Professional XL-100 sewing machine. This model provides every type of stitch and application required by a seamstress. Many of the controls are operated by touching liquid crystal display (LCD) screens as seen on the right of the machine

Howe's machines into his own design which he patented in 1850. He had trained as a machinist and early in his working life had patented a machine for drilling rock and one for carving metal or wood. It was whilst he was mending an existing sewing machine that he had the idea of making his own. The material was kept in position by a spring-loaded foot pressing down on it, and was moved forward by the rotation of a toothed wheel below it. The machine could be operated either manually by turning a handle or by a foot-operated treadle. When using the latter, both hands were free to manipulate the materials. Singer's company went from strength to strength despite having to pay compensation to Howe for patent infringements. Much of the success was due to Singer's partner, the lawyer Edward Clark, who introduced the first hire-purchase scheme to augment a door-to-door and mail-order selling campaign.

The Singer machine spawned many imitations. They could all sew more effectively than any human; they cut the cost of ready-made clothing; and they encouraged home dressmaking, as did the associated invention of paper patterns by Ebenezer Butterick in 1863. Modern machines are commonly driven by electricity and controlled by microprocessors ($\Rightarrow$p. 201). They can perform a wide range of sewing activities such as buttonholing and piping, and models are available for sewing shoes and other leather goods, and carpets.

KNITTING

Knitting involves converting a fibre, particularly wool, into a fabric by looping it together. It probably began as knotting in the making of nets but its precise origin is unknown though it was brought to Europe in the 15th century by Arabs. On a small scale it is done by using two needles (without eyes) held in the hands but in 1589 a Nottinghamshire clergyman, the Revd William Lee, invented a stocking frame on which it could be done more efficiently by using rows of fixed and movable hooks. Its use was not immediately encouraged for fear of causing unemployment and Lee sought refuge from his detractors in France but, by the 18th century, a knitting industry had begun in the East Midlands of England and is still there today. The frame was the precursor of the modern knitting machines that are used. For making hosiery, the hooks are mounted in a circle.

FASTENERS

Toggles and buttons

One of the oldest methods of joining two

pieces of cloth together was to use a toggle, a short piece of wood, sewn to one piece of cloth which was fitted into a loop on the other. Buttons fitting into slits (buttonholes) were introduced by the Romans but did not become common until the Middle Ages. They were originally made of horn, bone, leather, brass or wood, but are nowadays generally made of plastic.

Pins

A type of pin, made of bones, thorns, wood or metal has been used since about 4000 BC, but manufacture of today's pin, with a head and a point, only began around 1820 when an American, Seth Hunt, and an Englishman, Samuel Wright, took out patents for pin-making machines. The modern safety-pin was invented by Walter Hunt in 1849 in New York. He hit on the idea when he was trying to make a wire clasp to fit on to a rifle, and it is said that he transferred the patent rights to pay off a debt.

The zip-fastener

The first zip-fastener, originally intended for tying up shoes, was devised by an American, Whitcomb L. Judson, who spent most of his life trying, unsuccessfully, to develop a streetcar system driven by compressed air. In his idea for a fastener, patented in 1893, a series of metal hooks on one strip could interlock with metal eyes on an opposite strip, and the connections could be made either individually, by hand, or by moving a slide to draw the two strips together. The idea was taken up by an entrepreneur, Lewis Walker, who set up the Automatic Hook and Eye Co. and in 1905 marketed a fastener under the name of 'C-curity'. But it was neither reliably secure nor easy to make, and it was not until 1913 that one of the company's newer employees, a Swede, Gideon Sundback, designed a more reliable product. The main change has been that today's fasteners are generally made of plastic rather than metal.

Velcro

This consists of two strips of nylon, one having thousands of small hooks on its surface and the other thousands of small loops. It was patented by a Swiss engineer, Georges de Mestral, in 1957. The original idea had come to him in 1948 when he disovered, by microscopic examination, that the burrs which stuck to his clothing after he had been out shooting were covered with small hooks. The name derives from the French words *velours* (velvet) and *crochet* (hook).

The press-stud

This type of fastener, sometimes called a snap-fastener, was invented by a French manufacturer, Pierre-Albert Raymond, in 1886 and improved by another Frenchman, George Abraham, in 1901. A very small, springy metal or plastic cup is pushed into a slightly larger one.

Diagrams from British Patent No. 12,261 (1915) for the zip fastener

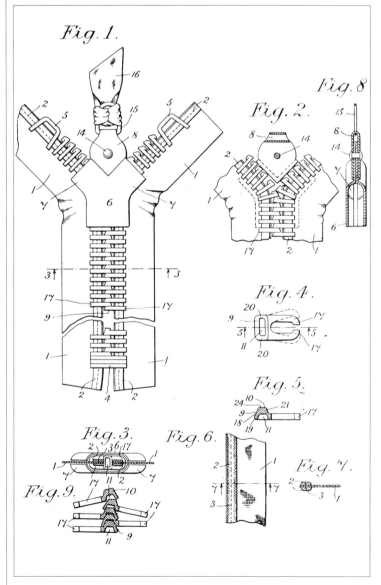

CHAPTER

9

TRANSPORT

'No single activity of modern man can be isolated for study, for each one is influenced by the others: housing, health, diet, recreation, wages, trade, transport - none is independent, for all are linked in a causal chain. The modern world is an organised whole, every part of which in its every activity is linked directly or indirectly to the rest. The link is that of transport and communications, for without the continual flow of goods and information which these provide, the modern world could not have come into being, nor could it maintain itself.'

F. SHERWOOD TAYLOR,
English scientific writer, 1940

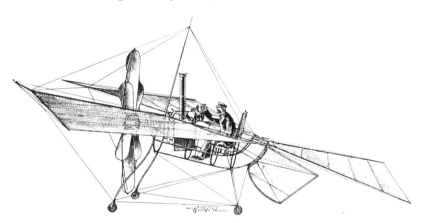

TRANSPORT

THE ANCIENT METHODS OF TRANSPORT were by boat or by some local animal such as a horse, dog, ox, bullock, ass, donkey, elephant, camel, llama, yak, or mule. In the Western world, from around 1850, the methods moved forwards dramatically with the invention and introduction of the railways, bicycles, motorcycles, motor cars and aeroplanes. Yet, though some people can now travel faster than the speed of sound and even into outer space, there are areas of the world where animals still provide the best and perhaps the only means of transport.

THE INFRASTRUCTURE

Originally, it was the horse that mattered most in the western world. The invention of the shoe, the padded saddle, iron stirrups and the bit, made the horse easy to ride; and the breast-band, padded collar, traces and shafts, enabled it to haul carts, stage-wagons, stage-coaches and barges. Individuals could travel quite quickly by riding post, which involved picking up new horses at convenient staging posts, but it was not until around 1800 that better roads allowed stage-wagons and coaches, first used a hundred years earlier, to travel more efficiently.

> *Water was gushing and fanning out all over the country.*
>
> J.BRONOWSKI
> *(1908–1974), Polish-born British scientist, on canals.*

Roads
At one time it was true that 'all roads lead to Rome' and the Romans had constructed more than 65,000 km (40,400 miles) of them before their Empire collapsed. Thereafter, the art of road-making declined until it was resurrected by French engineers such as Pierre Trésaguet in the middle of the 18th century. They used stone setts or laid small chippings on a layer of larger stones in a trench.

The French methods were developed in Britain, notably by John Loudon McAdam (1756–1836). He recommended that the subsoil of a road must be well drained, that the road must be built up above ground level, and that nothing which could retain water should be used in its construction. Crushed stones, of carefully measured size, were to be pressed down in layers and covered with smaller ones to give a smooth well-cambered 'macadam' surface. It was not, however, until the surface was protected from water by asphalt or tar, in the second half of the 20th century, that it became something like a modern road. Hence the use of the term 'tarmacadam'.

Today's roads are built mainly of reinforced concrete and their construction involves heavy machinery such as stone-crushers, bulldozers, steamrollers, concrete mixers and automatic tarring equipment. Even so, it is difficult to keep up with the ever-increasing demand.

Canals
A horse could move much heavier loads by pulling a barge than a stage-wagon so, at the same time as the roads were being improved, more rivers were made navigable by building weirs, and there was an enormous investment in canals.

The use of canals had been made possible by the invention of locks in China about AD 1000. They enabled barges to move up or down from one level to another, and they were first used in Europe on a Dutch canal in 1373. The boom came with the growth of industrial towns from 1760, and one new canal quickly followed another. By 1850, there were 6000 km (3730 mile) of canals in England, and 5500 km (3430 miles) in the USA.

The original lock gates, which slid up and down in vertical grooves, were replaced by hinged mitre-gates invented by Leonardo da Vinci during the 15th century. The two heavy gates closed to meet at an angle pointing upstream.

Bridges
The first bridges were simple beam bridges made from trees or planks of

A new £330 million bridge built across the River Severn by contractor Laing-GTM, a joint Anglo-French company. The bridge is 947 m (1035 yd) long, with a main central span of 456 m (499 yd). Work began in 1992 and the bridge was opened in 1996. A total of 1000 workers were employed at the peak of construction

wood laid across a stream. Alternatively, arch bridges, were made by placing shaped stones side by side on top of a wooden, semi-circular framework. When the keystone at the apex had been positioned, the framework could be removed.

The Englishman Abraham Darby, whose father had pioneered the use of coke in making iron (⇒p. 12), pointed the way forward when he built a cast-iron arch bridge over the River Severn at Coalbrookdale, in 1779. Later, bridge arches were built of steel or, sometimes, of concrete over a steel framework.

In a modern beam bridge, the deck is made of steel girders supported at each end and, if necessary, at intervals along its length. For a long bridge, the girders must be truss girders made up of upper and lower members joined by vertical or inclined struts, or welded box girders with a hollow rectangular cross-section.

The cantilever bridge is a modification of the beam bridge. Two supporting pillars are built in the river or ravine to be bridged at a distance of about half the total completed span apart. Girders are then used to construct projecting arms both inwards and outwards from each pillar. They are joined together where they meet in the middle of the span, and come to rest on supports at each end. The Forth Rail Bridge in Scotland, built in 1889, a good example.

In a suspension bridge, the deck is hung from massive, parallel cables made by binding many wires together. They are firmly anchored at each end before passing over tall supports. This provides a particularly lightweight structure, well exemplified in the Clifton Suspension Bridge over the River Avon in England, which was designed by Isambard Kingdom Brunel (⇒p. 125). The four main cables are 10 in (25.4 cm) in diameter.

Building the supports for any type of bridge has been simplified by the use of concrete (⇒p. 25). For foundations under water, the engineers either build a temporary dam, or sink a caisson or diving bell into the ground into which compressed air is pumped to keep water out.

Tunnels

Serious tunnelling began in the 17th and 18th centuries to accommodate canals and railway lines. It was done, at first, by pick and shovel, sometimes by sinking a number of shafts, excavating from the bottom of one to a neighbour, and hoisting the spoil up the shafts by horse-powered gins. The use of gunpowder, and then dynamite, dating from 1681, was a big step forward, as was the invention of pneumatic drills by a French engineer, Germain Sommeiller, in 1861.

It was particularly difficult to tunnel in soft or wet ground because of the danger of collapse and this led to the invention of shields. One of the first, patented by Sir Marc Isambard Brunel (⇒p. 125) in 1818, was used in constructing the first tunnel under the River Thames in London, England, between 1825 and 1843. It had a cylindrical cast-iron frame which was partitioned inside to accommodate 36 men. They excavated the face, which was held in place by boards except where they were working. The shield was pushed forward by jacks, 18 in (45 cm) at a time, as the tunnel was lined with masonry behind.

Today's big tunnels are bored by automatic machines. They act as shields and also have a rotating cutting head which drills into the tunnel as the machine is moved slowly forward. A huge machine, used for cutting the tunnel under the English Channel, was left in a lay-by in the tunnel when its work was finished in 1993.

TRAVEL BY SEA

The first boats were probably made about ten thousand years ago. They were rafts made by lashing logs or reeds together, or coracles, made by covering a wooden or wicker framework with hides, like those still used in Wales and Ireland today. They were propelled originally by paddles, but then oars took over, and the boats grew into craft which had banks of oarsmen on each side. First two in the bireme; then three in the trireme; and, eventually, five in the quinquereme.

There were disadvantages in using human labour to power boats. Initially, a good supply of slaves had to be found; they then had to be fed, housed and generally looked after. Stacking them in rows, one on top of the other, limited the design of a ship, making it top-heavy. So it was, that, perhaps as early as 5000 BC in Egypt, manpower was augmented by wind-power with the fitting of a sail.

6 Quinquireme of Nineveh from distant Ophir Rowing home to haven in sunny Palestine 9

JOHN MASEFIELD (1878 – 1947) English poet

SAILING SHIPS

The square sail
This sail, first used more than 5000 years ago, was formed by a square sheet, generally made of linen, which hung from a wooden pole, nowadays called a yard, along its top. The yard was tied rigidly to the top of the mast so that the sail lay across the length of the boat when it was unfurled. This greatly limited its usefulness because if the wind was blowing from the south, the ship could only move northwards, and vice versa. Therefore, the sail had to be used together with oarsmen.

The lateen sail
This sail is thought to be an Arab invention, which came to be used in Europe from the 9th century onwards. It is triangular in shape and is attached to a yard along its forward edge. The middle of the yard is loosely attached to the mast, near to the top, so that the sail can be moved from side to side by pulling on a rope at the rear, lower corner. In this way, the sail can be set at various angles across the boat, so that it can catch the wind on either side allowing the boat to beat into the wind.

The rudder
The lateen sail made it very much easier to handle a sailing ship, but it was the introduction of the rudder, an old Chinese invention, into Europe, at the beginning of the 13th century, that was decisive in making long sea voyages possible.

Previously, boats had been steered by dipping large oars into the water at the stern, but for big boats the necessary oars were too heavy for men to handle. The surface area of the new rudder could be much bigger than that of any oar and it was completely immersed in the water. It was attached to a long, vertical beam hinged to the stern of the boat, and the whole could be turned through the lever action of a tiller.

The impact of the sailing ship

By using more than one mast, by combining square and lateen sails, and by adding new topsails, sprit sails and front sails, it became possible to build ships which could undertake long sea voyages. They paved the way for the epic journeys of discovery undertaken by Magellan, Columbus, Vasco da Gama, and others, during the 15th and 16th centuries, which led to the foundation of European colonies overseas and to a vast increase in world trade. They also changed the face of naval warfare as exemplified in Drake's defeat of the Spanish Armada in 1588.

Sailing ships of increasing variety lasted well into the 20th century. They are, without doubt, a majestic sight, but whatever ingenuity was used in building and in sailing them they were always at the mercy of the wind. Their days were numbered once it became possible to replace wind power by the more reliable steam engine from the middle of the 19th century.

STEAMSHIPS

Paddle-wheels

The first steam-driven ships were propelled by paddle-wheels positioned either on both sides of the hull or, in the Mississippi river boats, in the centre of the stern.

The paddle-wheel was bulky, easily damaged, and inefficient because for much of the time the paddles were out of the water. It was, nevertheless, used successfully, usually with auxiliary sail equipment. In 1783, the Marquis de Jouffroy d'Abbans tested his 182-tonne *Pyroschape* successfully on the River Saône in France. In 1807, Robert Fulton, an artist as well as an inventor, launched the *Clermont* which was used to run a commercial service on the Hudson River between New York and Albany in the USA. Then in 1819 the *Savannah*, fitted with paddles which could be removed when not needed, crossed the Atlantic in 1819 in about 27½ days, but it used its sails for 87 per cent of the journey. Ships with paddles were still being built in 1860, and paddle-steamers continued, particularly for pleasure purposes in shallow waters, well into the 20th century.

Propellers

The basic inefficiency of the paddle-wheel was overcome by the invention of the propeller screw, which is totally submerged all the time. It is also much smaller and considerably more robust than a paddle-wheel.

The idea of using a screw had been studied at the start of the 18th century, but its superiority over the paddle-wheel was only demonstrated convincingly in ships, built in England, by Sir Francis Pettit Smith in 1836, and in Sweden by John Ericsson in 1837. Improved engines and metal hulls were required to bring propellers to the fore but, after 1850, the majority of ships used them, though for some years many of them still had sails as a back-up.

Metal hulls

For many years, most people thought that a boat with a metal hull would sink. However, John Wilkinson, a great English ironmaster and toolmaker, proved them wrong when he built a 21 m (69 ft) iron barge on the River Severn in 1787. He vowed that it would carry him to his grave and, when he died in 1808, he was buried in an iron coffin.

The English Channel was crossed by an iron ship in 1822 and slowly, thereafter, the advantages of iron over wood began to win the day. Wooden ships were limited in size both because very large timbers were scarce, and because they could not withstand the stresses and strains if the ship was longer than 90 m (295 ft). Metal ships could be built much larger and eventually became cheaper to operate. The three great ships built by Isambard Kingdom Brunel – the *Great Western* (1838), the *Great Britain* (1843), and the *Great Eastern* (1858) – pointed the way forward. They were 236 ft (71 9 m), 322 ft (98.2 m) and 680 ft (207.3 m) long respectively.

The *Great Western* was a paddle-steamer, with auxiliary sailing equipment, made of oak strengthened with iron; she made 67 crossings of the Atlantic over a period of eight years.

The *Great Britain*, with an all-iron hull and driven by a propeller, but with masts and sails, ran aground off Ireland on her maiden voyage and was not refloated for almost a year, but then did service for 30

❛...no ship ever went to sea carrying with her so much of the goodwill and interest of the nation...❜

THE TIMES, *on the launching of the* Great Eastern, *1859*

years, making frequent journeys to Australia. She was badly damaged rounding Cape Horn in 1866 and lay rotting off the Falkland Islands until 1970 when she was brought back to Bristol, England where she can still be seen.

The *Great Eastern* was a double-skinned, five-deck colossus, with an iron hull held together by about three million rivets. The ship was designed to carry 4000 passengers, and was fitted with propellers, paddles and sails. But she never saw the East. There was constant engine trouble and the ship was never commercially viable because the coal consumption was much greater than expected. However, she was successful as a cable-layer, laying the first one across the Atlantic in 1866.

Load lines
Since the passing of the Merchant Shipping Act 1876, ships have had to be marked with 'load lines' showing the minimum freeboard for the vessel under different conditions.

The PS Great Eastern *laying a cable in Heart's Content Bay, Newfoundland*

The first lines were known as Plimsoll lines after Samuel Plimsoll, the MP for Derby, in England, who became known as 'the sailor's friend'.

MODERN SHIPS

After 1900, all large ships were made of steel which had begun to replace iron in around 1880. Another advance was made with improved techniques in welding which replaced riveting for joining the metal plates, edge-to-edge, on to an inner framework. Riveting had given a particularly strong structure with the plates overlapping, but each rivet required the labour of two boys and two men.

Methods of propulsion also changed. First, there was the Parsons steam turbine (⇒p. 102) around 1910, then, the diesel engine in 1912, and, to some extent, the gas turbine from 1947.

Coal for firing the boilers to raise steam was replaced by oil, and, in a few ships, by nuclear power. Recently, there has been some return to wind power, which has the advantage of being free; large, computer-operated sails are used.

Specialized vessels
There have always been many types of ship which vary, depending on size, intended use and country of origin. There are, for example, still plenty of wooden Arab dhows and Chinese junks.

ISAMBARD KINGDOM BRUNEL
(1806–59)

THIS FAMOUS ENGINEER and inventor was born in Portsmouth, and began his working life by helping his father, Sir Marc Isambard Brunel (1769–1849), in the construction of the first tunnel to be built under the River Thames (⇒p. 122). He was seriously injured in an accident but, when recovered, he won a competition in 1829 for a design for the Clifton Suspension Bridge, and construction began in 1833. By then, he had been appointed chief engineer to the Great Western Railway. He was 27 years old and responsible for building the new line from London to Bristol and beyond, with all its bridges, tunnels and viaducts. He built, in all, about 2500 km (1553 miles) of railway track in England and Wales and was a consultant for many overseas lines. He also constructed or improved many docks.

It was his association with Bristol that gave Brunel the idea of building ships which could link the city with New York. After all his triumphs, it was sad that his last and most ambitious venture, the *Great Eastern*, was not fully successful. He was stricken with paralysis and died soon after her launch, still a young man but worn out by his stupendous efforts. A friend wrote that 'the greatest of England's engineers was lost, the man with the greatest originality of thought and power of execution, bold in his plans but right'.

Isambard Kingdom Brunel in front of the anchor chain of the Great Eastern

However, necessity has led to an increase in the number of ships which are built for specific purposes.

Nowadays, there are enormous oil tankers which need a kilometre to come to a halt; bulk carriers for transporting a single cargo such as coal, ore, cement, sugar or grain; refrigerator ships for meat; car and train ferries; container ships in which the cargo is packed in standard-sized containers; and pressurized ships for carrying natural gas as a liquid.

The hydrofoil
Traditional ships can be very big but their speed is limited by the drag of the water on their hulls, however well streamlined they may be. Welding provided some improvement by giving a smoother hull than riveting, but much better methods have been provided by the invention of the hydrofoil and the hovercraft, which are, in a sense, midway beween boats and aeroplanes. They are limited in size, but they travel faster than a comparable, conventional ship.

The hydrofoil has adjustable, wing-like structures beneath the hull which lift it out of the water as it moves forward. It can be driven by a propeller either in the water or in the air, or by jets.

The Italian, Enrico Forlanini, built a hydrofoil in 1905 which reached a speed of 80 km/h (50 mph) and Alexander Graham Bell, the inventor of the telephone, and Casey Baldwin achieved 100 km/h (62 mph) in their 1918 model. The Boeing jetfoil, first used in 1975, is driven by water-jets produced by pumps powered by gas-turbine engines, and the position of the foils are controlled by computer.

The hovercraft
The principle behind the hovercraft is that it is lifted up on a cushion of air so that it can either hover over or move across water, or reasonably flat land, free of drag. This essentially simple principle is used in today's hover grass-mowers.

*A Slingsby
Amphibious
Hovercraft*

The development of this method is mainly due to the Englishman, Sir Christopher Cockerell, who was born in 1910. After reading engineering at Cambridge University he worked on aircraft radio navigation and on radar. His inventive talent is recorded in the 36 patents he took out during that period, but more was to come when he started a boat hire business on the Norfolk Broads in 1950.

His early experiments on how to obtain an air cushion were carried out on empty tin cans but, by 1955, he had built a working model out of balsa wood and taken out his first patent. The *SRN1*, capable of carrying four men at 45 km/h (28 mph) was launched in 1959 and crossed the English Channel on 25 July, exactly 50 years after Blériot (⇒p. 143)

had first flown across. It heralded the dawn of a new method of transport, although it never quite fulfilled its original potential.

A modern hovercraft looks rather like a huge rubber dinghy. Powerful fans suck air in at the top of the craft and force it out below to form the air cushion. This is prevented from leaking away by a flexible skirt wrapped round the bottom. The craft is propelled by aeroplane-like propellers, mounted on top of the deck, and steered by swivelling the propellers, and by rudders on the rear tail fins.

The largest British hovercraft, the British *SRN4* Mk III, is 185 ft (56.4 m) long, can carry 418 passengers and 60 cars, and has a top speed of 120 km/h (75 mph); the fans are driven by gas-turbine engines.

RAILWAYS

The first steam locomotives began to be used in mines, around 1800, to replace the wagons which had been hauled along wooden rails by horses, women and boys since 1550. They were built by Richard Trevithick (⇒p. 101), and the most famous was used in 1804 to carry iron ore at the Pen-y-Darren works in South

Wales. It travelled for 14.5 km (9 miles) at a maximum speed of 8 km/h (5 mph) and proved that a machine with smooth wheels could run satisfactorily on smooth, cast-iron rails. However, Trevithick lost interest when he found that the rails broke under the strain, and that a second locomotive, nicknamed

'Catch-me-who-can', which he demonstrated in London in 1808, roused no real interest. Other locomotives for use in mines were built, however, by three Englishmen, John Blenkinsop, William Hedley and George Stephenson. Blenkinsop ran a colliery railway in Middleton, Yorkshire in 1812 using a rack system in which toothed rails engaged with cog-wheels on the locomotives; it was the forerunner of many of today's mountain railways. Hedley's locomotive (1813) was known as *Puffing Billy*, and Stephenson's (1814) as *Blücher*.

PUBLIC RAILWAYS

The first public railway, which ran from Stockton to Darlington in the north of England, was opened on 27 September 1825. The train had some 38 wagons, packed with coal and passengers, and was hauled by a newly built steam engine, called *Locomotion*, designed and driven by George Stephenson. Four years later, Stephenson and his son, Robert, designed the *Rocket* which, after beating four contenders in a competition at Rainhill, near Liverpool on 6 October 1829, joined in pulling the first 'inter-city' train from Liverpool to Manchester on 15 September 1830. The journey was not without incident because the Liverpool Tory MP, William Huskisson, was run over and killed; one of the trains was attacked by a mob; and, at the Manchester end, there were demonstrations against the Duke of Wellington, the prime minister, who was a passenger on the train.

THE GROWTH OF RAILWAYS

By 1850, 250,000 workmen were engaged in Britain on realizing George Stephenson's dream that the 'the railroads will become the great highway for the King and all his subjects'.

Rails
The rails in the old mines were originally made of wood; later, they were covered with iron bands; and from 1738 they began to be made of cast iron. A flange on the inner side of the rails held the plain wagon-wheels in position, this method

being adopted so that the wagons could also be used without rails. The present-day use of flat rails with flanged wheels was introduced by Richard Trevithick. Wrought-iron replaced the brittle cast-iron rails in 1820, and they were used until steel took over in the late 1860s. The standard type, nowadays, is the flat-bottomed rail first designed in 1837 by an Irish engineer, Charles Vignoles. The width of 4 ft 8½ in (143 cm), the traditional distance between the wheels of a north England coal wagon, was adopted as the standard gauge in both Britain and the USA by 1885.

Passenger accommodation
The Liverpool and Manchester railway set the early standards for passenger accommodation. First-class compartments were made by mounting three stage-coach bodies on a four-wheel base; second class had roofs but no sides; and third class were open wagons without seats. Eventually, more creature comforts crept in, particularly when George M. Pullman patented luxurious sleeping and dining cars in the USA, in 1865. In

Catch-me-who-can. A demonstration of a train built by Richard Trevithick on a track near Euston Square, London in 1808

> ❝*Rail travel at high speed is not possible, because passengers, unable to breathe, would die of asphyxia.*❞
>
> PROFESSOR DIONYSUS LARDNER (1793–1859), *Irish scientific writer*

In its early days, the Great Western Railway (GWR) was widely known as 'God's Wonderful Railway'.

Britain, first-class sleeping cars came in 1874; dining cars in 1879; electric lighting in 1881; and corridor trains in 1892. The Midland railway provided upholstered seats for all passengers in 1875.

The bogie

As locomotives and coaches got longer, they had difficulty in negotiating tight curves. The problem was solved in 1831 by the introduction of the bogie, which had been used on some older horse-drawn carriages. It consisted of an undercarriage of two or more paired wheels pivoted below the chassis at the front and rear of a coach and had been patented by an Englishman, William Chapman, in 1813.

Brakes

Two competing systems of automatic brakes began to replace manually operated ones in the 1870s. Air-brakes, patented in 1869 by a prolific American inventor, George Westinghouse, are operated by compressed air. In a modern version, the air is supplied to all the brakes on a train, through a single pipe, and they are applied by the driver lowering the pressure in the pipe. The alternative vacuum-brakes, first patented by James Nasmyth (⇒p. 53) in 1844 and improved by Joseph Armstrong and others some 30 years later, use a vacuum line instead of a compressed air line. The brakes are applied when the pressure in the vacuum line is increased.

All the brakes on a train work together, and they are applied automatically if the air- or vacuum-pipe is accidentally ruptured or the driver releases pressure on the 'dead man's' handle or pedal. They are both still in use today, in modified forms.

THE END OF STEAM

Steam locomotives were replaced by electric ones on the main lines in most western countries in the 1960s. The electricity was picked up from a conductor rail on the track or from overhead wires carried on gantries. Alternatively, the locomotives carried a diesel, or less commonly a gas-turbine, engine which drove a dynamo to generate electricity for the motors. The new electric trains were lighter and had much better acceleration; they were more efficient; they were much cleaner; and they could be operated more flexibly as, for example, when being turned round in a station.

Electric trains

The first electric railway using a conductor rail was designed by a

---

GEORGE WESTINGHOUSE
(1846–1914)

GEORGE WESTINGHOUSE, the son of a manufacturer of agricultural equipment, was born in Central Bridge, New York. He ran away from school at the age of 15 to fight for the North in the American Civil War and three years later joined the Navy. In 1865 he went back home to work in his father's workshop and began to pursue his interest in railways, taking out patents for a steam locomotive and for systems of air-braking and electrical signal control. Later, he turned his attention to improving the distribution of natural gas and the generation of electricity.

Whilst overseeing the successful adoption of his air-brake system by many of the world's railways, he played a key role in developing the transmission of alternating current electricity in America (⇒p. 73); organized the lighting of the first Columbia Exposition in Chicago (1893); and installed the generating equipment at the Niagara Falls power station (1893).

He was an irascible man with great energy and drive who, despite a lack of formal training as an engineer, took out 400 patents during his life. The Westinghouse Air Brake Co. which began in Pittsburgh in 1869 and which he controlled until 1907, is now a huge corporation.

Above: *A spray of optical fibres conducting white and green light* (⇒p. 21)

Right: *The gold death mask of King Tutankhamen found in his tomb in 1922 by Lord Carnarvon and Howard Carter* (⇒p. 12)

Above: *A British Steel plate mill for rolling steel. The plate is generally 5 to 50 mm thick and up to 5 m wide* (⇒p. 17)

Left: *A caesium fountain atomic clock being developed at the National Physical Laboratory at Teddington, England. The aim is to achieve an accuracy of at least one part in 10^{15} (one second in 30 million years)* (⇒p. 50)

Above: *A large solar energy complex in the Mojave Desert of California, USA. Flat mirrors in a circle on the ground are controlled by computers so as to reflect the Sun's radiation into a 20-storey tower (centre left) where it is concentrated on to a target area to boil water and raise steam to drive a turbine* (⇒p. 93)

Right: *Static electricity. The electric charge from the dome of a Van de Graaff generator passes into the girl's hairs which, because they carry like charges, repel each other* (⇒p. 66)

Above: *Welding a Rover car body by robots (⇒p. 139)*

Opposite: *The Rolls-Royce Trent gas turbine engine - the most powerful engine in the world today. It has a take-off thrust of 90,000 lb and is fitted in the Boeing 777 and Airbus A330 airliners (⇒p. 108)*

Right: *Elisha Otis demonstrating his safety elevator at the Crystal Palace Exposition in New York City in 1854. The ratchet bars can be seen on the inside of the two vertical supports below the loaded platform on which Elisha Otis is standing (⇒p. 146)*

Above: *Virtual reality - two players, fitted with headsets and data gloves, as shown, can play a game by 'inhabiting' the same environment within a computer. They can search for each other and use the data glove and a joystick to fire a gun. The* *headsets contain two miniature TV screens for stereo vision and headphones for stereo sound. They also contain sensors which enable the computer to calculate the direction in which each player is looking* (⇒p. 204)

Right: *Computer-aided design (CAD) - the hand rail of an escalator (⇒p. 203)*

Below: *A high-speed MRI scanner can perform a 50-slice brain scan in less than five minutes. The scanner and patient are in the background and the scans show on the computer screen to the right (⇒p. 229)*

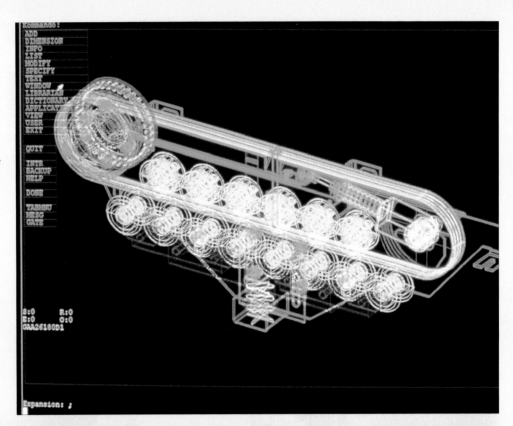

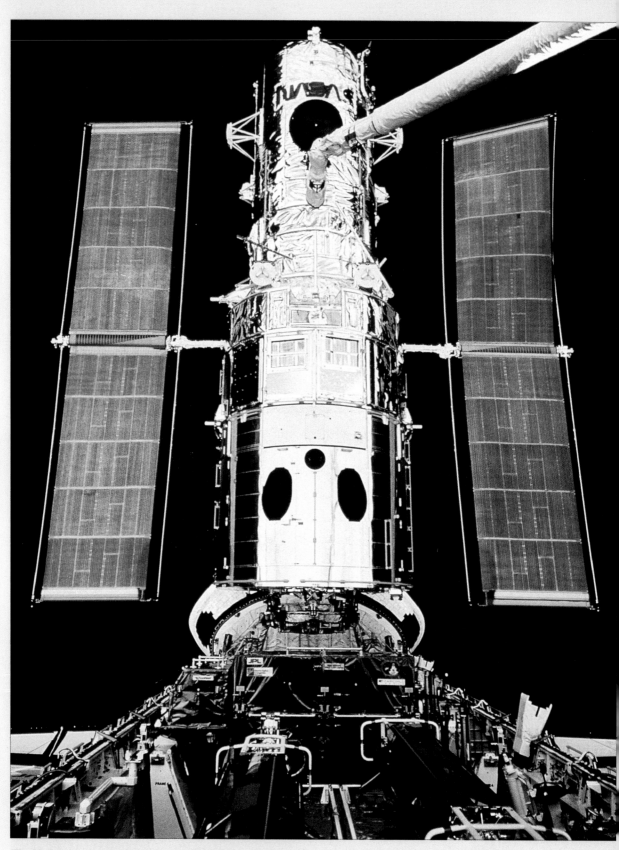

The Hubble space telescope seen shortly after capture by the shuttle Endeavour *in December 1993. In a series of five space walks the* Endeavour *crew replaced one of the telescope's cameras and its solar panels, and carried out other servicing tasks (⇒p. 251)*

GEORGE AND ROBERT STEPHENSON

GEORGE STEPHENSON (1781–1848) was born near Newcastle, England, the son of a miner. He began work almost as soon as he could walk and he drifted into the pits where he began work as an assistant fireman. He was very poor, spoke with an almost incomprehensible accent, and only began to learn to read and write by going to night school when he was 18. However, he was recognized as 'one of nature's gentlemen' and his skill as a mechanic led to his appointment as enginewright at Killingworth High Pit in 1812 on a yearly salary of £100. Whilst there, he built his first steam locomotive, *Blücher*, and in 1815 invented a miner's safety lamp which rivalled Davy's (⇒p. 29). After his success in designing the Stockton to Darlington and Liverpool to Manchester railways, he was responsible for planning many more both in Great Britain and in Belgium and Spain.

He formed a powerful team with his son, Robert (1803–59), whose more educated, cautious approach balanced George's self-confident aggression. Robert was as famous for the bridges he built as for the locomotives, and he became MP for Whitby in 1849. Both father and son spurned any state honours, but Robert was buried in Westminster Abbey.

George Stephenson experimenting with his safety lamp

❛*I will send them the locomotive to be the Great Missionary among them.*❜

GEORGE STEPHENSON (1781–1848), *English engineer*

German, Werner von Siemens, and exhibited in Berlin in 1879. Four years later, a similar railway was built along the sea front at Brighton, England by Magnus Volk, the son of a local clockmaker. It is still there, the oldest electric railway in the world, having carried over 60 million passengers since opening. The popularity of this type of train was enhanced when it was used on the London Underground in 1890, and on the line through the city of Baltimore in the USA in 1895.

Overhead cables were first used in road tramways which began in Germany, the USA and Britain around 1885. The first trams in England were in Blackpool, where they still run.

A French TGV train. This electrically driven high-speed train is the culmination of a French research project which began in 1967. It developed from a family of trains (the TGS, ETG and RTG) driven by gas-turbines.

Typical modern examples of electric trains are the Japanese 'Bullet' (1964), French TGV (Train à Grande Vitesse, 1978) and German ICE (Inter-city Experimental, 1985). A TGV recorded a speed of 515 km/h (320.2 mph) in May 1990. In 1967, British Rail began to build an electrical Advanced Passenger Train (APT), with a special hydraulic tilting mechanism to facilitate high-speed cornering, but the technical problems involved could not be solved and the project was largely abandoned in 1986. Modified TGV trains – transmanche super-trains – capable of speeds up to 186 mph (300 km/h) are used for travel through the Channel Tunnel.

Diesel–electric trains

Since 1912, diesel engines have been used to drive the wheels of a locomotive either directly, in much the same way as in a heavy lorry; through a hydraulic mechanism; or through an electric motor. The last method, used in a diesel–electric train, is the commonest. Its advantage is that the train can run on lines which have not been electrified, but the disadvantage is that it relies on only one kind of fuel. British Rail's High-Speed Trains (HST–125 and 225), used on the Inter-City services, are typical.

Magnetic levitation

Since the 1960s, inventors have tried to design trains without wheels which are lifted above a track by using powerful magnets in what is called magnetic levitation (Maglev). The idea was first proposed in 1909 by the rocket engineer Robert Goddard (⇒p. 247), and has been patented a number of times, for example by a German engineer, Hermann Kemper, in 1934.

In modern versions, the train is lifted either by repulsion or attraction between electromagnets on the train and on the track, and propelled by a linear induction motor (⇒p. 74) which makes use of some of the same magnets. Research began in Japan in 1962, and their most recent model, the MLU002N, is designed to travel at more than 500 km/h (310 mph). A 'Transrapid' system has been in operation in Germany since 1971, and it was agreed in 1994 to build a train which will cover the 284 km (176 miles) between Hamburg and Berlin in one hour. In England, a small coach has shuttled passengers between Birmingham Airport and the nearby Exhibition Centre since 1983, but only at 25 km/h (15.5 mph), and in the USA, a 14 mile (22 km) link from Orlando airport to Disney World is due to open in 1996. There is much renewed interest fostered by Henry H. Kolm's invention, in America, of what he calls a magneplane with a planned speed of over 250 mph (400 km/h). Yet the future of magnetic levitation is still very much in the air.

BICYCLES

Wheeled vehicles propelled by man are depicted on Babylonian bas-reliefs, and a contemporary of Leonardo da Vinci drew one, but the idea only developed slowly during the 19th century.

The 'bicycle' really began as a two-legged scooter, called a draisienne, invented by a German, Baron Drais von Sauerbronn, in 1818. The rider sat astride a wooden bar supported above two wheels and he propelled the contraption by pushing his feet against the ground. Improved versions with more comfortable seating arrangements were known as hobby-horses or dandy-horses.

None of these early bicycles was much more than a plaything but they did lead to the first pedal cycles, made in 1839 by Kirkpatrick Macmillan, a Scottish blacksmith. He used foot-operated pedals on each side of the front wheel of a hobby-horse to turn the rear wheel through connecting rods and cranks (⇒p. 59). His bicycle was cumbersome, and the velocipede, invented by Pierre Michaux and his son Ernest in 1861, was much easier to ride. The Michaux were manufacturers of perambulators and invalid chairs in Paris, and they fitted pedals directly on to the front wheels of a hobby-horse, as on a child's tricycle today. Their machine became popular, but it could not be ridden quickly because, with a front wheel about 0.9 m (3 ft) in diameter, it only moved about 3 m (10 ft) for each turn of the pedals.

This drawback was overcome by using a bigger front wheel in bicycles which came to be called penny-farthings. The first was designed by James Starley and William Hillman, in Coventry, England in 1870.

Penny-farthings used a lightweight frame, and wheels with adjustable metal spokes and solid rubber tyres, to make a bicycle which sold for £8 and could travel at 20 mph (32 km/h). But penny-farthings were difficult to mount and extremely precarious to ride.

THE MODERN ERA

Everything changed in the cycling world with the introduction of chain drive to the rear wheel by an Englishman, Harry J. Lawson, in 1876. The Rover Safety bicycle designed by John Kemp Starley, the nephew of James Starley, in 1884, was a particularly successful model with many of the features of today's bicycles.

By the year 1900, cycling was no longer associated with 'cads on castors', as the earlier riders had been dubbed; it was a common form of transport for everyone.

Gearing

In the first chain-driven cycles, a larger cog wheel on the pedals than on the rear axle gave a fixed gearing, and it was not possible to free-wheel. This was allowed for in 1894 by fitting a ratchet-type mechanism (⇒p. 59) on the rear wheel cog which only locked when pressure was applied to the pedals.

After 1899, variable gears were designed using either the Sturmey-Archer or the dérailleur systems which are both still in use today. In the former, there is a miniature gearbox within the hub of the rear wheel which allows three or four gear ratios. The latter depends on having a number of external, coaxial cogs of different diameters on the rear wheel

OLD BICYCLES

Left: *A draisienne, 1818;* centre: *the first Macmillan bicycle, 1839;* right: *a penny-farthing, 1870*

❛*People had reinvented the bicycle ten times a year, but basically a traditional bicycle was a collection of tubes and I suddenly realized it didn't need to be.*❜

MIKE BURROWS, *English engineer, 1993*

and, perhaps, on the pedal axis. The chain passes round a sprung wheel, so that its length can adjust, and the gear is changed by 'derailing' it from one cog to another. With five different cogs at the rear, and two on the pedal axis, up to ten gear ratios are possible.

A mountain bike, of the type first introduced in the USA in 1973, and proving increasingly popular today, even for riders who have absolutely no intention of going either up or down a mountain, may have up to 21 different gears ratios, provided by seven rear and three front cogs.

Pneumatic tyres

The ability to change gear made riding a bicycle much easier, and the fitting of Dunlop pneumatic tyres made cycling an altogether more comfortable activity, finally getting rid of the 'bone-shaker' label which had stuck to all previous models.

In 1887, John Boyd Dunlop (1840–1921), a Scot who had been a veterinary surgeon for 20 years, bought his nine-year-old son a tricycle fitted with solid rubber tyres. When the boy complained that the ride was bumpy, Dunlop replaced them with inflated rubber tubes under a canvas outer cover. The new pneumatic tyres were at first stuck permanently in position, but by 1890 the outer casing was designed to fit tightly within the rim of the wheel when the inner tube was inflated. It could be levered on or off.

Dunlop founded a business which grew into the Dunlop Rubber Co. and he became a millionaire, but it was not all plain-sailing because his idea had been patented by a Scottish engineer, R. W. Thomson, in 1845, which led to much legal wrangling.

The Bowden cable

This consists of a steel wire surrounded by a flexible, cylindrical cover. The cover can be fixed at each end, and the wire, pulled by a lever at one end, used to operate some mechanism at the other. It was patented by an Englishman, E.M. Bowden, in 1896 for operating the brakes on a bicycle but it has a much wider use today.

Racing bikes

The first cycle race was held in Paris in 1868 and the Tour de France began in 1903. Since then, racing has played an important role in the cycling world. It has also ensured the constant development of new designs and the use of new materials.

The racing bike invented by an Englishman, Mike Burrows, in 1982 is typical. He is a self-taught engineer who left school at 15 and began designing bicycles as a side-line in the 1970s. When his new machine was finally allowed to participate in international racing in 1986, and after development by Lotus cars, it was ridden to victory by the British cyclist Chris Boardman in the 4000-metre individual pursuit race in the 1992 Olympic Games.

Folding bikes

Alex Moulton, who lived in Bradford-on-Avon in England, designed a folding bicycle in 1958. It had small wheels with a diameter of 41 cm (16 in); a novel means of suspension; and it could be carried in the boot of a car when folded.

Large companies at first shunned Moulton's idea, so he began to manufacture the bike himself. Its success did much to halt the declining popularity of bicycling and led to the development of many similar small-wheel models such as the Raleigh Chopper, the BMX (Bicycle Moto Cross), and other folding models such as the Dahon and the Strida.

Electric bikes

A number of inventors have recently patented bicycles in which the normal pedalling process can be replaced or assisted by switching over, at will, to a battery-driven electric motor. Sir Clive Sinclair's Zike, Douglas Gatward's Citibike, and models such as the Boosta, City Blitz and Electra, are typical British models.

It remains to be seen whether such bicycles will be commercially successful or whether there is anything in the view of *The Times*'s leader writer that 'if bicycles were meant to be electrified, man would have been born with spark-plugs for feet'.

MOTORCYCLES

The limitations of human pedal power for propelling bicycles or tricycles were so obvious that inventors soon set about trying to devise better alternatives. The first serious attempts involved fitting a steam engine, which Pierre Michaux in France, and Howard Roper in the USA, managed to achieve in 1869. It came to naught because the engines, with their associated boilers, were bulky, hot, and tiresome to start. Nor could the inventors find a suitable place to fit them.

THE USE OF PETROL

Some progress was made when Edward Butler in England in 1884, and Daimler and Maybach in Germany in 1885, used small petrol engines, but neither machine went into production.

The French firm de Dion and Bouton had more success in 1895 with a ³/₄ hp, single-cylinder engine which was used very successfully to drive the rear wheels of a tricycle. It had a capacity of 120 cc and was fitted with external fins to facilitate air-cooling. But the big breakthrough came in 1902, when Eugene and Michael Werner, two Russian brothers living in Paris, fitted a similar engine to a bicycle in the position occupied by the pedals. It proved to be the ideal location because it allowed the crankcase of the engine to be built in as part of the bicycle frame, and there was room for the petrol tank below the crossbar. The engine was controlled by handlebar grips, and the rear wheels were driven by a belt from the engine, or by auxiliary pedals.

It was the shape of things to come. Over the next 90 years well over 2000 different models of motorcycle made their appearance. At first, production was concentrated in Europe and the USA with such favourite brand marks as Ariel, Triumph and Norton in Britain, Ducati in Italy, Harley Davidson in America, Peugeot in France and NSU in Germany. After the end of World War II, the Japanese companies – Honda, Kawasaki, Yamaha and Suzuki – began to make motorcycles and they completely dominate the market today.

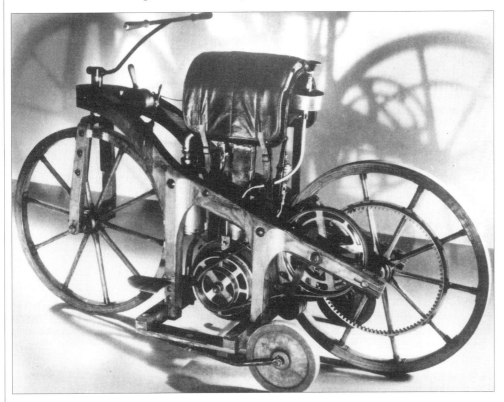

A replica of Daimler's original motorcycle. The original, made almost entirely of wood, was first driven by Daimler's son, Paul, on 10 November 1885. It was destroyed by fire in 1903

The rise of Honda is typical. Soichiro Honda, born in 1906, began as a garage apprentice but by 1934 had his own firm making piston rings. After World War II, he sold the firm, bought some surplus two-stroke engines and fitted them on to bicycles in a small shed. It was the start of the Honda Motor Co.

Technical advances

Today's motorcycles are streamlined, chromium-plated giants. The engines may have up to six cylinders, electrical starting, electronic ignition, multiple exhaust and inlet valves, water-cooling, and supercharging or turbocharging. They have capacities of over 1000 cc and horse powers over 150.

The machines themselves can have chain or shaft transmission, disc brakes, six-speed gearboxes with foot pedal controls, cast light-alloy wheels with tubeless tyres, sophisticated independent suspensions, and anti-locking brake systems. Since 1910 they have been linked to side-cars, and, in the 1950s, mopeds (motor-assisted pedal cycles) with small wheels, have been popular in hot countries.

The Honda Sabre 750S can accelerate up to 150 km/h (93 mph) from standing in just over 12 s, and has a top speed of over 200 km/h (124 mph). That compares with the 19 km/h (12 mph) achieved by the wooden-framed, Daimler–Maybach machine in 1885.

MOTOR CARS

In just over one hundred years, the manufacture of motor cars has become one of the world's greatest industries and over 33 million are manufactured annually worldwide. There is one car for every 1.3 persons in the USA and between 1.5 and 3 in many developed countries. That adds up to around 400 million car owners.

STEAM CARS

The earliest self-propelled road vehicle was designed in 1769 by Nicolas Cugnot, a French army engineer. It was driven by a steam engine and was really intended for dragging artillery pieces, but it could carry four people at a speed of just over 2 mph (3.2 km/h). Later, in 1803, Richard Trevithick (⇒p. 101) demonstrated one of his steam cars, in London but it aroused little interest so he turned his attention to railway locomotives.

In the 1820s and 1830s, however, a number of steam carriages were built and used to provide a limited bus service in London, Paris and other big cities, but development was hampered in many ways. Tolls had to be paid and the stage-coach proprietors and later the railway companies did all they could to deter any competition. Moreover, steam engines were tiresome to start; bulky, hot, noisy, and smoky; and the general public never regarded them as being very safe.

A few pioneers continued to make steam buses after they had largely disappeared around 1840 and there was some resurgence of interest towards the end of the century. In 1889 a Frenchman, Léon Serpollet, invented a boiler which produced steam by pumping water through a stack of red-hot coils of steel tubing heated by burning paraffin. In 1894, the well-known French firm de Dion and Bouton won the first motor-car race with a 15 hp steam carriage, which covered the 127 km (79 miles) from Paris to Rouen at an average speed of 18.7 km/h (11.6 mph). In the USA the Stanley brothers built a popular two-seater car which held the world land speed record of 205.5 km/h (127.56 mph) in 1906. However, the days of steam cars were numbered because, by then, the internal combustion engine was taking over.

EARLY PETROL-DRIVEN CARS

The modern car began to emerge in 1885 when Karl Benz fitted one of his engines over the rear axle of a tricycle to make a two-seater vehicle and, in 1886, when Gottlieb Daimler did likewise to a four-wheeled horse-carriage. The engines turned the rear wheels through belt drives and chains.

Benz's vehicle could travel at 8 mph

(13 km/h) and Daimler's at 12 mph (19 km/h).

In 1895 two French engineers, René Panhard and Emile Levassor, made what is generally regarded as the first saloon car. It had a front-mounted Daimler engine enclosed by a sort of bonnet; a propeller shaft to transmit the drive to the rear wheels; top- and side-covers together with a windscreen to protect the driver and passengers from the weather; solid rubber tyres; a clutch; and an enclosed gearbox. It laid the foundations of modern design.

It also inspired Daimler's son, Paul, to build a new car in 1901. It had a honeycomb radiator and a chassis made of steel; it could travel at 53 mph (85 km/h); and it won every race it entered. It was called a Mercedes after the name of the daughter of Emile Jellinek who backed it financially. It cost £2000.

Other early models were built by the Austrian Siegfried Marcus (1870); by the Frenchmen Armand Peugeot (1896) and Renault brothers, Marcel, Louis and Fernand (1899); Englishmen, F.W. Lanchester (1896) and Herbert Austin (1895); and American, Henry Ford (1896).

MASS PRODUCTION

In mass production, the manufacture of an object is broken down into a number of single operations which are then carried out in a carefully planned way by each of many workers doing just a single job repetitively. The method grew out of the American system of manufacture (⇒p. 115) in which articles were made from standard interchangeable parts.

In 1881 an American engineer, Frederick W. Taylor, working for a steel company, began what came to be known as time-and-motion studies. These involve a detailed investigation of how an individual worker carries out any particular job with a view to finding out how it might be done more efficiently.

Ransome E. Olds adopted these new methods in the manufacture of 18,000 Oldsmobile cars in the USA between 1901 and 1905, but they were exploited much more fully by Henry Ford when, in 1908, he added the idea of a moving assembly line which brought the car to the workers instead of them going to it. The car was conveyed along the line, at a suitable speed, so that individual workers could work on it at their particular task before it moved on.

Ford's method greatly increased the rate of production and cut the price of cars. His company, which he started in 1903, had made one million cars by the end of 1915. By 1921 it was making one million each year. The success of his method led to its adoption by all car manufacturers, particularly after the end of World War I when motoring grew in popularity.

Family saloons, small cars, and estate cars or station wagons, were made by, for example, the Austin and Morris companies in England; Citroën, Renault and Peugeot in France; Fiat in Italy; Volkswagen in Germany; and Ford, Chevrolet, General Motors and Dodge in the USA. At the end of World War II, Japanese companies also entered the field with, for example, Nissan, Honda and Toyota, and by the mid 1980s they had matched the American production of around 8 million cars per year. Each country now manufactures about 12 million cars each year.

TECHNICAL INNOVATIONS

Starting
An engine is started by rotating the crankshaft at about 50 rpm. At first, this was done by hand cranking which was both laborious and unreliable. The introduction of the electrical self-starter, designed by an American inventor, Charles F. Kettering, in a 1911 Cadillac, was therefore very welcome. The flywheel (⇒p. 106) attached to the crankshaft (⇒p. 105) was fitted with teeth so that it could engage with a gear wheel turned by the starter motor. Self-starting not only made driving much more acceptable to women, it also enabled engines with higher compression ratios (⇒p. 106) to be designed. For a while cars could be started either by hand cranking or by a starter motor but the crank was abandoned when it became too difficult to turn the engine over manually. Using the ignition key for starting, now universal, was pioneered by Chrysler in 1949.

6 It by no means follows that because one man has failed in a certain method that another man will not succeed. 9

HENRY FORD (1863–1947), American engineer

HENRY FORD
(1863–1947)

HENRY FORD was born in Greenfield, Michigan, in 1863, and began an apprenticeship as a machinist at the age of 15. He was employed by a number of different companies, and made money by repairing clocks and watches in his spare time, before he went to work for Thomas Edison in 1891. The two became life-long friends, but Ford's interest was in cars so, after making a petrol engine in 1893 and a car in 1896, he left Edison and became the chief engineer of the Detroit Motor Co. in 1899. He founded the Ford Motor Co. in 1903, when he was 40, and a year later one of his own racing cars, the '999', established a new world land-speed record of 147 km/h (91.4 mph) over a 1.6 km (1 mile) course.

His first cars, named after the letters of the alphabet, were replaced by the Model-T, popularly known as the 'Tin Lizzie', in 1908. It was a solidly built, easy-to-drive four-seater and though it originally cost $850, the price eventually fell to $360. Such value was only achieved by cutting out the frills. 'You can have it in any colour,' Ford said, 'so long as it's black.' Over 15 million were sold before it was replaced by the Model-A in 1928.

Ford was a fervent pacifist who travelled to Europe in 1915 to try to bring World War I to an end. He was also a considerable benefactor, setting up, for instance, the Ford Foundation in 1936 to encourage scientific, educational and charitable activities all over the world. Yet, in spite of his contribution to it, he always claimed that 'history is bunk'.

> **6 Exercise is bunk. If you are healthy, you don't need it: if you are sick you shouldn't take it. 9**
>
> HENRY FORD
> (1863–1947),
> American engineer

Henry and Edsel Ford with the first and 10 millionth car, 1928

The clutch

The drive still used in most cars is based on the arrangement of a clutch, gearbox, and propeller shaft originated by Panhard and Levassor. The purpose of the clutch is to disconnect the engine from the propeller shaft whilst the gear is being changed. It contains two lined plates, one of which is connected to the flywheel and the other to the gearbox. It is only when the two plates are pressed together, generally by a spring mechanism, that the engine can turn the propeller shaft, via the gear box. Depressing the clutch pedal separates the two plates and allows the gears to be changed.

Gear changing

Gear boxes were fitted on to early cars designed by Panhard and Levassor, by Renault, and by F.W. Lanchester, but for many years the gearbox was a relatively weak link in a motor car. A change of gear involves the uncoupling of a pair of gear wheels and the coupling of another pair, whilst the clutch pedal is depressed. As the gear wheels are rotating rapidly, it is not easy and it was originally a chancy and noisy operation.

Some improvement came when the teeth on the gears were cut helically ($\Rightarrow$p. 60), as on a screw thread, but the difficulty was not really overcome until the invention of syncromesh gearboxes in 1928. They have a clutch-like arrangement ensuring that any two gears which are to be linked will be rotating at similar speeds.

Completely automatic gearboxes, which do away with manually operated gear-levers, began to be used in the late 1930s. Continuously variable transmission systems (CVT), adopted recently on some small cars with front-wheel drive, use belts and different size pulleys instead of gear wheels.

The propeller shaft

Panhard and Levassor used chains in the final drive to the wheels of their early cars, but nowadays the propeller shaft is linked to two half-shafts, each connected to a rear wheel in a rear-axle assembly. This gears down the rotational speed of the propeller shaft and transmits it at right angles into the half-shafts. A differential gear arrangement, in the rear assembly, also allows the outside wheel to rotate more rapidly than the inside one when cornering.

The functioning of the propeller shaft was also improved in 1899 when Renault fitted it with universal joints at both ends which allowed it to adjust on bumpy roads. Nowadays, there is also a sliding connection which enables the length of the shaft to change.

Braking

Early cars were fitted with the type of brakes used on bicycles and carriages. They relied on brake linings made of wood, leather or metal being pressed against the propeller shaft or the rims of the rear wheels. Improved results were achieved in Renault and Merecedes cars, around 1902, by making the linings in the form of curved brake shoes which were pushed outwards on to the smooth inside of a cylinder attached to each wheel. They were known as drum brakes. Six years later, in 1908, an Englishman, Herbert Frood, patented brake linings (Ferodo linings) made from a composition of asbestos and high melting-point resins. They fitted on to a brake shoe and could be replaced when they wore away.

F.W. Lanchester experimented with disc brakes around the same time. Two lined pads were pressed tightly against the sides of a steel disc attached to the wheel, but the system, which keeps cooler than drum brakes, was not widely adopted until some 50 years later.

The earliest brakes were operated by cables or rods and only acted on the rear wheels, but a Scotsman, Malcolm Loughhead, invented a new method in 1924, which came to be known as the Lockheed hydraulic system. It used flexible tubes full of incompressible brake fluid to transmit the force applied on the foot pedal to the brakes on both front and rear wheels. Depressing the brake pedal moved a piston in a central, master cylinder which pushed the fluid on to other pistons in slave cylinders on the wheels. It was the movement of the slave pistons that actually operated the brakes, and because they were wider than the master piston the force they exerted was magnified, as in a Bramah press ($\Rightarrow$p. 53). The handbrake lever, fitted with a ratchet ($\Rightarrow$p. 57), still operated the brakes on the rear wheels by a mechanical linkage.

Servo-assisted systems, which function with a lighter touch on the foot pedal, were introduced in 1919. They have a mechanism between the pedal and the brake which boosts the pedal pressure.

'Fail safe', anti-skid and anti-locking systems are also available. The first lessens the risk of a complete brake failure if there is a leakage in the hydraulic system; the second lowers the chances of skidding; and the third ensures that the brakes will not lock when they are slammed on in an emergency.

Steering

The first cars were steered by a bicycle-style handlebar arrangement or a tiller as fitted to the top of a rudder on a boat. The steering-wheel appeared as early as 1894 in a Vacheron model and has been used almost universally ever since. Power steering, in which turning the wheel is facilitated by a motor, first appeared in 1951 in Chrysler and Buick cars.

The projection of a rigid wheel towards the driver proved to be dangerous in some accidents so that modern steering-columns are designed to collapse under presssure. Increasingly, cars are also being fitted with air bags, first patented in the 1950s, between the front seat passengers and the dashboard. They rapidily inflate when a car crashes.

Tyres

Pneumatic tyres, first used by Dunlop on bicycles (⇒p. 132), were fitted on the wheels of a Peugeot car by the Michelin brothers, Edouard and André, in 1895. At first they had a separate inflatable inner tube, but since 1948 the trend has been towards tubeless tyres which have an outer casing with an airtight rubber lining. An airtight seal is made between the wired edge or bead of the tyre and the inside of the wheel rim. Tubeless tyres are easier to fit and deflate more slowly if punctured.

The outer casing of a tyre is moulded from a mixture of synthetic rubber and additives such as glass fibre, carbon black, oil and sulphur. Detailed attention is paid to the tread pattern so that tyres for every sort of occasion are now available.

Underneath the outer rubber casing, there are overlapping layers of corded fabric, and the difference between a cross-ply and a radial-ply tyre, which is more expensive but lasts longer, depends on the way in which these layers are arranged. A bias-belted tyre is a hybrid of a cross-ply and a radial-ply. As different types of tyre have different steering characteristics they cannot always be used together.

Suspension

To ensure a reasonably smooth ride, even in old horse-drawn carriages, the body was supported on leaf springs, like those used by Ctesibius in 230 BC. They were made of a slightly curved strip of flexible steel, or a group of strips tied together, with the ends attached to the body and the centre to the axle.

Similar leaf springs are still used in many cars though they are made of much better spring steel and for many years have only been used on the rear axle. Since 1922, the front wheels have been connected, independently, to the car body by a coil spring or a torsion bar. Such an arrangement gives much better steering and comfort than the earlier rigid front axle.

Springs, however, cannot provide a smooth ride on their own. Bumps in the road would compress them, initially, and absorb the shock energy, but a very bouncy ride would result as the springs unwound. This is avoided by using dampers or shock absorbers. The simplest type consist of a piston, containing small holes or a valve, fitted inside a cylinder full of hydraulic fluid. As the piston moves and the fluid is pushed through the holes or valve the energy stored up in the springs is dissipated as heat.

In the 1950s, Citroën developed a pneumatic type of suspension system as an alternative to the hydraulic type; it used the compression of a gas to provide the springing. Then, in 1962, the use of hydraulic fluid was taken a stage further in the Moulton Hydrolastic system, first used in the Austin 1100, designed by Alec Issigonis, a Turkish-born engineer working in England. The separate springs and dampers on each wheel were replaced by single units which were hydraulically linked, and this gave a smoother ride. Within a few years, a combination of pneumatic and hydraulic springing was being used as in the Hydragas system.

Looking further ahead, it is possible that cars will be fitted with sensors to foresee the road ahead.

Car bodies

Car bodies have evolved from upright box-like affairs, suitable for passengers wearing top hats, to low, sleek, streamlined shapes not always easy to enter or leave. They were, at first, made by coach builders, mainly of wood. Nowadays car bodies are predominantly made of steel.

For many years the body was made in sections bolted together on top of a stronger, separate chassis. Nowadays, large parts of the body can be pressed from sheet steel into a structure which is so strong that the separate chassis has been discarded. When pieces have to be joined together it is generally done by spot welding (⇒p. 18) controlled by robots.

Catalytic converters

Since 1975, there has been growing concern about the atmospheric pollution caused by the unburnt hydrocarbons, the carbon monoxide and the oxides of nitrogen in the exhaust fumes of cars. Increasingly, stringent legislation to control the emissions, particularly in the USA and Japan and, recently, in Europe, has resulted in the development of catalytic converters. They are fitted into the car's exhaust system and contain catalysts, based on platinum, palladium and rhodium, which facilitate the conversion of the harmful gases into water, carbon dioxide and nitrogen. They are not cheap but in conjunction with well-designed and well-maintained engines they can be very effective.

Pollution-free motoring would be possible if electrically driven cars could be developed, but none of the many attempts to do that, since the first in 1896, has been very successful commercially.

ANCILLARY EQUIPMENT

External fittings

Bumpers came in 1905; electric lighting in 1911; direction indicators in 1913; wing mirrors, brake-stop lights and mechanically operated windscreen wipers in 1916; laminated windscreens in 1920; electrical windscreen wipers in 1922; chromium plating in 1927; windscreen washers in 1937; two-speed windscreen wipers in 1940; and iodine vapour bulbs in 1964.

Internal fittings

Speedometers were used as early as 1902; internal rear-mirrors in 1906; adjustable seats in 1914; petrol gauges in 1922; heaters in 1926; radios in 1932;

steering-column locks in 1934; air-conditioning in 1940; power-operated windows in 1946 and tinted glass in 1950. Seat belts, first patented by a Frenchman, G.D. Liebau in 1903, and well tested on aeroplane seats, were made compulsory in the front seats of all new British cars from 1967, and tachometers which log many of the details of a journey have had to be fitted into heavy goods vehicles in Great Britain since 1981. Some modern cars also use a modified 'black box' flight recorder.

ON THE ROAD

Traffic lights

A gas-lit 'Stop-Go' light, with red and green colours, was set up at the entrance to the British Houses of Parliament in London in 1868, but within a month it blew up and injured the policeman who operated it. The first electric light was installed in Cleveland, Ohio, in 1914. It, too, had only red and green lights. New York saw the first red-amber-green lights in 1918, and London in 1925.

Traffic lights operated by vehicles passing over a pressure pad in the road came in 1932.

Pedestrian crossings

Pedestrian crossings were introduced in Britain in 1934 by the then Minister of Transport, Leslie Hore-Belisha. They were indicated by an orange sphere on the top of a black-and-white post, which was called a Belisha beacon. When they were painted with black-and-white stripes on the road surface in 1951 they became known as 'zebra' crossings. Hore-Belisha also introduced the driving test and issued a new Highway Code in 1935.

Crash barriers

Crash barriers have saved thousands of lives. Some of them are extremely strong and will prevent a juggernaut going over the edge of a bridge. Others conceal a more subtle design, with legs which collapse more easily than the horizontal sections. When they are hit by a vehicle, the legs give way but the horizontal members act like a huge elastic band absorbing energy which would otherwise add to the injuries of passengers in the vehicle.

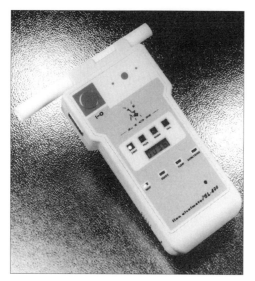

The Lion Alcolmeter

USA as Denver boots, first appeared in London in 1983.

Alcolmeters

It is an offence in many countries to drive under the influence of drink, and since 1967 the legal limit in Britain has been set at 80 mg of alcohol per 100 ml of blood in the blood stream or more than 35 µg in the breath. To implement the legislation, the police carry out roadside tests on drivers using alcolmeters made by Lion Laboratories, a subsidiary of the American firm, MPD. The devices rely on the fact that alcohol, which is not an electrical conductor, is readily oxidized to acetic (ethanoic) acid which is an electrical conductor. The amount of alcohol in a driver's breath is, therefore, measured by getting him or her to breathe into a tube and over an electrochemical cell where the acid is formed. The current which flows is proportional to the original amount of alcohol, and this is recorded either by indicator lights showing zero, pass, warn or fail, or as a digital read-out of the actual breath alcohol level.

Parking

Parking meters were invented by Carlton C. Magee, the editor of a local newspaper, and first tried out in Oklahoma City, USA in 1935; they came to Britain in 1958 when 625 were installed in the Mayfair area of London. The charge was 6d (2¹/₂p) for an hour. Wheel clamps, which originated in the

FLYING

The dream that man would defy gravity and fly like the birds, expressed by Leonardo da Vinci and others, began to be realized in June 1783. The scene was set in the town square of Annonay, near Lyons in France, where two paper-making brothers, Etienne and Joseph Montgolfier, lit a fire below a large, empty cloth-and-paper bag, and the entry of hot air into the bag caused it to rise to a height of 1800 m (5905 ft). In September, they used the same method to carry a sheep, a duck and a cock in a cage hanging below the 'bag'. And on 21 November another hot-air balloon carried two volunteer pilots, Jean Pilâtre de Rozier and the Marquis d'Arlandes, on an 8 km (5 mile), 25-minute flight from the Bois de Boulogne in Paris.

The record was beaten within a month when the French physicist, Jacques Alexandre Charles, used a hydrogen-filled balloon to carry himself and a passenger 44 km (27 miles) in two hours.

Ballooning became something of a

> *It was very beautiful to see this noble white bird sail majestically from the top of a hill... according to the set of its rudder, merely by its own weight.*
>
> SIR GEORGE CAYLEY *(1771–1857), English engineer*

craze throughout Europe and after a great many ups and downs, some of them distinctly hazardous, it is still practised as a hobby or for publicity purposes today.

AIRSHIPS

The original hot-air or hydrogen-filled balloons were at the mercy of the elements and the first successful attempt to convert them into a more controllable form of transport was made by a Frenchman, Henri Giffard, in 1852. He fitted a steam engine, which drove a propeller, on to a platform hanging below a 43 m (144 ft) long and 12 m (39 ft) wide, sausage-shaped, hydrogen-filled balloon. He drove the airship, standing on the platform, a distance of 27 km (17 miles) at a speed of 8 km/h (5 mph).

By 1900, a retired German cavalry officer, Count Ferdinand von Zeppelin, had flown a 117 m (384 ft) long airship in which Giffard's simple balloon was replaced by an aluminium framework covered by treated cotton. It contained 16 sealed bags containing hydrogen, and was driven by two 16 hp Daimler engines. Similar Zeppelins, as they came to be called, were used for pleasure trips and, much less pleasantly, for carrying the first bombs which were dropped on London in the early days of World War I.

Still bigger airships were built after the war, travelling in them became quite fashionable, and some regular services were instituted. However, this soon came to an end after a series of disasters. In 1930, the British *R101* (236 m/774 ft long) crashed into a hill in France on a maiden flight to India; in 1937, the German *Hindenburg* (245 m/804 ft long) caught fire when landing at New Jersey, USA. There has been some resurgence of interest in recent times and a helium-filled model is being built at the old Zeppelin factory in Friedrichshafen in Germany. It is 68 m (223 ft) long, and is planned to carry 12 passengers and to be able to stay aloft for 36 hours.

GLIDERS

An Englishman, Sir George Cayley (1771–1857), and a German, Otto Lilienthal (1849–96), were the first to make significant progress in designing gliders. Cayley drew a sketch of one in 1799 and invented an instrument for measuring air resistance in 1804. Over the next 50 years his experiments with model gliders enabled him to lay down the basic principles of aerodynamics. His ultimate practical successes came in 1853 when one of his gliders carried his reluctant coachman on a free flight. Some 40 years later, Lilienthal improved on that, piloting his own machines, which were not unlike today's hang-gliders, on many flights with great bravery. He discovered how to control a glider under different conditions but lost his life in the process when he fell from one of his machines near Berlin.

POWERED FLIGHT

It did not require much imagination to see that gliders could be converted into powered aeroplanes if only engines which were light and powerful enough could be found. There had, indeed, been a number of examples since 1850 of models and

machines being lifted from the ground by steam engines or compressed air or even twisted rubber or clockwork mechanisms. Clément Ader, for example, who originated the term 'aeroplane', travelled about 15 cm (6 in) off the ground for about 50 m (165 ft) in a steam-driven contraption in 1890. But the first sustained and controlled flight did not come until the Wright brothers achieved that rather special goal in 1903.

Their momentous feat was originally given no great publicity in America but it did alert the Europeans, particularly the French. So much so that, whilst the

The balloon in which Dr J. Jeffries and Jean-Pierre Blanchard crossed the English Channel on 1 January 1785. Pilâtre de Rozier was killed later that year attempting the same feat

WILBUR AND ORVILLE WRIGHT

WILBUR WRIGHT (1867–1912), born in Millville, Indiana, and his brother Orville (1871–1948), born in Dayton, Ohio, were the sons of a bishop. After attending the local high school in Dayton they ran a successful bicycle business and began to build their own gliders in the 1890s. They moved away from Lilienthal's 'bird-like' wings and opted for a biplane arrangement braced with struts. By 1903 they had built three gliders which they tested at Kitty Hawk, North Carolina.

After more than a thousand flights in their gliders, they fitted one with a specially designed, 12 hp internal-combustion engine and twin two-blade propellers. The propellers were placed behind the wings and driven by chains from the engine; the plane was fitted with elevators at the front and a rudder at the rear; and there were skids for landing on. The plane was launched from a carriage running along an 18 m (60 ft) track facing slightly downhill and into the wind. They called it *Flyer I*.

On 17 December 1903, Orville (who had won the toss to pilot it) took up his position lying on his stomach on top of the lower wing. The engine was started, the retaining rope was released, and *Flyer I* accelerated along the rail. It took off smoothly and covered about 36 m (120 ft) during the 12 seconds it was airborne. Later in the day, Wilbur completed a flight lasting almost a minute. Disaster struck when the plane was smashed by the wind whilst being stowed away, but the Wrights were not deterred and went on to build *Flyer II* and *Flyer III* in which, during 1904 and 1905, they made almost 150 flights with a record of 39 km (24.2 miles) in 38 minutes being set.

> ❛*I believe no financial profit will accrue to the inventor of the first flying machine...*❜
>
> *WILBUR WRIGHT (1867–1912), American engineer*

The Wright brothers' first flight at Kitty Hawk, North Carolina, USA on 17 December 1903

Wrights began to try to commercialize their planes, the first aircraft factory was set up near Paris in 1905 by Louis Blériot. It was there that he built a monoplane with a single propeller and an engine mounted at the front, and with wheels for take-off and landing. He flew it across the English Channel, on 25 July 1909, at an average speed of nearly 65 km/h (40 mph). This exploit won him a £1000 prize offered by the London *Daily Mail* and captured the whole world's attention.

The 'magnificent men in their flying machines' had truly arrived, and air power had come to rival land and sea power. It heralded a new period in transport and, alas, in warfare.

DEVELOPMENT OF THE MODERN PLANE

The significant differences between Wrights' and Blériot's planes and, even more, the exhibition of 38 different models at the Rheims aeronautical show in 1909, demonstrated the remarkably rapid changes that had been made in six years.

These went on apace during World War I so that by its end many of the essential features of a modern aeroplane were in place. Some of the machines were biplanes and some monoplanes, though the latter began to predominate, and they were built around a sausage-shaped fuselage with a cockpit for the pilot and a nose-mounted engine and propeller. There was a wheeled landing gear (often augmented by skids for safety), cantilevered wings fitted with ailerons (movable flaps) to give better control, and an elevator and rudder at the rear.

On 14 July 1919, Captain John William Alcock, born in England, and Lieutenant Arthur Whitten Brown, born in Scotland, were the first to fly non-stop across the Atlantic in a Vickers Vimy bomber fitted with special fuel tanks. It took 16 h 27 min to cross from St John's, Newfoundland to Clifden in County Galway in Ireland.

Between the wars

In the 1920s, new metal alloys were used increasingly in the so-called semi-monocoque (stressed-skin) method of construction for both fuselage and wings. It allowed the loads to be shared between the skin and an internal framework – this had not been possible in earlier planes which were largely made of wood and treated fabrics. Both the framework and the skin could be strengthened wherever necessary so that it was easier to introduce doors, mount the engines, and fit the retractable undercarriages first invented in 1911. The new method of construction also made it possible to pay much greater attention to streamlining.

The power of the engines that were available rose steadily and great strides were made in the design of propellers. When the Wright brothers first made theirs they had little or nothing to go on. The invention of the variable pitch propeller in 1924 by the British inventors H.S. Hele-Shaw and T.E. Beacham, was an enormous step forward because the pitch of the blades could be adjusted to suit different speeds.

The progress made was exemplified by the solo flight of an American, Charles Lindbergh, from New York to Paris in May 1927. He covered over 5630 km (3500 miles) in 33 h 39 min and became one of the world's all-time heroes. His plane was a Ryan NYP named *The Spirit of St Louis*.

In the 1930s long-distance passenger travel became possible, first in a series of giant flying boats, such as the Sikorsky S-40, and later in big land planes like the Boeing 247 and the Douglas DC-3, which could carry 21 people at 290 km/h (180 mph). Pressurization inside aeroplanes, which allowed flight at higher altitudes to avoid turbulence, began in 1938 and the first jet engines appeared towards the end of the decade.

Post World War II

By using jet engines developed during World War II, it was possible after the war to build high-speed and/or high-capacity passenger planes, planes which could take off and land vertically (VTOL planes), and planes capable of supersonic flight.

The British de Havilland Comet, which went into service in 1952, was the first in a long line of jet airliners, but its development was impeded following a crash in the Mediterranean in 1954 as a

❛...heavier-than-air flying machines are impossible. I have not the smallest molecule of faith in aerial navigation other than ballooning.❜

LORD KELVIN, *Irish-born Scottish physicist, 1896*

result of metal fatigue around the corners of the windows. It was quickly followed by the Russian Tu-104, the American Boeing 747 (1969), the first of the Jumbo jets capable of carrying nearly 500 passengers, the European Airbus (1973) and the Boeing 757, 767 (1978) and 777 (1995). Plans are laid for an enlarged Airbus, a still larger Boeing, and a McDonnell Douglas MD-12.

Vertical take-off and landing was pioneered by the British firm, Rolls-Royce, in an experimental model affectionately known as the *Flying Bedstead*, which was developed into the Harrier. For take-off, the nozzles of the four jet engines are directed downwards. As the plane ascends, the nozzles are rotated to point to the rear, which propels the plane forwards.

'Chuck' Yeager, flying a rocket-powered Bell X-1 aeroplane was the first to reach a speed above that of sound (greater than Mach 1) in the USA in 1947. The first supersonic airliner, the Russian Tu-144, was demonstrated in 1968, and the Anglo-French Concorde began its first regular supersonic passenger service in 1976. It flies at more than 1609 km/h (1000 mph) and can carry up to 100 passengers across the Atlantic in under three hours; it took Lindbergh nearly 40 hours to carry himself. Dick Rutan and Jeana Yeager flew their plane *Voyager* around the world in just over nine days without refuelling, in 1986.

At the other end of the scale, flying very light aircraft has become a popular hobby. Microlights weigh less than 150 kg (330 lb) when empty; ultralights less than 111 kg (245 lb).

MUSCLE-POWERED FLIGHT

Athenian legend has it that Icarus, son of Daedalus, flew from Crete to Santorini on man-made wings, and since then men and women have sought to use their own power to fly. Many attempts at jumping off piers or cliffs and trying to fly by flapping strapped-on wings have failed ignominiously, and all attempts to emulate a bird by flying a human ornithopter have so far failed. But the appropriately named Bryn Bird, in England, and workers in Canada still pursue that goal.

> 6 *It is impossible that men should be able to fly craftily by their own strength.* 9
>
> *Giovanni Borelli (1608–79), Italian mathematician*

There has been more success using pedal power to drive propellers through a system of gears. Moving an airship by such means is, in fact, relatively easy and Mrs Dixon flew one designed by her son in 1909. In 1992, a small helium-filled version, designed at Southampton University by Graham Dorrington, crossed from Southampton to the Isle of Wight and back.

In 1921, a French cyclist and aeroplane designer, Edouard Nieuport, built a winged machine which he called an aerocycle; it travelled over 16 km (10 miles) at a height of 1.5 m (5 ft). In 1977, Dr Paul McCready's *Gossamer Condor* flew a figure of eight, and, two years later, *Gossamer Albatross*, crossed the English Channel from Folkestone in England to Cap Gris Nez in 2 hr 49 min. In 1988, *Daedalus*, designed by Dr John Langford and a team from the Massachusetts Institute of Technology, flew from Crete to Santorini in four hours and turned the ancient Athenian legend into reality.

HELICOPTERS

A helicopter is driven by a rotor or rotors, made up of two or more wing-shaped blades, moving in a horizontal plane around a vertical axis. The basic idea is very old. Toy models, operated by winding string round a spindle, were known to the Chinese as early as AD 500. Leonardo da Vinci drew a 'helicopter' in about 1480 (⇒ p.7); and Sir George Cayley made a model which rose 27.5 m (90 ft) into the air in 1853.

A number of people claim to have made the first manned flight by helicopter at the start of this century but some of them rose only a few feet off the ground for a few seconds, and it was not until the 1930s that controlled flight was achieved. This came about as a result of the invention of the autogyro by a Spanish engineer, Juan de la Cierva, and the helicopter by a German aeroplane designer, Dr Heinrich Focke.

Cierva's idea was that the wings on a standard aeroplane might be replaced by a free-wheeling rotor on top of the plane. To test this, he built what he called an autogyro in 1923, and it was successful enough to warrant further research in a

number of countries. The idea was abandoned in 1939, but Cierva had by then discovered that the use of blades which were loosely jointed (articulated) to the central shaft and not rigidly fixed was beneficial. They were called flapping blades and they were incorporated into the design of Focke's helicopter in which the rotor was driven by an engine so that it took the place not only of the wings but also of the propeller of an aeroplane.

Focke designed blades with a variable pitch. For take-off, the pitch was so arranged that the blades pushed the air downwards. Then, by varying the pitch, some of the air could be pushed backwards or forwards to give two-way motion. The Focke Fa-61, built in 1936, had this arrangement in two four-blade rotors, one on each side of the helicopter. The spinning action of one on the flight of the helicopter was countered by rotating the other in the opposite direction. A similar arrangement is still used in today's large helicopters such as the Boeing Chinook, which has two counter-rotating rotors, one at each end of the fuselage. The Focke Fa-61 was followed in 1939 by the VS-300 built by a Russian, Igor Sikorsky, who was working in the USA. His machine had only one four-blade rotor and to counteract its spinning effect on the helicopter Sikorsky

fitted a small auxiliary rotor, which moved in a vertical plane, on the tail. By 1941 it was in production, and around 400 were used by the Allied forces during World War II.

The particular feature of the helicopter is that it can take-off and land almost anywhere, and, if landing is not possible, as for example on the sea, it can hover very effectively. It is widely used for military purposes, for linking airports, for crop spraying, for supplying oil rigs, and for emergency rescue work.

The main changes in basic design have come about with the use of jet engines. In the five-seater McDonnell Douglas Notar, for example, the blast from the jet engine is used to maintain stability so that the tail rotor is no longer necessary. In the Bell-Boeing V-22 Osprey, turbo-prop engines are used in the helicopter mode for take-off and landing and then swivelled through 90° for forward motion,

The original Sikorsky VS-300 was a single-seater which could reach 70 km/h (43.5 mph). Today's civil version of the EH 101, made jointly by Westland of Britain and Augusta of Italy, carries a crew of three and 30 comfortably seated passengers. At the other end of the scale, a man-powered helicopter driven by pedals stayed off the ground for 7 seconds in 1989.

The EH 101 Heliliner. This helicopter, made jointly by the British company, Westland Helicopters, and the Italian company, Augusta, carries 30 passengers in airline standard of comfort at a cruising speed of 278 km/h (173 mph) over 890 km (553 miles). Production began in 1995

LIFTS (ELEVATORS)

The Roman architect, Vitruvius, used a rope and pulley for lifting building materials during the 1st century BC, and Louis XV (1710–74) had a so-called 'flying chair' in his palace in Versailles on which he used to visit his mistress on a higher floor. However, today's lifts evolved from Elisha Graves Otis's invention in 1853 of a mechanism to make them safe. It was important because, together with steel girders, it is lifts which have made the modern skyscraper possible.

Otis's early life was a chapter of failures, but his luck changed when he became a master mechanic at a bedstead factory in Yonkers, New York in 1852. The factory hoisted beds from one floor to another on an open cage which moved up and down between two side supports. To ensure its safety, Otis built ratchets (⇒p. 59) into each of the side supports and fitted two spring-loaded levers, attached to the supporting rope, at the top of the cage. These levers were held inside the cage when the rope was in tension but, if the rope broke, they sprang apart and engaged in the ratchets.

He demonstrated his invention at the New York Fair in 1854 by being hoisted up on a fully loaded cage and then allowing his assistant to cut the supporting rope. When the safety mechanism worked perfectly, Otis waved his top hat and announced, 'All safe, gentlemen, all safe'. The first passenger lift was installed by the newly formed Otis Steam Elevator Co. in the five-storey china and glass store of E.V. Haughwout and Co. in New York City in 1857. It was operated through a series of shafts and belts driven by a central steam engine in the building and it could lift 453kg (1000 1 b) at 12.2m (40ft) per minute. Otis died four years later when he was only 50, but his sons took over and the firm has led the field ever since.

The actual load to be raised or lowered in a modern lift is not very great because the lift cage is connected to a counterweight over a pulley. For a low-rise lift, a hydraulic ram like a Bramah press (⇒p. 53) can be used to operate it. The ram fits into a cylinder built into the ground below the lift; it is raised by pumping oil into the cylinders, and lowered by releasing oil into a storage tank. Alternatively, electricity is used either to power a motor at the top of the shaft or, more recently, a linear induction motor (⇒p. 74) fitted into the counterweight.

Many safety features are built in so that it is safer to use the lift than the stairs, and the movement of a lift is controlled by microprocessors which respond to the signals they receive in sequence from top to bottom or vice versa. It is the lift system that largely determines the maximum practical height for a building, and very tall buildings need both local and express lifts. Their speeds are limited by the fact that too high an acceleration causes discomfort to the passengers.

Escalators

American patents for an early type of escalator were granted to Jesse W. Reno and George A. Wheeler in 1892, but they were bought by the Otis Elevator Co. who installed the first working system in Gimbel's store in Philadelphia in 1900.

When the first escalators were installed in the London Underground system in 1911 a man with a wooden leg was hired to allay public fears by demonstrating how safe they were to use.

In a modern escalator, each step has two pairs of wheels with the upper pair running in a concealed outer rail and the lower pair in an inner one. The steps are circulated by a chain passing round electrically operated gear wheels, at top and bottom, and the concealed rails guide the steps so that they level out at the top and bottom. Escalators are more efficient in moving greater numbers of people than lifts, but they occupy more space – hence the trial of a spiral escalator in Japan in 1985.

Travelators, common in airports and shopping malls, are moving walkways like flat or slightly rising escalators without steps. One of the first was installed at Erie Station in Jersey City in the USA in 1954.

NAVIGATION

Navigation is the determination of the position and course of a vessel, vehicle or person. Traditional methods, depending on the stars, maps and a variety of navigational instruments, have been improved upon by the use of electronic methods involving radio signals and satellites.

MAPS

A map is a diagrammatic representation of an area of the Earth or heavens; when it represents an area of sea it is generally called a chart. The earliest known example, showing Babylon as the centre of a part of Mesopotamia, was drawn on a clay tablet around 2300 BC. Many, at that time, regarded the Earth as flat, but by the 3rd century BC, Greek geographers had concluded that it was essentially spherical in shape and some maps were made in the form of globes.

Latitude and longitude

From the 3rd century BC any particular point on a globe was specified by reference lines drawn on it. Parallels or lines of latitude show the distance along the Earth's curved surface from the Equator. The latitude at the Equator is given a value of 0° and the latitude of any point on the Earth's surface is the angle to the north or south. Meridians run from the North to the South poles and the longitude of any point is given as the angle to the east or west of the meridian passing through Greenwich, England. It was internationally adopted as 0° longitude in 1884.

Map projections

Projection is a technique for converting a spherical map on to a flat sheet of paper; but this cannot be done without some distortion. The Mercator projection, devised by a Belgian, Gerardus Mercator, in 1568 is the best known method. It involves wrapping a sheet of paper around a globe of the Earth so that it is in the form of a cylinder touching the Earth at its Equator. An Imaginary light at the centre of the Earth, regarded as transparent, then casts a shadow map on

to the paper. When it is unrolled, the lines of latitude and longitude show up as parallel horizontal and vertical lines respectively, but the size of the land and sea areas is greatly distorted. South America, for instance, appears to be smaller than Greenland. Projections invented by Arnos Peters in 1977, and Arthur Robinson in 1988, show land areas having more correct relative sizes but at the expense of distorting their shapes. Other projections have their own advantages and disadvantages.

Surveying

The earliest maps were drawn from observations made by travellers and they could be notoriously inaccurate over large areas. Considerable progress was made using the information brought back by the explorers of the 15th and 16th centuries, but more precise methods of mapping began with the invention of the theodolite, by a self-educated English mathematician, Leonard Digges in 1570, and triangulation in 1617.

The theodolite is based on an instrument first designed by Hero (⇒p. 99) around AD 100 and is used for measuring horizontal and vertical angles. It consists of a telescope mounted between two side supports in a trunnion so that it can be moved up and down in a vertical plane, whilst the trunnion can also be rotated horizontally. The whole is mounted on a tripod fitted with levelling screws and a compass. The angles through which the telescope moves are measured from circular, graduated scales.

In triangulation, surveyors use a measured base line, XY, from each end of which they measure the angles to a point, P. Since the length of XY is known it is then possible to calculate the lengths of XP and YP and find the position of P. The process can then be repeated using PX or PY as new base lines. The original base line on which the British Ordnance Survey maps are based was laid down on Hounslow Heath in 1784. Modern mapping also depends on taking stereophotographs from aircraft or satellites, and measurement of lengths using a laser or radar beam.

❝It is by God's almighty Providence and great chance, and the wideness of the sea, that there are not a great many more misfortunes and ill chances in navigation.❞

SAMUEL PEPYS (1633–1703), English diarist and Secretary to the Admiralty

TRADITIONAL NAVIGATIONAL AIDS

The sextant

Early mariners used the Sun by day, and the North pole star by night, to estimate their position and this was developed into a more accurate navigational method by the invention of the astrolabe. It was first mentioned around 200 BC but popularized by the Portuguese explorers around 1500. It consisted of a disc graduated in degrees with a central vane which could be rotated. When the disc was held vertically and the vane rotated to align with a star, the altitude of the star above the horizon could be measured and this enabled the latitude to be discovered.

The astrolabe led, via the octant and the quadrant, to the more accurate sextant which was first made to resemble its present form by a Scot, Captain John Campbell in 1757. In use, the horizon is viewed through a telescope and a fixed half-silvered mirror, whilst a second, index mirror is rotated so as to bring the Sun or a particular star into view alongside the horizon. The angle of rotation, read off from a graduated scale, gives a measure of the altitude of the Sun

This traditional navigational aid enables the user's latitude to be determined

or star from which the user's latitude can be calculated.

The compass

A freely suspended magnet points to the Earth's magnetic North or South poles and this can be used for navigation because the varying distance of those poles from the true geographic North and South poles (which are joined by the line around which the Earth rotates) can be read off from tables.

The magnet used in the very first compasses, perhaps dating from 500 BC in China, consisted of a piece of naturally occurring iron ore, which came to be known as lodestone. Around the 11th century, in China, and the 12th in the West, it was replaced by a magnetized iron needle which was either pivoted or floated in a liquid. In later improvements the magnet was attached to a card which was free to rotate and which was marked with the points of the compass; the card was immersed in a fluid to damp down oscillations; and the distorting effect of nearby iron, as in an iron ship, was countered by fitting Flinders bars made of soft iron around the compass. To keep the compass level in a tossing ship or aeroplane it was mounted on gimbals (⇒p. 62) or attached to a gyroscope.

Since about 1910, such magnetic compasses have been largely replaced by electrically controlled gyroscopes (⇒p. 62) known as gyrocompasses. They maintain the true north–south orientation on which they are initially set and have the added advantage that they are not affected by external iron.

An inductor or flux-gate compass works on the basis that the current passing through an easily magnetized material is at a maximum when it is orientated in a magnetic north–south position. This can be detected electronically.

The chronometer

Because the Earth rotates through 360° once every 24 hours, a ship sailing east to west for one hour changes its longitude by 15°. However, it was not until the invention of the chronometer (⇒p. 49) that a ship's captain knew for how long he had been sailing so that he could use this method to fix his longitude.

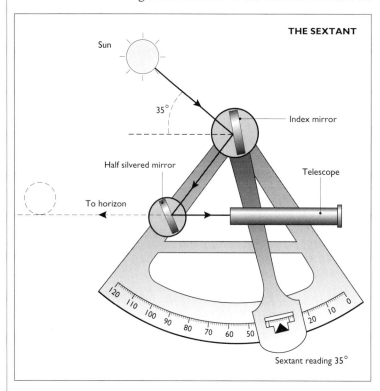

THE SEXTANT

Sun

35°

Index mirror

Half silvered mirror

Telescope

To horizon

120 110 100 90 80 70 60 50 20 10 0

Sextant reading 35°

Greenwich Mean Time (GMT) is the local time at longitude 0°. Places to the east are ahead in time by one hour for every 15° of longitude; those to the west are behind. Time zones, invented at the International Meridian Conference in Washington in 1884, cover approximately 15° of longitude and all clocks within one zone show the same time. There is, generally, a difference of one hour from zone to zone.

RADAR

Radar – *Ra*dio *d*etection *a*nd *r*anging – began its life by using pulses of high-energy, short wavelength radio waves to detect aeroplanes and other targets. The pulses, emitted by a transmitter, are reflected by the target and picked up by a detector and the target distance can be obtained from the time taken.

The early discoverers of radio waves (⇒p. 184) all realized that they could be reflected. Early experiments were carried out by the Austrian, Karl Hülsmeyer in 1921, and in 1924 Sir Edward Appleton, an English physicist, measured the height of the Heavisde layer, one of the layers in the part of the upper atmosphere known as the ionosphere, at a height of 95 km (59 miles), by reflecting pulses of radio waves from it. However, it was not until 1935 that the full implications of the method were realized. Then, R.M. Page, in the USA, used radar to find the position of an aircraft and Sir Robert Watson-Watt, in Britain, found that receiving equipment, 16 km (9.9 miles) away from the powerful short-wave transmitter at Daventry, UK, picked up waves reflected from an aircraft flying at 1.8 km (1.1 miles) high, about 13 km (8 miles) away.

Converting this basic idea into a practical proposition required extensive research into the development of radar transmitters and receivers, but by August 1938 a chain of five radar stations had been built around London, and this was rapidly extended to cover more and more of the country. This screen of detectors was vital in repelling the vast German air raids launched on Britain in the latter half of 1940.

Thereafter, radar went from strength to strength, to a large extent because of the invention in 1940 of the cavity magnetron by J.T. Randall and H.A.H. Boot working at Birmingham University in England. It was a special type of valve which provided 25 kW pulses of 10cm waves lasting about one-millionth of a second about 1000 times a second. Because it was small and light it enabled radar equipment, fitted into individual aeroplanes, to be used for finding targets and guiding bombs. Other uses included

SIR R.A. WATSON-WATT
(1892–1973)

ROBERT ALEXANDER WATSON-WATT was born in Brechin, Scotland. James Watt, the inventor of the steam engine, was one of his ancestors, and his father was a master carpenter. He won a scholarship to Brechin High School where he found that learning science was 'fun and endlessly entertaining', and he completed his education at St Andrews University where he studied engineering and physics. He joined the British Meterorological Office in 1915 and developed a successful method of detecting thunderstorms which depended on picking up the radio pulses produced by lightning. To that end he patented a cathode-ray detector in 1924. He subsequently worked in England in the National Physical Laboratory at Teddington, as superintendent of the Radio Research Station at Slough, and as scientific adviser to the Air Ministry.

He led the team in Britain which developed radar and their work was recognized in 1951 by an award of £87,950 from the Royal Commission on Awards to Inventors. Watson-Watt's share was £52,000. He had been elected to the Royal Society in 1941 and knighted in 1942, and his wife directed the Women's Auxiliary Air Force from 1939 to 1943. Few married couples can have done more to promote victory.

Traffic control by radar at the London Area and Terminal Control Centre at West Drayton, England

reflection from the ground to provide a 'map' of the terrain over which a plane was flying; the directing of searchlights and anti-aircraft guns on to a target; and the detection of U-boats. Fitting radar into naval ships revolutionized their role.

Post-war uses

Since the end of World War II, the use of radar to provide a defensive shield for detecting the approach of aircraft or ballistic missiles has been widely adopted. There are chains of radar stations across northern Canada and Alaska, and at Fylingdales in Yorkshire, England. Radar has also become a general navigational aid on all shapes and sizes of vessels. It has also been used for measuring long distances; detecting swarms of locusts; making contact with, and mapping, the Moon and Venus; tracking the flight of rockets; air traffic control at airports; and police speed traps. In Lidar, which is used for some purposes, radio waves are replaced by laser beams (⇒p. 160).

RADIO NAVIGATION

Beams of radio waves, either pulsed or continuous, emitted from two transmitters, A and B, can be used to direct a plane along a fixed path. If the pilot keeps the time difference between receiving each signal at zero, he will fly along a course which bisects the line, AB, perpendicularly. By maintaining some other fixed time difference he will fly along a specific parabola. By using two other transmitters, one parabola will cut another so that a particular location can be pinpointed. This was the basis on which a number of flight direction systems were invented during World War II, and similar methods, for example the Decca navigator, have been widely used since.

More recently, radio signals have been transmitted from radio satellites to enable aeroplanes, ships and land vehicles to determine their position. The first system, which was developed by the US Navy in the 1960s, has now been extended, at a cost of billions of dollars, into the Navstar Global Positioning System (GPS). By using signals from any three of the 18 available satellites, it is possible to fix a position to within 3 to 4 m (9 to 13 ft). GPS, which was originally, developed for military use, now has many civil applications. A small, portable appliance, costing about £200, can pick up the necessary signals to provide a direct map-reference. A larger appliance, costing about £4000, fitted into a car, will give the driver the necessary instructions to find any destination.

LIGHT *and* SOUND

'The surprised and pleased clubwomen saw a small pine box standing on the floor. In the top of the box was a hole perhaps an inch in diameter. As they looked through this hole they saw the picture of a man. It bowed and smiled and waved its hand and took off its hat with the most perfect naturalness and grace. Every motion was perfect.'

A newspaper report on a National Federation of Women's Clubs' visit to see a kinetoscope in Edison's laboratory in 1891

LIGHT AND SOUND

IN THE 17TH CENTURY, Isaac Newton (⇒p. 159) thought that switching on a light was rather like firing a mini-gun and that the light beam consisted of tiny, fast-moving particles. On the other hand, Christiaan Huygens, a Dutchman, and Augustin Fresnel, a Frenchman, thought it was more like dropping a stone into a pond of water and that the light had a wave nature similar to the ripples moving across the surface. Much argument ensued, but to account for all the known experimental facts it is now necessary to accept both viewpoints. Light sometimes has a wave-nature and sometimes a particulate-nature. Thought of as a wave, its wavelength measures the distance between one peak, or one trough, and the next (see below).

THE ELECTROMAGNETIC SPECTRUM

Wavelength (m)		Frequency (Hz)
10^1	Radio waves	10^7
10^0		10^8
10^{-2}	Micro-waves	10^{10}
10^{-4}		10^{12}
10^{-6}	Infra-red waves	10^{14}
	Visible waves	
10^{-8}	Ultra-violet waves	10^{16}
10^{-10}	X-rays	10^{18}
10^{-12}		10^{20}
10^{-14}	Gamma rays	10^{22}

The different types of electromagnetic radiation together with their wavelengths in metres (m) and frequencies in 65 km (40 miles) Hertz (Hz). The wavelengths of visible light are given on p. 158

ELECTROMAGNETIC RADIATION

Visible light is the only form of what is technically known as electromagnetic radiation that can be detected by the human eye. It appears to be colourless but is, in fact, made up of a mixture of all the colours of the rainbow – red, orange, yellow, green, blue, violet – which differ in wavelength from 700 nm for red to 420 nm for violet (⇒p. 158).

Gamma rays, X-rays, ultraviolet rays, infra-red rays, microwaves, and short, medium and long radio waves are other forms. Together with visible light, they make up what is sometimes known as the electromagnetic spectrum. They all have a velocity of almost 3×10^8 m per second in a vacuum but they have different wavelengths ranging from 10^{-14} m to 10^3 m. Those with the lowest wavelength have the highest frequency and the highest energy.

MIRRORS

The first mirrors were made long ago by polishing metals. What could be achieved is exemplified by the lighthouse built in Alexandria harbour in 280 BC on the island of Pharos. It reflected the light from a fire of resinous wood nearly 65 km (40 miles) and was one of the original seven wonders of the world.

It was not until the 3rd or 4th centuries AD that glass was used for making mirrors. At first the surface of the glass was coated with tin foil. Then, during the 16th century in Venice, the tin coat was applied by using tin amalgam – an alloy of tin with mercury. Some modern mirrors used in optical equipment have a deposit of aluminium on their front surfaces, but the majority are silvered on the rear. The silvering process was invented by Justus von Liebig, a German chemist, in 1840, and was developed into a continuous process by the British firm of Pilkington Brothers Limited in 1931. It is applied nowadays to make many different shapes of mirror, the commonest of which are plane, spherical (convex and concave) and parabolic.

The laws of reflection were probably known around the 4th century AD. Light is reflected from a plane mirror at an angle equal to that at which it impinges on the mirror. For a concave, spherical mirror, a narrow beam of light parallel to the axis of the mirror, is converged through what is known as the focal point, F, of the mirror. For an object closer to the mirror than the focal point, the image is magnified in size, as in a shaving mirror. For a convex mirror, a narrow, parallel beam is diverged as though it came from the focal point, F. The image of any object seen in such a mirror is reduced in size, as in a rear-view car mirror. A parabolic mirror reflects all the light from a source placed at its focus into a nearly parallel beam, as in a torch.

REFRACTION

Because the speed of light is smaller in glass than in air, a beam of light is refracted (bent) when it passes into or

6Nature and Nature's laws lay hid in night: God said, Let Newton be! and all was light.9

ALEXANDER POPE (1688–1744), English poet

out of a glass surface. This was known to Ptolemy about AD 140 but it was not until 1620 that W. Snell, a Dutch professor, discovered that the ratio of the sine of the angle of incidence (*i*) to the sine of the angle of refraction (*r*) had a constant value. It was called the refractive index; the value varies depending on the type of glass and the wavelength of the light involved, but is around 1.5.

Lenses
When light passes through a lens, it is refracted in different ways depending on the type of lens. A double convex lens

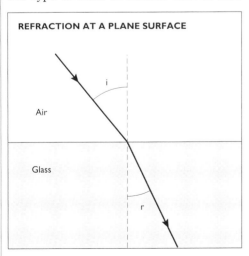

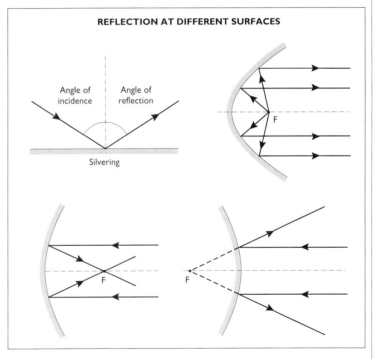

Top: *Old print of the Pharos lighthouse. It was built by Ptolemy Philadelphus (308-246 BC), the King of Egypt, and was one of the Seven Wonders of the Ancient World*

Above: *A plane surface (top left); a parabolic mirror (top right); a concave mirror (bottom left); a convex mirror (bottom right)*

Left: *The ratio sin i/sin r is equal to the refractive index*

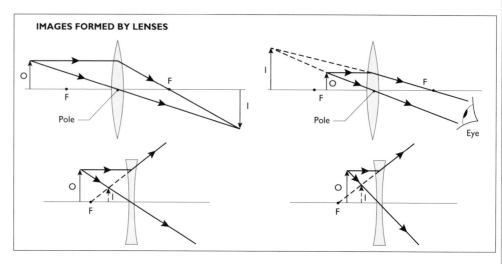

IMAGES FORMED BY LENSES

Top: *Image (I) formed of an object (O) by a convex lens. If the object is outside the focal length of the lens, the image is real and inverted* (left). *If it is inside, the image is erect, virtual and enlarged* (right)

Bottom: *The images formed by a concave lens are diminished and virtual.*

converges the light. A narrow beam, parallel to the axis, will pass through the focal point (F) of the lens; a ray passing through the pole of the lens will not be deviated. The distance between the focal point and the pole of a lens is called its focal length.

For an object placed outside the focal length of a convex lens, the image formed will be inverted. That is why the slide has to be put into a projector upside down. It is possible to pick up the image on a screen so it is said to be real. If the object is inside the focal length of the lens, it is not possible to pick up the image on a screen; it is said to be virtual. To the eye it appears to be enlarged, as when a convex lens is used as a magnifying glass.

A concave lens causes a beam of light to diverge. A narrow beam, parallel to the axis, diverges as though it originated from the focal point (F) of the lens; a ray passing through the pole will not be deviated. The image of any object will always be virtual and diminished in size.

Chromatic aberration

When a beam of white light is passed through a single lens, each of the various colours making up the light is refracted slightly differently so that the colours are not all focused at the same point. This causes the image to be blurred. The phenomenon is known as chromatic aberration, and around 1700 it seemed as though it might prevent lenses being used successfully in accurate optical instruments. The problem was overcome by the invention of an achromatic lens in 1758 by John Dollond, an English silk weaver who became a practising optician at the age of 46. He cemented a convex lens made of crown glass to a concave lens made of flint glass (⇒p. 20). The two glasses had different refractive indices and the aberration caused by one was corrected by the other.

Total internal reflection

When a ray of light passes from glass into air, it may be either refracted, according to Snell's Law, or reflected, depending on the angle of incidence within the glass. For a small angle of incidence, x, the ray will be refracted at an angle, y, such that $\sin y / \sin x$ equals the refractive index of glass which is about 1.5. But as x is increased there comes a time when y is 90° so that the refracted ray passes along the glass-air surface. The value of x at this point is approximately 45°; it is known as the critical angle. For higher angles of incidence, the ray is totally internally reflected.

Making use of this phenomenon, right-angled isosceles, glass prisms can be used to reflect light through 90°, as in periscopes used in tanks and submarines, or through 180° as in binoculars (⇒p. 155).

TELESCOPES

The first telescope was probably built by Hans Lippershey, in 1608. He was a Dutch spectacle-maker, and the story goes that he found, by accident, that looking at something through two lenses in line caused magnification. The Dutch government, who were interested in the

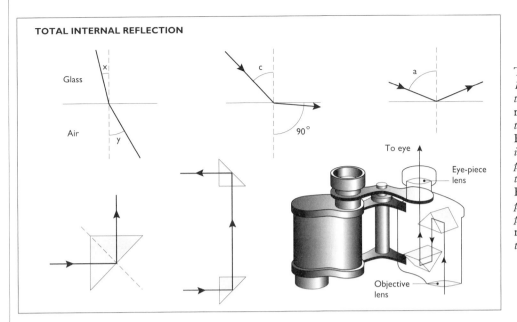

TOTAL INTERNAL REFLECTION

Top left: *sin y/sin* x = *1.5.* Top centre: *c is the critical angle.* Top right: *Angle a is larger than the critical angle.* Bottom left: *Total internal reflection in a prism, which enables it to function as a mirror.* Bottom centre: *The path of light through a periscope.* Bottom right: *The path of light through binoculars*

invention for military purposes, gave him 900 florins. When, a year later, Galileo (⇒p. 45) heard of the invention he made a telescope of his own. He used a convex lens, with a long focal length, inside one end of a lead tube to form an image of a distant object, within the tube, and he viewed it through a concave lens, with a short focal length, at the other end. His telescope had an eventual 32-fold magnification and gave an erect (upright) image. He used it to discover the mountains and valleys on the surface of the Moon, the stars in the Milky Way,

Galileo using his telescope to show the satellites of Jupiter to Venetian senators

and the four satellites revolving round Jupiter.

Galileo's telescope was improved in 1611 when a German astronomer, Christoph Scheiner, built one with two convex lenses and claimed to be the first to discover sunspots. The front lens, with a long focal length, forms an image at its focal point, just within the focal length of the eye-piece, which serves as a magnifying glass (⇒p. 154). Scheiner's telescope, now known as an astronomical telescope, gave an inverted image. This is avoided in what is generally referred to as a terrestrial telescope by incorporating a third convex lens.

Isaac Newton was very interested in making telescopes but he came to the conclusion that it would not be possible to make a good one using lenses because those available to him caused chromatic aberration (⇒p. 154). So he turned his attention to making a reflecting telescope using mirrors. His first, made in 1688, was only 6 in (15 cm) long but magnified 40 times. Light from the object being viewed was focused on to a second mirror and observed, from the side, through a convex lens acting as a magnifying glass (⇒p. 154).

Newton's telescopes had mirrors with a diameter of about 50 mm (1.97 in), so that they could not collect much light and gave only dim images. By 1789, a German-born British astronomer, William Herschel, was using a mirror 1.25 m (49.2 in) in diameter in a telescope installed at La Palma on the Canary Islands, and so it went on. The telescope at Mount Wilson (1917) in California, USA, has a 100 in (2.54 m) mirror; at Mount Palomar (1948) in California it is 200 in (5.08 m); and at Zelentchouskaia in Russia (1976) it is

236 in (6 m). The mirror in the Keck telescope, on the top of Mount Kea in Hawaii (1992), is made up of 36 hexagonal parts each 1.8 m (71 in) in diameter and has an effective overall diameter of 10 m (393.7 in)

Binoculars

Prism binoculars, sometimes known as opera or field glasses, were first made by Hans Lippershey but they were developed towards the end of the 19th century, mainly by the German Ernst Abbé who worked in Jena. They contain two compact telescopes side-by-side so that they allow two-eyed vision which gives a stereoscopic effect. Each half contains an objective lens and an adjustable eye-piece but the light passing between them is twice turned back on itself by total internal reflection in two prisms set at right angles to each other. The prisms serve two purposes. First, they lengthen the path of light so that binoculars give the same magnification as a much longer telescope. Second, they produce an image which is the same way up and the same way round as the object being viewed. The first of the two figures on a pair of binoculars, for example 10 x 25, indicates the magnification; the second gives the diameter of the objective lens in mm, which determines the light-gathering power.

MICROSCOPES

Optical microscopes were first used during the second half of the 17th century, particularly by Antoni van Leeuwenhoek in Holland and Robert Hooke in England. They could magnify about 200 times, and they revealed the secrets of bacteria, blood vessels, and plant and animal cells from a previously unexplored world, which opened up vast new avenues of understanding and research.

Van Leeuwenhoek's simple microscope was basically a glorified magnifying glass (⇒p. 154). It had a single convex lens, which looked like a small round glass bead, held in a hole in a metal plate. The specimen under examination was mounted on an adjustable pin or, if living, placed in a glass tube, just in front of the lens.

‹I had prepared for myself a very excellent instrument.›

GALILEO GALILEI,
Italian astronomer, 1610

Newton designed this telescope in 1688 to avoid the chromatic aberration caused in contemporary telescopes using lenses

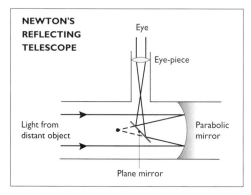

NEWTON'S REFLECTING TELESCOPE

Eye

Eye-piece

Light from distant object

Parabolic mirror

Plane mirror

Robert Hooke used a compound microscope, with two lenses, probably based on an earlier version made by the Dutch spectacle-maker, Hans Janssen, around 1590. It contained a convex lens – nowadays known as the objective – mounted at the bottom of a tube, which gave a magnified image of a specimen under examination. This was formed within the tube inside the focal point of a second convex lens, the eye-piece, which acted as a magnifying glass. In a modern compound microscope both the objective and eye-piece consist of a group of lenses, and it is possible to rotate different objectives into position for different purposes. The specimen is well illuminated by a separate arrangement of mirrors and lenses, the whole is mounted on a sturdy framework, and all the lens systems can be moved very accurately for focusing. In many cases, the beam coming into the eye-piece arrangement is split so that two-eyed vision is possible, and cameras might also be fitted.

The electron microscope

The magnification that can be achieved by an optical microscope is limited to about 2000 because objects too much smaller than the wavelength of visible light cannot be clearly detected by the light because it is not affected by them. It is rather like the inability of a blind person to detect a 1 cm hole with a 2 cm diameter stick.

To achieve higher magnifications it is, therefore, necessary to use radiation with shorter wavelengths than visible light. This can be done by using ultraviolet rays or X-rays, but much more effectively, by using a beam of electrons which has an equivalent wavelength thousands of times lower. In this way magnification of over a million times is possible in electron microscopes. The first were built by two Germans, Ernst Ruska and Max Knoll in 1931, and they became available commercially in 1935. They function in much the same way as optical microscopes but use beams of electrons, focused by electric and magnetic fields, instead of rays of light focused by lenses. The magnified image is displayed on a fluorescent screen or photographed. In a transmission electron microscope, electrons are passed through a thin

specimen. In a scanning electron microscope, a beam of electrons is scattered from the surface of an object; it can be used on thick specimens and gives an almost three-dimensional image.

In 1988, the Americans, James Van House and Arthur Rich, invented a microscope which used positively charged electrons – positrons.

Other types

Field-emission microscopes examine the surface of a material by making it into a fine point, within a vacuum, and giving it a high negative charge. The electrons emitted from the point create an image on a nearby fluorescent screen giving something like a contour map of the surface. Alternatively, in a field-ion

The principal mirror of the Keck telescope

microscope, the point is positively charged, within a gas at low pressure, and the image is formed by the emission of positive ions from gas adsorbed on the point. Both these methods, invented by a German–American, E.W. Mueller in 1936 and 1951, respectively, give good images of individual atoms. This can also be achieved by a scanning tunnelling microscope invented by a German, Gerd Binnig, and a Swiss, Heinrich Rohrer in 1980. This scans the surface of a specimen by moving a finely-pointed tungsten electron emitter closely over it.

SPECTACLES

Spectacles were invented, probably in Italy, towards the end of the 13th century but they were not commonly used until the middle of the 16th century. The lens in the eye is convex, but it is flexible so that the eye muscles can, normally, adjust its focal length to ensure that the light from any object is focused on to the retina at the back of the eye. For people suffering from long sight (hyper-metropia), the eye lens cannot converge the light from a nearby object sufficiently to focus it on the retina. The fault can be corrected by using spectacles containing convex lenses, which converge the light from the object, to some extent, before it enters the eye.

In short sight (myopia), the eye of the lens converges the light from a distant object too much. This is corrected by using spectacles with concave lenses, which diverge the light before it enters the eye.

Benjamin Franklin (⇒p. 68) improvised bifocal glasses in 1784 by cutting two lenses in half and mounting them in the same frame, but one-piece bifocal lenses were not made until 50 years later. The first contact lenses, which fit directly on to the eye-ball, were tried around 1890 but were not successful until 60 years later.

THE SPECTROSCOPE

In 1666, Issac Newton (⇒p. 159) made a small hole in the window shutters of his room and let the beam of sunlight which entered fall on to a glass prism. The sunlight was refracted at the two glass–air surfaces but it was also dispersed into its component colours (wavelengths) to form a spectrum on the wall. It appeared to him to be a continuous 'rainbow', but in 1814, a German, Joseph von Fraunhofer, discovered that there were about 700 dark lines crossing the spectrum, quite haphazardly, when he viewed it through a simple spectroscope which he had invented. It was the first example of what came to be called spectrum analysis which grew, once better instruments were designed, into a powerful new analytical technique.

Modern spectroscopes are based on Fraunhofer's and on that designed in 1859 by two Germans, R. W. Bunsen, the inventor of the Bunsen burner, and G.R. Kirchhoff. They have a slit, through which the light enters, situated close to the focal point of a nearby convex lens. This provides a parallel beam of light which is directed on to a prism to form a spectrum which can be examined through a telescope. The prism may be replaced by a diffraction grating which also produces a spectrum. It consists of a series of very close, parallel lines ruled on a glass plate; the first was made by Fraunhofer, in 1823, using a diamond tip. A spectrometer is like a spectroscope but contains arrangements for measuring the wavelengths of the component parts of a spectrum; and cameras are fitted in a spectrograph. Modified instruments can also be used to examine ultraviolet-, infra-red and X-ray spectra.

Spectrum analysis can be used to detect different atoms or molecules, even if they are present in only minute quantities, because each different atom or molecule will absorb its own particular spectrum of radiation, or emit that same radiation when it is excited (⇒p. 161).

❝The microbe is so very small You cannot make him out at all But many sanguine people hope To see him through a microscope.❞

HILAIRE BELLOC (1870–1953), French-born British writer

A spectrum formed by dispersion of white light within a prism. The wavelengths of the coloured components of the white light are given on the right

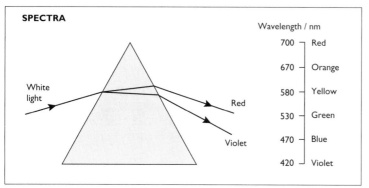

SPECTRA

White light

Red

Violet

Wavelength / nm

700	Red
670	Orange
580	Yellow
530	Green
470	Blue
420	Violet

ISAAC NEWTON
(1642–1727)

ISAAC NEWTON was born at Woolsthorpe Manor in Lincolnshire, England in the year that Galileo died. He was educated at the Grammar School in Grantham and went to Trinity College, Cambridge in 1661, where he spent the next 40 years, apart from a period during 1665-66 when he returned to Woolsthorpe because the fear of Plague closed the university. That short period was the most productive of his life. In his own words: 'In those years I was in the prime of my age for invention, and minded Mathematics and Philosophy more than any time since'. He worked out the methods of the binomial theorem and of calculus. His observation of an apple falling from a tree led him to the law of gravitation. He bought a prism to 'try therewith the phenomena of colours' and called the 'rainbow' that he cast on to the wall of his room a spectrum. Later, when he returned to Cambridge, he propounded his laws of motion, he designed a reflecting telescope, and he wrote his two great works: *Philosophiae Naturalis Principia Mathematica* (1687) in Latin, and *Opticks* (1703) in English.

He was elected to the Royal Society in 1672 and was the President from 1703 until 1727; he was MP for Cambridge University between 1688 and 1690; he became Warden of The Mint in 1696; he was knighted in 1705; and he was ceremoniously buried in Westminster Abbey.

Despite all he achieved, he likened himself late in life to a 'boy playing on the seashore, and diverting himself in now and then finding a smoother pebble or a prettier shell than ordinary, whilst the great ocean of truth lay all undiscovered before me'.

❛*If I have seen further it is by standing on the shoulders of giants.*❜

ISAAC NEWTON *(1642–1727), English scientist*

Newton using a prism to obtain a spectrum, 1666. In his own words: 'Having darkened my chamber, and made a small hole in my window shuts, to let in a convenient quantity of the Sun's light, I placed my Prisme at this entrance, that it might be thereby refracted to the opposite wall'

The composition of stars, for instance, can be determined by comparing their spectra with that of known elements. Spectrum analysis can also be used to 'look inside' atoms and molecules. It was, for example, a study of the spectra given by the elements that contributed greatly to the elucidation of atomic structures (⇒p. 89), and similar methods are still used today to unravel the internal structure of molecules.

POLARIZATION

In an ordinary beam of light, vibrations are taking place in all directions at right angles to the direction of the beam but, if the vibrations are limited to one plane, the light is said to be plane polarized. Such polarized light can be obtained by passing ordinary light through a polarizer such as a piece of synthetic material known as Polaroid, or through a Nicol prism, which was invented by a Scottish chemist, William Nicol in 1828; it contains pieces of a naturally occurring mineral called Iceland spar mounted in a special way. The polarizers act like a slit which will transmit vibrations which are parallel to the slit but stop all others.

Polarized light causes less glare than ordinary light so that Polaroid is used in making sun-glasses. As the plane of polarization of a beam of light is rotated on passing through solutions containing asymmetric molecules, such as sugars, measuring the extent of that rotation can be used to find the concentration of the molecule in the solution; the instrument used is known as a polarimeter. Polarized light is also used to measure stresses in transparent materials.

OPTICAL FIBRES

These are very fine fibres of ultra-pure glass with an outer cladding of a glass with a lower refractive index. They are flexible enough to bend into smooth curves and light will pass along them because it is totally internally reflected (⇒p. 155) at the walls. They are used for making ornamental 'trees'; in endoscopes for examining internal parts of the body (⇒p. 229) or inaccessible parts of machines; and for transmitting electrical signals (⇒p. 183).

The fibres were first used in 1955 at Imperial College in London by Dr Narinder Kapany.

LASERS

Lasers produce beams of light so fine that they can be focused on to a point 1 millionth of an inch across. They can be millions of times less powerful, or many millions of times more powerful than a 100 W bulb. Initially the beams did not seem to be very useful but they have had a quite dramatic impact in the last 30 years. For example, beams of varying intensity are used to read the bar codes on items being checked out of a supermarket; to record and replay music on a compact disc (⇒p. 171) or information on a computer disc; in laser printers where the beam acts as a pen; in transmitting several thousand telephone messages through a hair-thin glass fibre; in sound-and-music shows; in surgical operations; in cutting or drilling many materials including diamonds; in measurement, surveying and range-finding; in endless research projects; for military purposes, in identifying a target for bombing, or setting up a possible 'star wars' space defence system against missiles; and for fusing mixtures of deuterium and tritium in nuclear fusion research (⇒p. 243).

What is a laser beam?

Ordinary light from the sun or an electric lamp consists of light of many wavelengths which are not in phase, i.e. the peaks and troughs of the waves do not match up. The light is said to be incoherent. It can be concentrated into beams by mirrors and/or lenses, but it remains incoherent and this limits its intensity. A laser beam contains light of only one wavelength and all the waves are in phase; it is coherent. It is similar to a professional chorus line – all of the same height and all in step – as compared to the relative chaos on a normal dance floor.

When a material is heated or has an electric current passed through it, most of the energy is absorbed by electrons in the various atoms moving into higher energy levels. It is rather like being pushed up on to a higher step on a flight

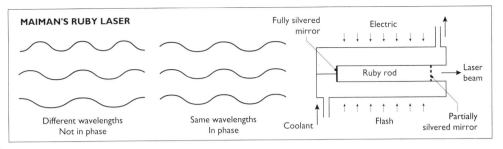

MAIMAN'S RUBY LASER

Different wavelengths
Not in phase

Same wavelengths
In phase

Fully silvered mirror

Electric

Ruby rod

Laser beam

Coolant

Flash

Partially silvered mirror

Incoherent light (left);
coherent light (centre);
*and the principle of the
ruby laser* (right)

of stairs, and the atoms are said to be excited. Once the external stimulus is removed, the electrons move back into lower energy levels (fall down the stairs) and as they do so they release their energy in the form of light or heat radiation. There are many ways in which this can happen which is why the radiation is incoherent. It is like compressing millions of springs in varying degrees and then releasing them over a period of time.

In a laser it is like compressing millions of springs to the same extent and releasing them all at once. Theodore Maiman, a relatively unknown American electrical engineer, achieved this when he produced the first pulse of laser light on 16 May 1960. A contemporary, A. Javan, made the first continuous laser beam in 1961.

Types of laser
In Maiman's so-called solid-state laser, the central component was a rod of ruby (aluminium oxide containing some chromium) surrounded by a coolant. It had flat, parallel ends, one of which was completely silvered and the other partially silvered. When it was illuminated with a powerful flash of light, from an external source, most of the chromium atoms were excited. As the electrons in some of them returned to a lower level they emitted radiation which was reflected to and fro along the rod. This stimulated more atoms to radiate in the same way so that a high intensity of coherent radiation built up which passed out through the partially silvered end as a deep red pulse of laser light. Javan used a gas laser in which a mixture of neon and helium was initially excited (pumped) by an electric discharge.

The word laser was chosen because the *l*ight was *a*mplified by the *s*timulated *e*mission of *r*adiation and the ruby and

neon-helium mixtures were called the lasing materials. They have been replaced, to some extent, by yttrium aluminium garnet containing some neodymium, argon, carbon dioxide and dyes. Different materials give beams with different wavelengths and powers.

Other lasers, however, work on different principles. The commonest are made from minute semiconductor chips ($\Rightarrow$p. 81); they can give a laser beam with a power as low as a thousandth of a watt. At the other end of the scale, however, big lasers in which a fast-moving beam of electrons is deflected by a series of magnetic fields, or a mixture of hydrogen and fluorine reacts to form excited hydrogen fluoride molecules, can generate laser pulses with a power of many millions of watts lasting for a minute fraction of a second.

Masers
The maser, which came before the laser, does for microwaves what the laser does for light waves. It was invented by C.H. Townes, a professor at the University of California in 1958, when he made the pyramidal NH_3 molecules in ammonia gas invert repeatedly, like an umbrella turning inside-out, in such a way as to emit coherent microwaves. Because the radiation had a precise frequency it was used in early atomic clocks ($\Rightarrow$p. 50). Masers are also used as amplifiers and oscillators in radar and communication systems. Townes shared the 1964 Nobel Prize for physics for this work with two Russians, N.G. Basov and A.M. Prokhorov, and, together with his brother in law, A.L. Schawlow, first suggested the idea of a laser.

Holography
This is a technique for forming a three-dimensional image of an object, first mooted by a Hungarian, Dennis Gabor,

⁶In a few minutes I had calculated on the back of an envelope, the critical condition for oscillation...⁹

C.H. TOWNES (1915–), American physicist, on his invention of the maser

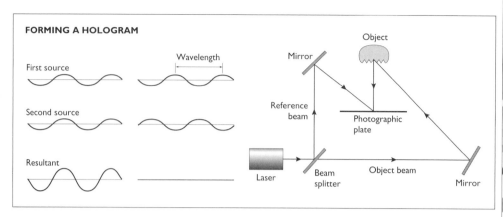

FORMING A HOLOGRAM

Left: *Two light waves reinforce each other.* Centre: *Two light waves cancel each other out.* Right: *The paths of light in forming a hologram*

in 1947. He worked in Germany until driven out by the Nazis in 1933, when he settled in Britain. He won the Nobel Prize for physics in 1971. The method depends on the fact that two sources of light, of the same wavelength and intensity, will interefere with each other if they are brought together. If the peaks and troughs of the two waves match, they will reinforce each other and give brighter light. If there is a complete mismatch, one wave will cancel the other out and there will be no light.

The invention of the laser enabled the idea to be developed by two Americans, E. Leith and J. Upatnieks in 1963. A laser beam is split into two. One, called the reference beam, is directed on to a photographic plate by a mirror and a convex lens. The other, the object beam,

is directed on to the object being photographed and then on to the plate. Because the light reflected from different parts of the object travel different distances to the plate, some of it reinforces the reference beam whilst some of it cancels it out. The plate records a pattern of lighter and darker areas, known as a hologram. When it is illuminated by a replica of the original reference beam, a realistic three-dimensional image of the object can be seen.

Holograms are used in research, in industrial design and as an art form. In everyday life, they are beginning to appear on credit cards, bank notes and stamps to make counterfeiting more difficult. The technique is, at present, limited to still photographs – holographic movies are something for the future.

A hologram of a bird on a VISA credit card to deter counterfeiters

PHOTOGRAPHY

Photography grew out of the camera obscura which was first described around AD 1000 by an Arab scholar, Alhazen of Basra. In its simplest form it is a light-proof box with a pin hole in one face which casts an image of the external scene on to a ground glass screen on the opposite face. A simple convex lens was first fitted into the hole by an Italian, G. della Porta in 1558, and the camera came to be used as an aid by artists, but the image was only transient. To develop a satisfactory photographic process required the invention of a way of ensuring a reliably bright and sharp image and of recording it permanently. This was done for black-and-white photographs in 1839, and for colour in 1907.

RECORDING THE IMAGE

The first permanent photograph was taken by a Frenchman, Joseph Nicéphore Niepce, in 1826. It was the view from the window of his house and it was recorded on a pewter plate coated with a thin layer of a kind of asphalt known as bitumen of Judea. This hardened, depending on how much light fell on to it, and, after exposure, the unhardened bitumen was removed by treating with petroleum spirit. The photograph required an eight-hour exposure and was far from clear, but it survives to this day.

Daguerreotypes

Improved results were obtained in 1835 by a partner of Niepce, Louis Jacques Mandé Daguerre, who was a scenery painter accustomed to using the camera obscura as an aid. He made use of the fact, discovered in 1725 by a German professor of anatomical science, J.H. Schulze, that silver salts were blackened by exposure to light. It is now known that this occurs because some of the salt, depending on how much light falls on it, is converted into silver which, when finely divided, appears black. The amount of silver formed in a short exposure is invisible, but it can be built up by a chemical process known as developing.

Daguerre's plate was made of copper coated with polished silver which was treated with iodine vapour to produce a layer of silver iodide. After an exposure to light of about 30 minutes, a latent image was produced by the varying amounts of silver formed. The plate was then developed by treatment with mercury vapour, which deposited black-looking mercury in proportion to the amounts of silver. It was then fixed by treatment with hypo (sodium thiosulphate) to remove unaffected silver iodide, which revealed the polished silver. The photograph was known as a daguerreotype.

Calotypes

In 1835, an Englishman, William Henry Fox Talbot, took photographs, which he called calotypes, using paper coated with silver iodide made more sensitive by treatment with gallic acid. After an exposure of some 30 minutes the photograph was developed by chemical treatment with more gallic acid and warming. When the photograph was fixed, by removing unaffected silver iodide with hypo, what is now known as a 'negative' remained with the highlights of the original showing up as dark deposits of silver and the shadows as white paper. It could be used over and over again to produce 'positives' by placing it over more calotype paper, which was exposed to light for a long time so that no developing was necessary, and then fixed.

Talbot, educated at Harrow and Trinity College, Cambridge, England, was very clever and by the age of 32 he had been elected Fellow of the Royal Society and become MP for Chippenham. In 1844 he published the first photographically illustrated book, *The Pencil of Nature*. He also took out patents for a number of internal-combustion engines, one of which was operated by pellets of gun-cotton; helped to decipher the cuneiform inscriptions of Nineveh; and wrote *English Etymologies*. His ancestral home at Lacock Abbey in Wiltshire, England, where he lived for the last 44 years of his life, is now owned by the National Trust and contains a museum of his work.

How charming it would be if it were possible to cause these natural images to imprint themselves durably.

W.H.FOX TALBOT (1800–77), English scientist

The use of glass plates

Glass plates were first used for photography around 1850 by a Frenchman, Louis-Désiré Blanquart-Evrard, and an Englishman, Frederick Scott Archer. A solution of collodion and potassium iodide in ether was poured on to a glass plate and, when the ether had largely evaporated to leave a film, the plate was dipped into silver nitrate which formed silver iodide within the film. The plates produced good photographs but they had to be made in the dark, immediately exposed, and then developed immediately once again in the dark. This meant that a tent had to be used for any outdoor work, and it took 20 minutes to take one photograph.

The numerous attempts to make dry plates, notably by R.L. Maddox, a British microscopist in 1871, culminated in 1879 when George Eastman took out patents for a new method of manufacturing them. It had taken him two years of experimentation in his mother's kitchen after a day's work to perfect the method. The dry plates were still bulky and each photograph required a new plate but they could be stored for months and exposed and developed at the photographer's convenience.

The use of film

The possible use of flexible film instead of plates was patented in 1855 by Scott Archer, but the idea lay dormant until resurrected by Eastman in 1885. Then, in collaboration with W.H. Walker, a camera maker, he invented a way of using a strip of paper coated with the sort of photographic emulsion used on dry plates. The film was known as stripping film or American film because the paper, which was opaque, had to be stripped away during development. This involved a complicated procedure which limited the sale of the film, so in 1886 Eastman employed a research chemist, Henry Reichenbach, to help him make something better. In 1889, they came up with a 70 mm film with a celluloid base. This could be developed without any stripping because the celluloid was transparent; it was sold in rolls which could easily be loaded into a camera; and it was strong enough to be used by Edison in the kinetograph (⇒p. 168)

which he invented around 1890.

Celluloid in film was replaced by the non-flammable cellulose acetate in 1908. Today's film, commonly 35 mm wide, is made with different sensitivities or speeds which are denoted by an ISO (International Standards Organization) number – the higher the number, the faster the film. In a DX-coded film, there is a pattern of perforations along its edge which is 'read' by sensors within the camera to ensure correct exposures.

Charge-coupled devices

An alternative, revolutionary method of taking photographs has been developed in the past 25 years. It uses the optical arrangements in traditional cameras but the light is focused on to a charge-coupled device instead of on to a film or a plate. The device consists of a grid of a very large number of separate cells, which are known as pixels (picture elements), printed on to the light-sensitive surface of a semiconductor (⇒p. 79). When exposed to light, each pixel builds up an electrical charge depending on the amount of light falling on to it, and the different charges can be recorded on a magnetic disc. The result is an 'electronic' photograph which requires no chemical processing. About 50 colour photographs can be stored on a 2-inch disc and can be viewed through a television set, a video player or a computer screen.

This new method does not, at present, give such a good photograph as the old one but it has other advantages. Charge-coupled devices (CCDs) can be used over and over again; they are much more sensitive to light than any photographic plate or film so that they are widely used, for example, in investigating distant stars; and they do not use expensive and increasingly scarce silver compounds. Furthermore, the charges built up in the CCD can be digitized (⇒p. 183) if required, and a photograph so recorded can be transmitted along a telephone line or fed into a computer where it can be edited in a number of ways.

Existing photographs can also be scanned and converted into digitized images which can be stored electronically on a disc, transmitted by telephone line, or manipulated in a computer.

> *The ideal large corporation is the one that makes the best use of the brains within it.*
>
> GEORGE EASTMAN
> *(1854–1932),*
> *American inventor*

GEORGE EASTMAN
(1854–1932)

EASTMAN was born in Waterville, New York. His father died when he was eight years old and he was brought up, with something of a struggle, by his mother. He left school when he was 14 and began to work as an errand boy for an insurance company, studied accountancy in the evenings, and became a bookkeeper for a bank at the age of 20.

He took to photography, as a hobby, in 1878 but when he found that the existing equipment was so poor he set about trying to improve it. By 1881 he had left the bank and founded the Eastman Dry Plate Co. in Rochester. In 1885 he began to make photographic film, and he used it in a camera which he marketed in 1888. He called it a Kodak camera because K, he said, was 'a strong and incisive sort of letter'. These early inventions greatly simplified photography and made it universally popular. What became the Eastman Kodak Co. in 1892 has continued that process ever since.

Eastman was a reticent bachelor who devoted almost his whole life to photography. He had a shrewd business acumen and he invested heavily in both research and advertising. He also instituted many modern benefits, such as profit sharing and medical and dental care for his employees. Much of the money he made was given away, sometimes anonymously, and his passion for music was reflected in the founding of the Rochester Symphony Orchestra and the Eastman School of Music at Rochester University.

Despite all his success, his life ended in tragedy when, after progressive disablement by arteriosclerosis, he shot himself.

George Eastman (left) *and Thomas Edison* (right)

THE CAMERA

The first cameras, used in the 1840s, were made of one wooden box which could slide into another. Lenses of different focal lengths, and aperture rings of different sizes, were screwed into the centre of the front half, and the plate was positioned at the rear of the back half. Focusing was achieved by sliding the back into the front. The photograph was taken by removing the lens cover for the

Advertisement for an early Kodak camera which featured a slogan coined by Eastman - 'You press the button, we do the rest'

estimated exposure time. In the late 1850s, the front and back halves were connected by flexible bellows, made of leather or cloth.

Early Kodak cameras

The first Kodak camera, designed by W.H. Walker and George Eastman in 1888, brought photography to the masses. It was a hand-held box, measuring 82.6 x 92.3 x 165 mm (3.25 x 3.75 x 6.5 in), fitted with a lens and a roll of stripping film (⇒p. 164) which would take 100 photographs. It cost $25 and when the film was finished the whole camera had to be sent to the Kodak company who developed the film and replaced it with a new one for $10. The advertising slogan was 'You push the button – We do the rest'. The camera had an aperture of fixed size, a shutter which opened for 1/20th of a second to take the picture, and a film that would give good photographs on a sunny day. On a dull day the film was underexposed; on a very sunny day it was overexposed.

The Pocket Kodak camera, using celluloid roll film, was marketed in 1895, and a folding model followed in 1898. The Box Brownie camera, developed by the American Frank Brownell, and costing just $1 arrived in 1900.

Apertures and shutters

In a modern camera, the exposure can be adjusted by using apertures of different sizes and shutters with different speeds. They were introduced at the end of the 19th century and two types are still in general use. In the diaphragm shutter, built into the lens system, overlapping thin metal leaves open to form the required aperture as the photograph is taken, and then close. In the focal-plane shutter, a blind with a horizontal slit in it is moved across, and just in front of, the plate or film.

Single-lens reflex cameras

In a cheap compact camera, a simple lens is used for the viewfinder whilst a standard lens system, generally of fixed focal length, is used for taking the photograph. In a more expensive single-lens reflex (SLR) camera, one lens system serves both purposes. Prior to taking a photograph, light passing through the lens is directed by a mirror and a prism into the viewfinder but, as the shutter is opened, the mirror moves and allows the light to fall on to the film. This ensures that the film records exactly what is seen through the viewfinder. The lens system in an SLR camera can be unscrewed and changed at will enabling, for example, telephoto, wide angle or zoom lenses to be fitted.

In the now less common twin-lens reflex (TLR) camera an upper lens is used for viewing and focusing whilst the actual photograph is taken through a separate, lower lens.

Modern refinements

Since the late 1960s, battery-powered cameras fitted with silicon chips have provided automatic control of the focusing, the aperture setting, the shutter speed and the loading, rewinding and advancing of the film. Together with automatic flash bulbs, which operate for a time determined by the amount of light received from the view by a photo-cell, these devices allow good photographs to be taken under almost any conditions by almost anyone.

It is, perhaps, truer today than in

Eastman's time, almost 100 years ago, that 'You press the button – We do the rest'. Yet, with the increasing availabilty of electronic or digital cameras (⇒p. 164), Eastman's method of photography may be coming to an end.

COLOUR PHOTOGRAPHY

Any method of taking a colour photograph depends on the fact that white light is made up of three primary colours – blue, green and red. The early methods, such as those introduced in France by two brothers, Louis and Auguste Lumière (1907), and by Louis Dufay (1908), took photographs through a screen coated with the primary colours.

Modern colour photographs are made by recording the primary colours on a single film coated with a number of different layers of emulsion. All the layers are sensitive to blue light, but two are treated with dyes so as to be also particularly sensitive to green or red. The untreated top layer, which the light reaches first, records blue. The light then passes through a yellow filter to remove any remaining blue on to a layer which records green. Finally, it passes on to a layer which records red. The film can be processed after exposure to produce a coloured slide or picture. Making such a colour film which is suitable for amateur use is technically difficult, but the first, marketed as Kodachrome in 1935, has been followed by many others.

OTHER APPLICATIONS

The basic photographic process can be applied in many different ways. It is possible, for example, to take ultraviolet, infra-red, X-ray and γ-ray photographs. Photographs can also be taken from aeroplanes or satellites; they are particularly useful in wartime and for surveying and weather forecasting purposes. In stereophotography, two shots of a scene are taken from slightly different angles; viewing through a stereoscope, with each eye looking at only one shot, gives a three-dimensional effect. Very rapid movement, as of an explosion or a moving bullet, can be captured on film by high-speed photography in which the camera shutter is kept open and the object is illuminated by an electrically operated flash. In time lapse photography, a slow process, such as the growth of a plant, is photographed at regular intervals over a long period of time and the series of shots is then projected at normal speed. Micro-photography is the photography of, for example, business records at greatly reduced size so that they can be stored, in much less space, on microfilm or microfiche sheets, and viewed as required through a magnifier.

Instant photography

A black-and-white photograph could be taken almost instantly in 1924 in a photobooth invented by a Hungarian, Anatol Josepho. It was operated by two attendants until 1968 when coin

A Kodak Professional DCS 420 digital camera. It weights 3.75 lb (1.7 kg) and is 6.7 in (170 mm) wide, 4.5 in (114 mm) in depth and 8.32 in (208 mm) high

operation and colour photography were introduced. Meanwhile, in 1947, Edwin H. Land, an American inventor, who took out more than 500 patents, had marketed his hand-held Polaroid 95 camera which enabled anyone to take instant photographs. It contained two sheets of special film which were processed within the camera by passing them through rollers which ruptured a pod containing the necessary chemicals in a suitably viscous state. The first model, which gave sepia-coloured prints in one minute, was soon improved to give black-and-white prints. It was followed by models such as the Swinger 20, in 1965; the SX-70 which gave coloured prints in one minute, in 1972; and today's 636 CloseUp, Impulse, Image and Vision cameras.

Long legal battles over patent rights were settled, in 1991, when Kodak paid the Polaroid Corporation $924.5 million.

CINEMATOGRAPHY

The brain retains any image for a short time longer than the eye actually sees it and that phenomenon, known as the persistence of vision, was first studied by an English doctor, P.M. Roget in 1824. It formed the basis of a number of toys such as the thaumatrope and the zoetrope or wheel-of-life. A thaumatrope is a disc with, for example, a drawing of a bird on one side and an empty birdcage on the other. When it is spun the bird appears to be inside the cage. In a zoetrope, an impression of motion is obtained by viewing a sequence of drawings, on a strip, through slots in a rotating cylinder.

In 1878, an Englishman, Eadweard Muybridge, who had been found not guilty of murdering his young wife's lover only three years earlier, used a row of 24 cameras, 1 ft (30.5 cm) apart, to take a series of pictures of a galloping horse at Palo Alto in California. The cameras were triggered, in turn, as the horse rode through twenty-four thin threads at chest height or, later, by electrically operated switches. Muybridge was able to portray the way in which the horse moved by mounting the 24 photographs round the edge of a rotating glass disc and projecting them. A Frenchman, Étienne-

Jules Marey, improved on that method in 1888 when he took a series of photographs of flying birds on a roll of film. But he was unable to control the movement of the film accurately and it could not be projected clearly.

The kinetograph

The basic idea of moving pictures was made to work by Edison and his English assistant, W.K.L. Dickson, when they invented a camera called a kinetograph for taking a series of photographs around 1890. They slit some 70 mm Eastman roll film down the middle and put rectangular perforations along each edge. This enabled the 35 mm film to be kept in good alignment as it was fed, by electrically driven sprocket wheels, through what came to be known as the gate of the camera. A series of pictures was taken by moving the film intermittently through this gate. When it was stationary, the shutter of the camera was opened and one photograph (frame) was taken. When the shutter closed, the film was moved on in preparation for the next frame to be taken.

Edison's films were viewed in what he called a kinetoscope which contained a continuous loop of about 15 m (49 ft) of film. By inserting a coin a single person could view the film through a slit; it ran for about 15 seconds. The kinetoscopes were set up in so-called parlours in America and the idea moved to Europe in 1894.

The cinématographe

It seems rather odd that Edison did not choose to project his films on to a screen. It is odd, too, that such an experienced inventor only patented his new ideas in America. So it was that the first successful projection of a motion picture was made by the Lumière brothers (⇒p. 167) in France in 1895. They invented a camera called a cinématographe, very much like Edison's, but they also adapted it to act as a projector and used it in making and showing the first public movie, *La Sortie des Ouvriers de L'Usine Lumière*, in Paris in 1895. The film was shot at 16 frames per second (24 frames per second is generally used today). Separate cameras and projectors introduced by another Frenchman,

6 *I have a photographic gun, which kills nothing and which takes the picture of a flying bird in less than 1/500th of a second.* **9**

Étienne-Jules Marey (1830–1903), French physiologist

Charles Pathé, in 1897, embodied the same basic principles and were not unlike today's equipment.

Adding the sound

The first attempts to provide talking pictures used a phonograph (⇒p. 170) as the source of sound, but they were not very successful because the sound was not loud enough and it was difficult to synchronize it with the picture. Edison tried, and the Frenchman, Léon Gaumont, was partially successful between 1900 and 1910. The first major 'talkie', *The Jazz Singer* starring Al Jolson, did not appear, however, until 1928. It used the short-lived Vitaphone system pioneered by the near-bankrupt Warner Bros.

Thereafter, more progess was made with sound-on-film systems as in *Fox Movietone News*. Typically, the sound track consisted of darker or fainter lines along the edge of the film. When light was passed through them it operated a photo-electric cell connected to a loudspeaker which reproduced the original sound from which the track had been made.

During the early 1950s, sound began to be recorded by magnetic means, as in tape recording (⇒p. 171), and this allowed the simultaneous use of up to eight sound tracks. It was developed into optical stereo-sound by R.M. Dolby (⇒p. 171) in the 1970s.

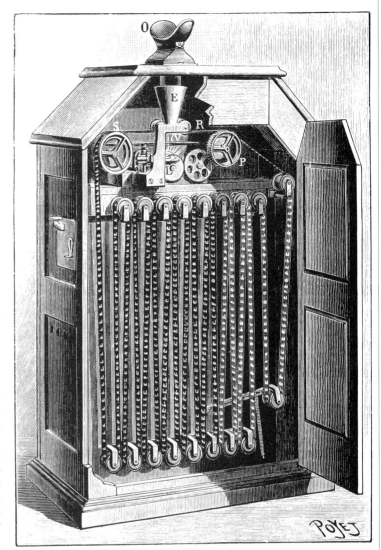

Adding the colour

The first colour films were hand-painted, but a two-colour process called Kinemacolor was invented by G.A. Smith in 1909. A black-and-white film was photographed through a rotating colour filter whch gave one frame of red–orange and the next of blue–green. Technicolor, also in two colours, began in 1917; it had red and green films cemented back-to-back, but it was replaced by three-colour technicolor in 1930. In that process, the film was treated with dyes, as in the taking of still colour photographs (⇒p. 167), so that red, green and blue images could be recorded on it through colour filters. Other systems followed, and in the 1980s it became possible to colour old black-and-white films using a computer.

Special effects

Projection on to a wide screen, to try to match a normal eye-view, began in America with Fred Waller's Cinerama in 1952; it used three projectors and a curved screen. Cinemascope came a year later; it used an anamorphic lens, which is a lens made up of cylindrical components giving distorted photographs of tall, thin figures. They are 'stretched', laterally, by another lens in the projector. Other sytems include Todd-AO (1955), IMAX (1970) and OMNIMAX (1973).

Attempts have also been made to produce three-dimensional effects on a screen. One method uses two cameras, or one camera with two lenses, to project two images side-by-side about 65 mm (2.6 in), the distance between a person's eyes, apart. If one image is blue and the

Edison's kinetoscope, 1893, showing the roll of film which could be viewed through the opening at the top

other red, a three-dimensional effect will appear when they are viewed through glasses with one red and one blue lens. Alternatively two images made with light polarized (⇒p. 160) at different angles can be viewed through two lenses, each of which will transmit only one form of the light.

Cartoons

Newspaper cartoon strips first appeared around 1900 and it was an English-born cartoonist, J. Stuart Blackton, who made the first cartoon film for the Vitagraph Co. of New York in 1906. Other pioneers were the Spaniard, Segundo de Chomon; the American, Winsor McCay; and the Frenchman, Emile Cöhl; but the major contributor was Walt Disney. His first cartoon film featuring Mickey Mouse was made in 1928, and many others followed including *Snow White and the Seven Dwarfs* (1937), the first full-length coloured cartoon film, and *Fantasia* (1940), the first 'musical' cartoon. He built the first theme park, which he called Disneyland, in California in 1955.

SOUND

Sound waves are caused by in-and-out vibrations, as from a tuning fork, resulting in a pulsating movement of the air which can, within limits, be picked up by the human ear. They are unlike electromagnetic waves, such as light, because they consist of a series of compressions and rarefactions. They will not traverse a vacuum, because there must be something to compress or rarefy, and they travel much more slowly than light waves. That is why thunder is always heard after lightning is seen.

THE GRAMOPHONE

6 I was always afraid of things that worked the first time. 9

THOMAS EDISON (1847–1931), on his invention of the phonograph

Thomas Edison invented what he called a phonograph in 1877; it later became the record player or gramophone. It grew out of an automatic recorder for Morse code signals (⇒p. 180), which consisted of a paper disc rotating horizontally about a vertical axis. The dots and dashes were embossed in the paper along a volute spiral and, when the disc was rotated in a similar transmitting machine, the indentations lifted a lever up and down to make electrical contacts which relayed the original Morse message. It was when Edison noticed that the rotating disc produced a crude musical note, if it was turned quickly enough, that he began to make what he originally thought might be a useful dictating machine.

It consisted of a 10 cm (3.9 in) diameter, brass cylinder fitted with a flywheel and covered with a sheet of tin foil. As it was manually rotated about a horizontal axis, it also moved laterally. A steel stylus, attached to a diaphragm at the lower end of a conical horn, was used to cut into the foil as it rotated. The depth of the cut corresponded to the vibration of the diaphragm, and the words spoken into the horn were played back when the cuts were retraced. When Edison recited 'Mary had a little lamb' into the horn he found that it was very well reproduced and he quickly realized the potential of his discovery.

However, the full potential was not realized immediately because only short messages could be recorded, their reproduction was inconsistent, and the tin-foil wore out very quickly. In 1887, Edison replaced the tin foil with hard wax cylinders which could record longer messages, were more durable, and could be shaved down for reuse. A year later, a German, Émile Berliner, working in the USA, turned to flat discs, instead of cylinders. They were made of metal coated with beeswax and the vibrations of the stylus were recorded side-to-side and not by depth of cut. After recording, the pattern was etched into the metal with acid. He then used this disc to make a nickel-plated 'negative' from which he pressed other records, first from rubber and then from a shellac composition. A 10 in (25 cm) record rotating at 78 rpm was generally adopted and shellac eventually replaced by vulcanite or vinyl plastics.

By 1910, cylinder machines had largely disappeared, and clockwork motors were being replaced by electric ones to give more reliable rates of rotation. In 1925, an electrical microphone replaced the horn, and lighter electrical pick-ups were used in playing the record. They converted the vibrations of the stylus into electrical signals which were amplified and fed into a loudspeaker. Stereophonic recording, using two microphones and speakers, was pioneered by the Englishman, A.D. Blumlein in 1933, but stereo records did not arrive until 1958. Long-playing (LP) records 12 in (30 cm) rotating at $33^{1}/_{3}$ rpm and extending the playing time became available in 1946; EPs (extended play) 7 in (18 cm) rotating at 45 rpm were first made in 1949; and quadraphony, using four speakers, began in 1971.

TAPE RECORDING

This is a magnetic method of recording sound, invented by a Dane, Valdemar Poulsen in 1898. In what he called a Telegraphone, a steel wire was wound on to a drum as it passed an electromagnet linked to a microphone. This magnetized the wire in a pattern determined by the sound entering the microphone, and the sound could be reproduced by rewinding the wire past the electromagnet connected to a headphone. The idea was taken up in 1929 by a German, Louis Blattner, in his Blattnerphone. It used steel tape but required about 3 km (1.9 miles) to record for half an hour and was not sensitive enough for music.

In the 1930s, the German companies AEG Telefunken and I.G. Farben replaced the steel tape by a plastic tape coated with very finely divided magnetic iron oxide, and this was used in making the first commercial tape recorders in the 1950s. At first, they were cumbersome and expensive but the use of transistors and narrower tape, commonly contained in a cassette instead of larger open reels, made them smaller, cheaper and more reliable as in the Sony Walkman, a highly successful portable stereo cassette player first launched in 1979.

Today, cassettes are used in dictating machines, telephone answering machines, language teaching, and for operating computers. Beginning in 1966, R.M. Dolby invented various systems for lowering the background noise when a tape is replayed.

Digital audiotape recording

Digital audiotape recording (DAT) is an alternative method of recording on tape, invented in the 1980s. A sound wave is sampled 40,000 times a second, as in pulse code modulation (⇒p 183), so that it can be digitized and represented by a series of numbers which can be converted into a binary code (⇒p. 195) using 1's and 0's. These numbers are then imprinted on to a magnetic tape and used for replaying the original sound.

Compact discs

Compact discs (CDs), which consist of a disc of aluminium with a clear plastic coating, were invented by the Dutch company Philips, and the Japanese company Sony in the early 1980s. A sound wave is digitized, as in digital audiotape recording, and the numbers, and hence the original sound, are imprinted on the rotating disc using a binary code of 1's and 0's (⇒p. 195). This is done by using a laser beam to

Berliner's gramophone, 1901

make millions of pits (indentations) on the disc in a spiral pattern. There is a pit to represent a 1 but no pit to represent a 0. When the disc is replayed and scanned by a laser beam, the pattern of pits is reflected back into photo-detectors which convert it, first, into electrical pulses and then into a nearly-exact version of the original sound.

CDs give better sound reproduction than records or ordinary tape recorders because they are only touched by a laser beam and this eliminates any background noise. A typical disc is 5 in (127 mm) in diameter and can hold 75 minutes of music or sound. The discs were slow to catch on because the deck on which to play them was, originally, very expensive, but they have now almost completely replaced records, and have been widely exploited. The technique can be used for video-recording to make video discs; CD-ROMs (read-only memory) can carry an enormous amount of data and can be used for storing the information formerly printed in large catalogues and encyclopedias; and recordable discs, WORMS (write once read many times), are used in computers.

ULTRASONICS

The pitch of a sound depends on the frequency of the vibration, and this is measured in vibrations (cycles) per second or hertz. Middle C on a piano keyboard, represents a frequency of 261 hertz; a shrill whistle would have a frequency of several thousand hertz; and that of a low-pitched hum would be around 100 hertz. Whatever the frequency, all sound travels at the same speed. It is approximately 340 m (1115 ft) per second in air depending on the temperature, pressure and humidity. It is about four times higher in water and 14 in steel.

The human ear can only detect sounds with frequencies between about 20 and 20,000 hertz but some animals, for example dogs and bats, can hear more high-pitched notes with frequencies well above 20,000 hertz. Ultrasonics is the name given to the study of such high frequency sound. It can be focused in much the same way as light by shaped reflectors or ultrasonic lenses and has found many applications in recent years.

Generation and detection

Ultrasound waves are most commonly produced and detected by an instrument using a synthetic piezoelectric ($\Rightarrow$p. 76) material such as lead zirconate titanate. A thin disc, covered on each side by silver electrodes, is supported on a backing block and fitted with a converging lens at the front. When used as a transmitter, an alternating current is passed between the electrodes. In use as a detector, they are connected to an amplifier.

Underwater detection

Radio waves do not travel well through water so that they are ineffective for detecting underwater objects, but a beam of ultrasonic sound can be used instead. In 1915, the British Navy had begun to detect the position of German U-boats by fitting their ships with underwater microphones (hydrophones) to pick up the noise from the U-boats. The hydrophone can, however, only detect a submarine if it is making a noise, so that it can remain hidden by keeping silent. The Allied Submarine Detection Investigation Committee was set up in the early 1920s to investigate how this problem could be overcome. The new method which it pioneered was originally called Asdic after the committee's initials. Nowadays, it is known as Sonar from the American SOund NAvigation and Ranging programme. A pulse of sound is transmitted and the time is measured for its echo from a target to be picked up on a receiver. The method is also used for finding the depth of the oceans, and the positions of wrecks or shoals of fish.

Medical applications

In ultrasonography, ultrasound waves are used to 'see' inside a body. The waves entering the body are reflected back and can be detected and converted into a moving display on a cathode-ray screen. The technique was pioneered particularly by Dr Ian Donald at Glasgow University in the 1950s. He used it to monitor the foetus during a pregnacy and found that it was much safer than the use of X-rays. It is now used in the examination of the heart, breast, liver, gall bladder and spleen; to destroy diseased tissue in the brain; to treat arthritis; and to break up kidney stones.

COMMUNICATION

'This is a great day with me and I feel I have at last struck the solution of a great problem – and the day is coming when telephone wires will be laid in to houses just like water or gas, and friends converse with each other without leaving home.'

ALEXANDER GRAHAM BELL,
Scottish-born American inventor, 10 March 1876

COMMUNICATION

COMMUNICATION HAS BEEN DESCRIBED as the cement of society and it would certainly be an odd world without the free dissemination of information, news, gossip, ideas, knowledge, entertainment and literature with which most of us are familiar. Speaking and writing came first; then printing, widely used from the 15th century; and then the various forms of telecommunication such as telegraphy, telephony, radio and television in the 19th and 20th centuries. 'Tele' means 'distant' and these new methods enabled written, verbal or pictorial messages to be transmitted almost instantaneously all around the world.

WRITING

Today, in most countries, writing involves the use of words made up of letters – but it all began with pictures. Ancient civilizations drew pictures on rocks and cave walls which by about 3500 BC developed into the first languages. In Sumeria, in the southern part of Mesopotamia, inscriptions were made in soft clay using a length of reed with a triangular-shaped end. Because the impressions were wedge-shaped the writing became known as cuneiform from the Latin *cuneus* for a wedge, and because the clay was baked in the sun it became hard enough, like a brick, to survive over the years. The inscriptions were at first pictorial but, later, they became more symbolic and consisted of a number of strokes not always very closely related to the original picture they were intended to represent. This cuneiform writing spread throughout most of the Near East, but a different system grew up in Egypt where they used pictures and symbols, known as hieroglyphs, written in ink on papyrus (⇒p. 21) using a brush or a reed.

A cuneiform tablet from Sippar, Mesopotamia dating from c. *6th century BC*

Alphabets

Selected lists of symbols – the first alphabets – were first used during the 2nd millennium BC. At Ugarit, in Syria, 32 cuneiform symbols were chosen around 1500 BC and, somewhat later, 22 hieroglyphic symbols were being used in Phoenecia. These early alphabets, modified in turn by the Greeks, the Etruscans and the Romans, led to the 26-letter alphabet of the western world. In Chinese, several hundreds of symbols, each representing one word and many of them dating back to around 1300 BC, are used.

Braille

In 1786 a Frenchman, Valentin Hany, used raised letters which could be identified by touch to enable blind people to read, and a compatriot, Louis Braille, who had been accidentally blinded when he was three, invented an improved system in 1829. In its modern form it comprises six dots raised in different patterns to represent each letter and common words such as 'the' and 'of'.

Shorthand

The first successful shorthand (rapid writing) system was invented by an Englishman, Sir Isaac Pitman, who had begun work as a clerk but became a schoolmaster when he was 19. He began to teach his system, which depends on the phonetic sound of a word rather than its spelling, in Bath in 1839. His system was introduced into the USA by his younger brother Benjamin, but from 1893 it had to compete with a rival invented by an Irish immigrant, J.R. Gregg.

Esperanto

Esperanto is the best known of a number of international languages. It was invented by a Pole, Dr Ludwig L. Zamenhof in 1887 and is based on 28 letters, each representing a single sound. There are 16 grammatical rules and a vocabulary of about 12,000 words. Ido and Novial are simplified forms of Esperanto.

Pencils

Modern pencils were invented by a Frenchman, J.N. Conté, in 1792. They contain a thin rod of graphite and clay inside a wood casing, and the rod is still sometimes called a lead because it was originally made of metallic lead. Today, it is made by extruding a mixture of graphite, clay and water through a hole and baking it. The more graphite, the softer the pencil.

Propelling or mechanical pencils use a finer lead which is moved, as required, in or out of the body of the pencil either by screwing or by a clutch mechanism. The first was invented by Rokuji Hayakawa in Japan in 1915.

Fountain pens

The quill was the main writing implement for many years. It was made from a feather, preferably of a goose, with the end sharpened, cut diagonally, and split to form an embryonic nib. It lasted until the first half of the 19th century, when it became possible to make metal nibs which could be mounted on wooden holders to make dip-in pens, or in fountain pens carrying their own ink supply. The first nibs were made of flexible steel; later ones of gold or platinum, perhaps tipped with a hard alloy.

The first successful fountain pen was patented by an American insurance broker, Lewis E. Waterman, in 1884. He had lost an important order when the pen he used to sign the contract produced a large blot. In his first pen, called the 'Regular', the flow of ink from the barrel through the nib was controlled by allowing air to enter through a capillary tube, and it was refilled with ink using an eye-dropper. Later, the ink was stored in a flexible rubber container within the barrel. It could be squeezed by using a lever which enabled it to be refilled when empty. The ink cartridge, which could be discarded when empty and replaced by another full one, was patented in 1935 by M. Perrand who worked for the Jif-Waterman Co.

Ballpoint and fibre-tip pens

The ballpoint pen was invented by Laszlo Biro and his brother Georg in 1938. In 1940, they fled to Argentina from Hungary and patented their new product in 1943. The pen has no traditional nib. Instead, the special quick-drying ink that it contains flows past a ball set in a casing at the tip of the pen. It was popularized in the 1950s when a Frenchman, Marcel Bich, who had started his career as a door-to-door salesman, manufactured a cheap disposable model and founded the Bic empire.

In 1960, the first fibre-tipped pen, called Sign Pen, was launched by the Japanese Pentel company, founded by Yukio Horie. It pioneered an improved version of the ballpoint pen with a cushioned alloy point in 1970.

Typewriters

The first modern typewriter was patented by C.L. Sholes in the USA in 1868, but it was not a commercial success because it was expensive, bulky and difficult to use. By 1900, however, there were at least 40 different models. Most of them had characters, mounted at the ends of individual bars, which struck the paper through an inked ribbon when the

❛Evil communications corrupt good manners. ❜

1 CORINTHIANS

❛The pen is mightier than the sword. ❜

BARON LYTTON
(1803–73), English
politician and poet

appropriate key was pressed. The QWERTY keyboard, with commonly used letters positioned far apart, was designed to minimize the chance of the bars hitting each other if adjacent keys were pressed too quickly.

During the 1960s, the old-fashioned, mechanically operated machines were replaced by electrical or electronic systems, in which the type-characters were set into rotatable, circular 'daisy-wheels' or spherical 'golf balls' so that a different type could be inserted simply by changing the 'wheel' or the 'ball'. But, despite the advances made, the typewriter has been made largely redundant by the much more versatile word processor ($\Rightarrow$p. 203).

PRINTING

> *We should note the force, effect and consequences of inventions which...were unknown to the ancients, namely, printing, gunpowder and the compass. For these three have changed the appearance and state of the whole world.*
>
> FRANCIS BACON *(1561–1626), English philosopher*

For many years, printing depended on making a plate in a number of different ways, inking it, and then transferring the ink on to paper or some other surface in a printing press. However, in recent times it has been revolutionized, first, by the impact of photography and then by computers and laser techniques. So much so that some methods no longer require plates or presses.

RELIEF OR LETTER-PRESS PRINTING

This began with the use of seals long ago. They were small discs of stone or fired clay carrying an embossed pattern and used for impressing that pattern, probably as a mark of ownership. About 1300 BC, in China, they were embossed with mirror-image letter symbols which could then be printed on to paper. The first known book was printed from carved wooden blocks, $2^{1}/_{2}$ x $1^{1}/_{2}$ ft (76 x 45 cm), in AD 868. It was a Buddhist scriptural piece, known as the *Diamond Sutra*, and a 4.9 m (16 ft) long scroll survives in the British Museum in London.

Between 1040 and 1050, a Chinese alchemist, Pi Sheng, adapted the method by fashioning individual characters (movable type) in baked clay and mounting them as required in an iron frame. At the start of the 15th century, type was being cast in metal in Korea.

The Gutenberg Bible
Johannes Gensfleisch (1400–68) was born in Mainz in Germany in a house called Gutenberg which became the adopted family name. He began work as a goldsmith, but around 1450 turned to printing. He set up a page of type by hand, using cast metal type probably made by pouring a molten alloy of tin and lead into a brass mould. The page was held in a metal frame (forme) and was placed, face up, on the base of a screw press. After inking by hand, a sheet of paper was pressed down on to the forme.

Gutenberg began work on his bible, in Mainz around 1453, in collaboration with Johannes Fust, but the partnership broke up because of a wrangle over debts in 1455, and the bible, illustrated by hand, was completed by Fust and his son-in-law, Peter Schöffer.

By 1490 presses were at work throughout Europe, and William Caxton established his in London in 1476. A year later, he printed the first English book – *The Dictes or Sayinges of the Philosophers* – and went on to print one hundred more.

Setting the type
In Gutenberg's time, it took a day to set one page of text and it remained a slow, manual process until the advent of the first typesetting machine, invented by Ottmar Mergenthaler, a German working in the USA, in 1884. His machine enabled a line of letters (a slug) to be cast from molten metal, in individual moulds, under the control of an operator working a typewriter-like keyboard. It was four times faster than hand setting. In 1887, it was followed by the monotype machine invented by an American civil servant, Tolbert Lanston. Its keyboard produced a punched tape which was fed into a machine casting individual letters.

Making the plate
Printing can be carried out from an original forme but if this is done for a large book a considerable amount of type is needed, and, if the forme has to be kept for a later reprint, all that type is simply

being stored. The original forme is, therefore, used to make a replica which can be used for printing and for storage, whilst the original type is dismantled and reused. These stereotypes were first made by a Scotsman, William Ged, in 1727, using plaster of Paris (⇒p. 25) to make the mould. It was replaced, in 1827, by a papier mâché material, known as flong, which had the advantage that it could be curved to make a semi-cylindrical plate suitable for rotary printing presses.

Today, a plate can be made from a plastic material (photopolymer) by exposing it to a photographic image. This hardens some areas of the material which allows the softer areas to be etched away. Alternatively, laser engraving can be used. In this, the material to be printed, set up on a flat plate or a rotating cylinder, is scanned and the information is digitized on a computer which is then used to control the engraving of a matching printing plate generally made of rubber.

INTAGLIO OR GRAVURE PRINTING

In this system, first used in 1477 for printing maps, and now for colour supplements and magazines, the design is cut or etched into a printing plate, generally made of copper or plastic, which is then inked. After wiping the surface clean, so that the only remaining ink is in the recessed grooves, the plate is pressed against paper which absorbs the ink.

In photogravure, invented by the Austrian Karl Klac, in 1895, a photographic image is formed on the plate and the recesses are made as a series of holes of different depths corresponding to the tone of the image. Where it is dark a deep hole is made and where it is light a shallow one. Today, this is done automatically using a scanner and a computer to control a laser cutter. On printing, the deeper holes, containing more ink, produce darker spots than the shallower holes.

LITHOGRAPHY

Lithography was invented by a Bavarian actor and playwright, Aloys Senefelder, in 1796, and has now largely taken over from letterpress printing for large-scale work. It depends on the fact that water

will repel a greasy ink, so that any pattern can be recorded on a surface by drawing it in a greasy material and then treating it, first with water to wet the non-greasy areas, and then with a greasy ink. It is claimed that Senefelder made the invention when he drew, by chance, on a piece of limestone with a wax crayon. Hence the word lithography meaning stone writing.

In today's photolithography, metal, plastic or paper plates are used which are treated with a light-sensitive coating. The pattern to be printed is then transferred to the plate as a photographic image so that some areas of the plate receive more light than others. This enables the plate to be treated so that different areas will hold more ink than others as in an original lithograph.

Part of William Tyndale's translation of the New Testament printed in Worms, Germany in 1526

PRINTING PRESSES

The ink is removed from any sort of printing plate by pressing it against a sheet of paper or some other surface. The first effective press for doing this, made of wood and hand-operated by turning a screw, was invented by Gutenberg but it could only print about 15 pages an hour. An improved design by a Dutchman, Willem Blaeu, in 1620, lifted this to about 150 an hour, and in 1800 a German, Frederick König, invented a steam-driven press in which the printing plate and paper positioned on a flat base was passed under a cylindrical roller, under pressure; it could print 400 pages an hour. The idea of using cylindrical rollers was taken further by an American, Richard Hoe in 1844 when he patented a rotary press in which the printing plate was wrapped round a cylinder. Today, it is possible to print very rapidly on both sides of a roll (web) of paper by using two cylinders, each with a different plate, one on each side of the paper.

In an offset press, the ink from the printing plate is transferred on to a rubber-covered (blanket) cylinder before being printed on to its final surface. This gives better printing, particularly on a rough surface.

In colour printing, four separate plates are used for printing the four colours – cyan (bluish green), magenta (purplish-red), yellow and black. Accurate superimposition of the four printings provides good reproduction of the original colours.

PRINTING WITHOUT PLATES OR PRESSES

Large-scale printing still employs plates and presses but there are a number of modern methods widely used on a smaller

> *I grew up in poverty and making and selling an invention struck me as one of the few possible avenues through which one could quickly change one's economic status.*
>
> CHESTER CARLSON (1906–68), American inventor

scale as in word processors, cash tills and desk-top computers. They have been invented mainly by computer manufacturers. In a dot-matrix printer, marketed by IBM in 1957, the characters are formed from a vertical row of needles which impinge, through an inked ribbon, on to a sheet of paper as it passes the print head. Others followed in the 1970s. In an ink-jet printer, fine, electrically charged droplets of quick-drying ink are directed on to a sheet of paper. A laser printer uses a beam of laser light to cast an image of characters on to an electrically charged drum, which is then treated with toner as in xerography. A daisy-wheel printer operates as in a typewriter.

Xerography

This is a dry, non-chemical process for copying printed material which is used in most photocopiers. It was invented by Chester Carlson, who studied physics at the California Institute of Technology, and then law, before becoming a patent lawyer. Dissatisfied with the laborious nature of the existing copying methods, he turned his attention to improving them and took out his first patent in 1937. But it was only after lengthy development work that his idea finally came to fruition in the late 1950s.

The process uses a metal plate coated with a photoelectric material, such as selenium, which is electrically charged in the dark. When a photographic image of what is to be copied is focused on to the plate, the loss of charge from the plate depends on the intensity of light falling on it. The darker areas, which remain most fully charged, are blackened by dusting the plate with a charged black powder (toner). This is then transferred to a sheet of paper where it is fixed by heating. Colour copying is also possible.

TELEGRAPHY

The first extensive system of transmitting written messages over a distance was invented by a Frenchman, Claude Chappe, in 1791. It was known as semaphore from the Greek *sema* (sign) and *phero* (bearing), and consisted of a series of towers which could be seen, one

from the other, through telescopes or field glasses. Each tower carried an H-shaped projection, the arms of which could be set in a number of different positions to represent letters and numbers. In 1793, Chappe was appointed telegraph engineer to the French government and within a year he had built 15 towers linking Paris to Lille, 140 miles (225 km) away. Pressure of work caused him to commit suicide in 1805, but building went on for another 40 years until 2500 miles (4000 km) of France was covered by 556 towers. By then electrical telegraphy, with which Chappe had himself experimented, was well under way, but the semaphore persisted, particularly in the use of flags between ships.

ELECTRICAL TELEGRAPHY

A Scotsman known only by the initials CM put forward the first theoretical idea of an electrical telegraph in 1753. It was described in a magazine as being made from 26 different wires. A current passed along each wire would electrify a pith ball at its other end which would attract the appropriate letter written on a piece of paper. This theme was pioneered by a number of workers, particularly after the invention of the Voltaic pile ($\Rightarrow$p. 68) provided a reliable source of current. However, the main breakthrough came when patents were granted to the Englishmen, Charles Wheatstone and William Cooke, in 1837, and the American, Samuel Morse, in 1840.

Wheatstone and Cooke
Charles Wheatstone (1802–75) was born in Gloucester, England, and he began to work with his father who made musical instruments when he was 14. He invented the concertina and a speaking machine, and experiments he carried out on the transmission of sound through rods led to a friendship with Faraday and to an appointment as professor of experimental philosophy at King's College, London, in 1834.

He was a good scientist but very shy, and his idea for an electric telegraph only came to fruition when he met William Cooke (1806–79) who possessed more business acumen. Cooke had studied medicine at Edinburgh University in Scotland before leaving, at the age of 19, to become an officer cadet in the East India Co. He resigned due to ill-health in 1833, and two years later he saw, by chance, a demonstration of an early German telegraph invented by Dr S. von Sömmering. This persuaded him to try to

make something better and, shortly after going into partnership with Wheatstone, they obtained a joint patent in 1837.

Their first telegraph was operated by wires connected to five electromagnets adjacent to five magnetized needles pivoted in front of a dial on which 20 letters and 10 numbers were printed. By changing the direction of the current sent along the wires, each needle could be made to swing to the right or the left. Any particular number was picked out by pointing only one needle in its direction. Letters were picked by pointing two needles. Messages could only be sent very slowly and the absence of six letters led to some odd spelling. 'Quick', for example, became 'kwick' because there was no

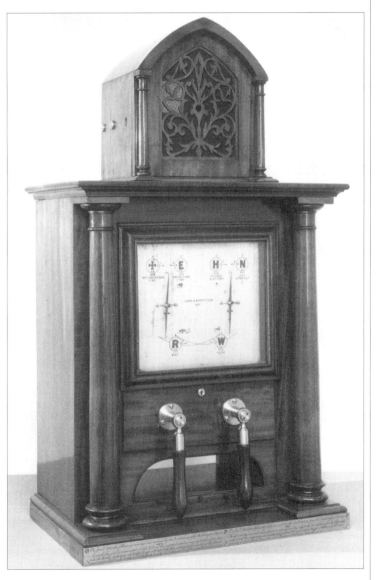

A Cooke and Wheatstone double needle telegraph, as used at Paddington Station, London, c. 1850

letter 'Q'. In 1858, they simplified it so that it worked with only one needle.

The English railway companies were the first users of the new telegraph system, and the first line connected the station at Euston Square in London to that at Camden Town, 2.4 km (1½ miles) away. Paddington was then connected to West Drayton, 21 km (13 miles) away, and later to Slough. In 1844, news of a royal birth at Windsor Castle was carried by horse to Slough and then by telegraph to Paddington; it took 11 minutes. The first cable across the English Channel was laid in 1850 but was cut by a French fisherman and not replaced until 1851. The first successful cable link across the Atlantic was laid in 1858.

As telegraphy became more popular, both Wheatstone and Cooke became rich and they were both knighted. However, they quarrelled about who had actually made the invention. Wheatstone had the stronger claim, he went on to invent a dynamo and a typewriter, and he was still wealthy when he died. Cooke, alas, lost his money and had to survive on a small government pension.

Samuel Morse

Samuel Morse (1791–1872) was born at Charlestown, Massachusetts in the USA, the eldest son of a congregational minister and distinguished geographer. After an education at Yale University, where he first became interested in electricity, he intended to make a living as a painter. To that end, he made two trips to Europe, but his life changed whilst he was returning home in a sailing ship in 1832. A fellow passenger explained to him the workings of an electromagnet (⇒p. 71), and this gave him the idea for his telegraph. Back home, he abandoned a position as professor of the art of design at the University of New York to spend all his time on its development.

His system was patented in the USA in 1840. It depended on the Morse code in which numbers and letters were each represented by a different combination of dots and dashes. The international distress signal SOS, for example, was three dots, three dashes and three dots. The telegraph operator transmitted the message by pressing a key on a transmitter and holding it down for a

shorter or longer period to tap out the required dots and dashes. In the receiver, at the other end of the line, each pulse of current through an electromagnet actuated an inked wheel which printed the dots and dashes on to a moving strip of paper.

Morse had difficulty in launching his invention, even though he was appointed superintendent of United States Telegraphs, and he had spent most of his money before, in 1843, the US Congress provided funds to build a 40 mile (64 km) experimental link between Washington and Baltimore. The first message, sent on 24 May 1844, read 'What hath God wrought'. Thereafter, Morse's system was widely adopted and he became rich and famous, with his achievements being commemorated by the erection of a statue in Central Park, New York.

THE TELEPRINTER

Early telegraphy required skilled operators at both ends of the line but it all became much more user-friendly, and much quicker, when the teleprinter (teletypewriter in the USA) was adopted. This enabled a message to be typed out, relayed by telegraph line, and reprinted at the receiving end. An early teleprinter had been invented in 1855 but it was not until the early 1930s that improved machines became fashionable. The characters, tapped out on a typewriter-like keyboard, were transmited by electric signals, in the form of a code invented by a French engineer, Jean-Maurice-Émile Baudot. Five pulses of positive or negative electricity were used. For example, – + – + – stood for R or 4, and + – – – – for E or 3. Baudot's name lives on in the baud unit, defined as a rate of data transmission of 1 bit (⇒p. 195) per second.

In today's telex or teletex service a message typed on to a teleprinter or a word processor is conveyed, through an exchange, to receivers where it is reproduced. Each transmitter and receiver has an identifying code (like an address), and a central, computerized terminal allows messages to be stored and distributed as required. However, the system is limited to typed messages and is being replaced by fax machines (⇒p. 184) which are more versatile.

6Across the wires the electric message came: "He is no better, he is much the same".9

ALFRED AUSTIN (1835–1913), English poet, on the illness of the Prince of Wales (later, Edward VII)

TELEPHONY

Following the success of telegraphy, many inventors turned their attention to finding a way of converting sound waves into electric currents which could be transmitted along a wire and reconverted into sound waves at the other end. A working model which did that was demonstrated in 1860 by a German teacher of physics, J.P. Reis, and he coined the word 'telephone'. However, he died before he could develop the idea and a practical telephone did not emerge until 1876 when, on the same day, two very similar patent applications were filed in the USA. One came from Alexander Graham Bell, a teacher of the deaf, and the other from Elisha Gray, a manufacturer of telegraphic equipment. Bell's was first, by a few hours, and his claim to be the inventor of the telephone was eventually upheld after almost ten years of litigation.

BELL'S TELEPHONE

Bell used identical devices, connected by a wire, for transmitting and receiving the sound. They consisted of a circular diaphragm of stretched parchment carrying a magnetized, flexible steel reed, which was placed next to an electromagnet. Speaking into the diaphragm of the transmitter caused it to vibrate and this produced a small undulatory current in the nearby electromagnet. The current passed through the wire into the electromagnet in the receiver, causing its diaphragm to vibrate in unison with that of the transmitter so that the original voice could be heard. The first sentence heard on a telephone was 'Mr Watson, come here, I want you'. It was a cry for help from Bell, when he spilt some acid on his clothes, to Thomas Watson, his assistant, in a nearby room.

Bell set about exploiting his idea and demonstrated his telephone at the Centennial Exposition in May 1876 in Philadelphia, but it was not until Thomas Edison invented an improved transmitter in 1878 that the telephone had sufficient range and clarity to become commercially successful. The new transmitters had a metal diaphragm behind which granules of carbon were packed. As the diaphragm vibrated, it compressed the granules and changed their electrical resistance so that a current passing through them undulated in phase with the vibrations. The new transmitters gave a much stronger signal because they depended on the sound waves continuously changing an external current and not on producing a current on their own.

MAKING A CONNECTION

The existing network of telegraph cables consisted of single wires with an 'earth' return to complete the circuit. They were adequate for carrying the pulses of current from a telegraph transmitter, but not for the weak, undulating currents from a telephone. It was therefore necessary to construct a new network of overhead lines and underground or underwater cables using two-wire circuits. At first, calls could only be made at all clearly over very short distances. There was some improvement when iron wires were replaced by copper but, even then, expensive 5 mm (0.2 in) thick wire was needed, and for distances over about 100 km (62 miles) it was necessary to fit repeaters (amplifiers) to maintain the signal strength. It was difficult to design repeaters which would operate successfully in sealed containers under 6 km (3.7 miles) of sea water, so that it was not until 1956 that the first submarine transatlantic cable (TAT-1) between Scotland and Newfoundland was laid. It had over 50 repeaters along its 3620 km (2250 miles) length and provided 36 channels. TAT-7, laid in 1983, had 4000 channels.

Early telephone exchanges

The first exchange, linking only eight local customers, was established in New Haven, Connecticut in 1878. The caller rang the operator, who inserted a plug into a socket to make the connection to the receiver. The first British exchange opened in Coleman Street, London, in 1879; it had ten customers.

Automatic exchanges began to take

❛Well informed people know it is impossible to transmit the voice over wires and that were it possible to do so, the thing would be of no practical value.❜

BOSTON POST, *1865*

ALEXANDER GRAHAM BELL
(1847–1922)

BELL was born in Edinburgh into a family where sound was of the utmost importance because both his father and grandfather were well-known speech therapists and Alexander's first job was as an assistant in that activity. When, in 1870, he was stricken with tuberculosis, from which both his brothers had died, the family emigrated to Ontario, Canada. A year later they moved to Boston, USA, where Alexander set up a school for teaching the deaf which was so successful that he was appointed as professor of vocal physiology in the new University of Boston. It was the wealthy parents of two of his deaf pupils who sponsored his early research in telephony.

The Bell Telephone Co. was formed in the USA in 1877 and Bell travelled to England where he demonstrated the new device to Queen Victoria. Existing telegraph companies tried to impede its progress, and there were many legal battles over patent rights, particularly those involving Elisha Gray and Edison. Bell's idea was, nevertheless, widely adopted and though he was no business man he became very rich. He invested much of the money in the Volta Laboratory in Washington for developing new inventions, and the Volta Bureau to advance the interests of deaf people. Meanwhile, he continued to be very active in different spheres, inventing an improved version of Edison's phonograph, an early type of iron-lung and a metal detector; founding the journal *Science*; and taking an active interest in the possibility of manned flight. 'Don't keep for ever on the public road,' he wrote. 'Leave the beaten track occasionally and dive into the woods.'

Alexander Graham Bell making the first call between New York and Chicago on 18 October 1892

over after the end of World War I. They had been invented in the 1890s by an American undertaker, Almon B. Strowger. The story is that he suspected a competitor's wife, who was a telephone operator, of putting his calls through to her husband. In his automatic exchange, a contact was both lifted and rotated, in stages, to make the right connection. The caller used a phone fitted with three buttons which were later replaced by a rotary dial numbered zero to ten.

PULSE CODE MODULATION

The undulating current emanating from a telephone mouth-piece weakens (attenuates) as it passes along a wire so that the background noise becomes a nuisance. To avoid this, A.H. Reeves, a British engineer working in France, invented pulse code modulation (PCM) in 1937. His idea was that the signal strength, represented as an undulating wave, could be sampled at intervals, and each sample could be allotted a number (quantized) which could then be transmitted in a binary code (⇒p. 195) as a particular arrangement of on–off electrical pulses.

To reproduce speech clearly by this method requires samples to be taken about 8000 times a second, and this only became possible in the 1960s, with the invention of the chip (⇒p. 81). It was known as digital transmission to distinguish it from the older analogue transmission. To convert one type of signal to the other requires a device known as a modem (modulator/demodulator). If it can handle two-way transmission it is known as a full duplex modem; if only one way, as a half-duplex. Its speed of operation is measured by its baud (⇒p. 180) rate, which for a fast modem may be 9600 or 14,400 bits per second.

PCM had two very important consequences. First, it became possible, in the late 1960s, to replace the electric current transmitted along a metal wire by light pulses sent along an optical fibre. Second, it enabled the use of electronically operated exchanges, with no moving parts, which could function much more rapidly than the previous automatic ones.

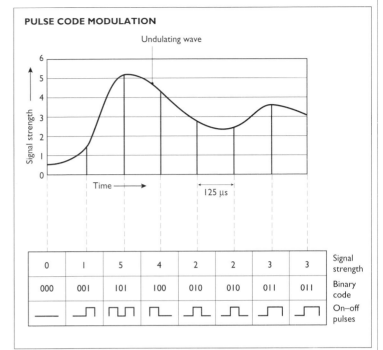

PULSE CODE MODULATION

0	1	5	4	2	2	3	3	Signal strength
000	001	101	100	010	010	011	011	Binary code

THE USE OF OPTICAL FIBRE

In digital transmission by optical fibre, the electric current generated by the sound is converted into pulses of light either by a laser or a light-emitting diode. They travel along the fibre and are reconverted at the receiving end, first into electric current and then into sound waves.

This use of optical fibre was first suggested by Dr Charles K. Kao in 1966. He was born in Shanghai, China and trained as an engineer at London University before going to work in the Standard Telecommunications Laboratories in Harlow, England. Once it became possible to make the fibres of sufficiently pure glass, new optical fibre cables began to replace the old metal ones, both in Britain and the USA, in the late 1970s. They are cheaper and last longer; they require fewer amplifiers (regenerators); they are very thin so that they fit readily into existing ducts; and they can carry many more simultaneous signals with less interference.

The first transatlantic optical fibre cable (TAT-8) was laid in 1988, and an integrated services digital network (ISDN), now being installed in Europe, can transmit data at speeds up to 64,000 bits per second. The time may well come

The signal strength, in the form of an undulating wave, is sampled at very small time intervals, so that it can be represented as a series of numbers. By expressing them on a binary scale, they can be transmitted using on-off electrical pulses

when metal cables can be completely replaced.

OTHER DEVELOPMENTS

Fax machines

Fax is an abbreviation for facsimile, and fax machines enable a copy of a picture, drawing or printed document to be transmitted to a receiver with an individual fax number, over a telephone line. The general idea was patented by a Scot, Alexander Bain, in 1843, and an Italian physicist, Giovanni Caselli, in 1866, but they were ahead of their time and it did not become popular until the 1970s in Japan where the complex language is not suitable for teleprinters.

In a modern fax machine, the material to be transmitted is divided into a number of tiny squares. They are scanned by a light source and the emission from each square is converted into an electric current by a light-sensitive diode. The various currents are passed over a telephone link and reconverted into images at the receiving end.

Visual contact

A videophone allows two people to see each other in colour whilst they talk. It contains a phone with an in-built 3 in (7.6 cm) television screen and a concealed video camera (⇒p. 192). Similar

6 We can hardly realize the blissful quietude of the pre-telephone epoch. 9

NORMAN DOUGLAS
(1868–1952), Scottish essayist

combined cameras and screens together with telephones, set up in different locations, enable different groups of people to see and speak to each other just as if they were all around the same table. It is called video-conferencing.

The mobile (cordless) phone

This is a portable radio-telephone (⇒p. 188), which became available in the 1970s. It operates through a nationwide network of cells each allotted their own short-range, high-frequency radio band so that they do not interfere with each other. The cells vary in size from 2 to 30 km (1.25 to 18.6 miles) in radius depending on whether they are in built-up or rural areas, and a transmitter/receiver within each cell is used to connect a mobile phone user into the national network through an exchange. As the mobile phone is moved from one cell to another, it is automatically retuned to the new frequency.

Radiopaging provides an alternative method of making contact. A doctor, for example, may carry a pocket-sized radio receiver which can be made to bleep by a coded message transmitted to it. The doctor then knows that he has to ring a previously arranged number on another phone. In a more sophisticated system the radiopager can receive a short written or spoken message.

RADIO

James Clerk Maxwell, a Scottish professor of physics, proposed in 1864 that light was just one rather special type of, what he called, electromagnetic radiation and that other types were likely to exist. Another physics professor, the German, Heinrich Hertz, confirmed this when he discovered what came to be called radio waves in 1888. He was using an alternating current to create an electric spark between two separated spheres when he found that an electric current was set up in a loop of wire some distance away. He also found that the radio waves given out by the spark could be reflected like light and had the same velocity. The development of radio was concerned with controlling the transmission of these waves, broadcasting them and receiving them.

WIRELESS OR RADIO TELEGRAPHY

The first successful application, known as wireless or radio telegraphy, was pioneered by Marconi (⇒ p. 185) and was satisfactory for transmitting the dots and dashes of a Morse code message, but could not transmit music or speech. It used a spark generator, like that of Hertz, which could be switched on and off by the Morse key operator. The pulses of radio waves which were emitted were picked up on a coherer, invented in 1890 by a Frenchman, Professor Edouard Branly, and improved by an Englishman, Sir Oliver Lodge. In a simple form it consisted of a tube full of metal filings in a circuit with an electric battery and bell. The conductivity of the filings was

MARCHESE GUGLIELMO MARCONI
(1874–1937)

MARCONI was born in Bologna, Italy of a wealthy Italian father and his second wife, the daughter of a well-known Irish whiskey distiller. He had little formal education but did receive some tuition in physics at the Technical Institute in Leghorn. When he read about Hertz's experiments (⇒p. 184) in 1894 he was inspired to try to repeat them at his family home. Despite his early success, the Italian government refused to help him with his invention so he set sail for England where, backed by the Post Office, he was granted a patent in 1896.

In 1897 he founded the Wireless Telegraph and Signal Co. which ran the first wireless installation at The Needles in the Isle of Wight and in 1900 became the Marconi Wireless Telegraph Co.,

based in Chelmsford, England.

Marconi's single-mindedness and business acumen enabled him to transform radio from a novelty to a central feature of everyday life. In 1909, he shared the Nobel Prize for Physics with Karl Ferdinand Braun (⇒p. 77), and during World War I he began to investigate ways of transmitting and receiving short wavelength beams, similar to those on which radar (⇒p. 149) was eventually based. From 1921, he made his steam yacht *Elettra* both his home and his research station, and he continued his work even though he was stricken with a number of heart attacks. He was awarded an Italian marquisate in 1929, and on the day after his death, radio transmitters across the world closed down for two minutes.

> ❛*Signor Marconi has the sublime confidence of genius that the signals he received at ... Newfoundland were ... from Cornwall.* ❜
>
> THE DAILY TELEGRAPH, *16 Dec 1901*

Guglielmo Marconi with the wireless equipment he brought to England in 1896

increased when radio waves passed through them so that the bell rang.

Initially, Marconi transmitted a radio signal across a room in his parents' house. He increased the distance in stages, making great progress when he fitted both his transmitter and receiver with aerials and earths. By 1895, he could transmit

over a distance of 1 mile (1.6 km); in 1899, he sent a message across the English Channel; and on 12 December 1901, he sent the three Morse dots of the letter S from Poldhu in Cornwall, England, to St John's, Newfoundland. Thereafter, radiotelegraphy was used, particularly in ships, until it was overtaken by radiotelephony (⇒p. 188) in the 1930s. Radiotelegraphy facilitated navigation by enabling ships to be kept informed of Greenwich Mean Time (⇒p. 148), and was responsible for saving many lives. In 1909, for example, the American *Republic* collided with the Italian *Florida*, but a rescue vessel, called by telegraph, arrived within half an hour and saved 1700 lives. In 1912, the *Carpathia*, picking up a call from the sinking *Titanic* 95 km (59 miles) away, was able to rescue 705 survivors though it could not help the 1513 who drowned.

BROADCASTING

The first transmissions of music and speech were made in 1906 by a Canadian, R.A. Fessenden, from Brant Rock in Massachusetts, and a spoken radio message crossed the Atlantic in 1915. In 1920, the Marconi company broadcast twice daily from Writtle, near Chelmsford, England, and the Westinghouse station, KDKA, began its broadcasts from Pittsburgh. Radio-Paris went on the air from the Eiffel Tower in 1921; the British Broadcasting Company (BBC) was set up in 1922; and programmes began in Germany in 1923. By that time there were already over 500 licensed transmitters in the USA.

Wave bands

Today there are tens of thousands of radio transmitters used for broadcasting , for radiotelephony, for military and police communications, for amateur and citizen's band radio, for communication in space, for television and for radar. All this is possible because radio waves can vary in wavelength from 1 cm to over 1 km. Dividing the wavelength, in metres, into the velocity of light (299,792,458 m/s) gives the corresponding frequencies in hertz. Thus, a 1 cm wavelength has a frequency of 30 GHz and a 1 km wavelength 300 kHz. These wavelengths are divided into wave bands which are designated for particular uses by the International Telecommunucation Union

Radio broadcasting, for example, takes place on frequencies chosen from the long wave (above 1 km), medium wave (100 m to 1 km), short wave (10 to 100 m), or very high frequency, VHF (30 to 300 MHz) bands. Ultra-high frequencies, UHF (300 to 3000 MHz) are used for television; and microwaves (10 to 100 cm) for telephony. Each transmitter has its own allotted wavelength or frequency, though two can operate on the same value if they are far enough apart not to interfere with each other.

Transmission

A modern radio transmitter produces waves of its own allotted radio freqency by using a valve oscillator, first invented in 1915, to produce a fixed alternating current which is then amplified and fed into an aerial or antenna. The frequency of these waves is far too high for them to be audible to the human ear, but they can travel long distances without weakening much. They are used as carrier waves for

In amplitude modulation (bottom left) the amplitude of the carrier wave is changed by the audio sound wave. In frequency modulation (bottom right), it is the frequency that is changed

AMPLITUDE AND FREQUENCY MODULATION

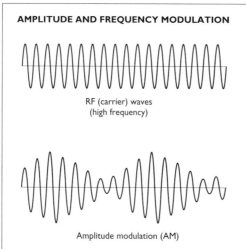

RF (carrier) waves
(high frequency)

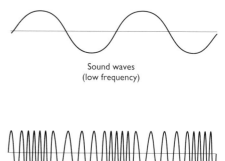

Sound waves
(low frequency)

Amplitude modulation (AM)

Frequency modulation (FM)

the much lower audio frequencies coming from a microphone when anyone speaks into it. The audio frequency is superimposed on to the radio frequency in one of two ways. In AM (amplitude modulation), as originally used by Fessenden (⇒p. 186), the amplitude of the carrier wave is changed by the audio wave. In FM (frequency modulation), invented in 1933 by an American electrical engineer, E.H. Armstrong, it is the frequency that is changed. FM reduces the background noise caused by static electricity and is generally used in VHF transmissions. AM is used by short-, medium- or long-wave stations; it has a longer range than FM and requires less expensive equipment.

Reception
The modulated signal made up of radio and audio frequencies is picked up by the receiving radio when the listener tunes in until its aerial responds to the signal. The signal is then amplified before it is demodulated by separating out the radio- and audio-frequency components. The audio-frequency part is then reamplified before being led into headphones or a loudspeaker.

An American, H.H.C. Dunwoody, first achieved this in a crystal set which he invented in 1906. It relied on the fact that some crystals, for example galena and carborundum only allow current to pass in one direction. The electrical connection to the crystal was made by playing a thin wire, known as the 'cat's whisker', over its surface to find the optimum position for good reception. It was fun to see what could be achieved but it was highly unreliable.

Everything changed at the start of the 20th century with the invention of valves or tubes (⇒p. 77). They allowed the necessary operations of modulation, amplification, tuning and rectification to be achieved much more efficiently and they revolutionized the design of radio equipment, until the advent of transistors in 1948 (⇒p. 80). Because they are much smaller than valves or tubes and require less power, smaller batteries can be used, so that pocket-size radios became possible in the early 1950s. They were popularized, particularly by the Japanese Sony Corporation.

Microphones and loudspeakers
A microphone is a device for converting sound waves into an electric current, and a loudspeaker does the reverse. The early devices, invented by Bell and Edison for use in telephones, were unsatisfactory for music because they had to be held close to the source of sound and, even then, they only responded to a limited range of frequencies. They were replaced, first, by moving coil microphones in which a light aluminium coil attached to a diaphragm is surrounded by a permanent magnet. As the coil moves in and out of the magnetic field, under the influence of sound waves on the diaphragm, an alternating current is produced. They were invented by an American, Charles Cuttris, and a German, E.W. Siemens in 1877. Later, the coil and diaphragm were replaced by a thin, corrugated aluminium ribbon which vibrated in a magnetic field as sound waves fell on to it. It was invented by two Germans, W.H. Schottky and Erwin Gerlach, in 1923.

Other models depend on the electrical changes which occur when sound waves impinge on a diaphragm which serves as one plate of a capacitor (⇒p. 67); on a heated wire; or on a piezoelectric material (⇒p. 76).

Refinements
Over the years, there have been many technical refinements. Aerials, pioneered by the Russian Alexander Popov in the 1890s, have become more sophisticated, both for transmission and reception. In 1918, an American electronics engineer, E.H. Armstrong, invented the super-heterodyne, or superhet, radio in which the incoming signal was mixed with an internal signal. This required some extra components but gave a reciever which was more selective and easier to tune. Stereophonic recording, which uses two microphones and two loudspeakers, began in 1961.

Since then, printed circuits (⇒p. 81) and integrated circuits (⇒p. 81) have made radio equipment still smaller, cheaper and more reliable. So much so that there are numerous models available which will pick up radio broadcasts, and play records, tapes and compact discs, all with high-fidelity (hi-fi) sound reproduction.

Above left: *An artist's impression of* Telstar, *the first communications satellite, launched in 1962*

Above right: *The Hoy microwave transmission tower in the Orkney Islands, Scotland*

RADIOTELEPHONY

The first transatlantic telephone call by radio was made in 1915 from Arlington, Virginia, USA to the Eiffel Tower in France. Radio waves travel in straight lines but they can traverse the curved surface of the Earth because they are reflected by different electrically charged layers in the upper atmosphere (the ionosphere) – the E-layer at a height between 110 to 120 km (68 to 75 miles) reflects waves with a medium wavelength; the F-layer at 250 to 400 km (155 to 250 miles) reflects shorter wavelengths.

A transatlantic, commercial radio telephone link was opened between Rocky Point, New Jersey and Rugby, England in 1928. Calls were expensive (£15 for three minutes), not reliably clear, and they had to be booked in advance because the link would only carry one call at a time. Direct dialling began in 1970.

Australia and England were linked by radio-telephone in 1930.

COMMUNICATION SATELLITES

Making long-distance telephone calls was greatly facilitated by the launch of the first communication satellite, *Telstar*, in the USA in 1962. Radio signals were transmitted to the satellite from a ground station via an antenna in the shape of a parabolic reflector known as a dish. They were amplified by equipment on the satellite and relayed to a second dish at a receiving station.

The disadvantage of Telstar was that it circled the Earth in about two hours so that it had to be tracked by a dish as it passed over and was only accessible for 20–30 minutes at any one place. This problem was overcome in 1965 when a second satellite, *Early Bird*, was put into orbit at a height of 36,000 km (22,500 miles) above the Equator. At that height, it travelled at the same rate as the Earth rotated on its axis so that it encircled the Earth once every 24 hours. This meant that it was always above the same point on the Earth (it was said to be geostationary) and a dish could be

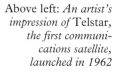

constantly pointed at it without having to move.

Early Bird was the first of many satellites to be launched by Intelsat (the *International Tele*communications *Sat*ellite Organization). The first three, positioned over the Indian, Atlantic and Pacific oceans provided worldwide coverage and turned the 1945 suggestion of the British science-fiction writer, Arthur C. Clarke, into reality. Today, there are over 130 communication satellites of all shapes and sizes serving many purposes. Relaying telephone calls from London to Sydney is typical. First, the call is carried by cable to the British

Telecom Tower in London (built in 1966 and now capable of handling 90,000 simultaneous calls) where the signals are converted into microwaves by a modulator. These waves are of higher frequency than radio waves so that they can be focused into a narrower beam. The beam is transmitted to the Goonhilly Downs Earth Station in Cornwall, England, where it is reflected to a satellite by a dish. The call is received at a ground station at Gnangara in Western Australia and transmitted onwards from there.

Other satellites deal with calls to other parts of the world and from ship-to-shore or air-to-shore.

TELEVISION

Television, the transmission and reception of moving pictures, depends on scanning a picture by breaking it down into many dots, measuring the light intensity of each dot, and transferring this information on to a distant screen either via a cable or by a radio carrier wave. It developed alongside radio broadcasting but at a rather slower pace because the problems were more intractable.

BLACK-AND-WHITE TELEVISION

The first realistic idea as to how television might work came in 1884 when a German, Paul Nipkow, suggested that an illuminated picture might be scanned by using a rotating disc containing a spiral of holes. The light passing through each hole would fall on to a selenium photocell ($\Rightarrow$p. 78) and provide a current, depending on its brightness. The various currents would then light a bulb whose image would be projected on to a screen through a second disc, perforated exactly like the first and matching its rotation.

Cathode ray tube receiver
Nipkow's idea could not be made to work successfully until the advent, around 1905, of valves ($\Rightarrow$p. 77) and more sensitive photocells ($\Rightarrow$p. 78) to allow amplification of the minute currents involved. By then, the cathode ray tube ($\Rightarrow$p. 77) had been developed,

and in 1907 a Russian professor, Boris Rosing, suggested its use as a receiver for pictures by feeding the various currents coming from a Nipkow disc scanner into it. The idea was that the currents would be used to control the intensity of an electron beam moving across the phosphor-coated screen of a cathode ray tube. The beam would start at the top left-hand corner and move very rapidly across, and down, in nearly horizontal lines. When it struck the screen it would cause a glow proportional to its intensity so that the original picture would be reproduced in black and white.

The early development of this system was largely due to a Scot, John Logie Baird, but the Americans, Charles F. Jenkins, Herbert Ives and Ernst Alexanderson, also made significant contributions. Baird began his work in 1923 and he gave the first public demonstration of television three years later. He called it 'seeing by wireless'. In 1927, he relayed pictures along a telephone wire from London to Glasgow, 700 km (435 miles) away, and in 1928 he spanned the Atlantic. Similar progress was made in the USA, Germany and France but all these early pictures were ill-defined and flickering because the number of lines scanned was too low and too slow.

The iconoscope
In 1908, a British scientist, A.A. Campbell-Swinton, suggested that it

‘We must not lose track of the fact that ... inventions are made by individuals and almost invariably by individuals with very limited means.’

PHILO T. FARNSWORTH (1906–71), American engineer

might be possible to replace the mechanically operated Nipkow disc by a camera based on a cathode ray tube. The idea was eventually put into practice when Vladimir Zworykin invented the iconoscope in 1923. He had been a pupil of Boris Rosing's before moving, penniless, to the USA, where he worked in the Westinghouse laboratories in Pittsburgh and, later, for the Radio Corporation of America (RCA) of which he became vice-president. His iconoscope contained a 10 cm (3.9 in) square sheet of mica, with a metal backing, fitted inside a cathode ray tube. The sheet was covered with a mosaic of tiny photoemissive cells (⇒p. 78), insulated from each other. When an image of the picture to be transmitted was cast on to the sheet, each photocell became positively charged according to the amount of light falling on to it. The charged mosaic was then scanned by passing an electron beam over it. This negatively charged beam reduced the positive charge on each cell, and what remained was fed out from the metal backing of the mosaic. The resultant currents, proportional to the amount of light which had fallen on to each cell, were amplified and eventually passed to a cable or superimposed on a high-frequency carrier wave (⇒p. 186) for transmission from an antenna.

The first commercial iconoscope was made by RCA in 1930 and two competitive products, working on similar lines, appeared about the same time. They were the Emitron, designed by American Isaac Shoenberg working for Marconi-EMI, which had been formed by a merger of the Marconi company with Electrical and Musical Industries Ltd (EMI), and the image dissector invented by Philo Farnsworth, a freelance American inventor. Another camera, the image orthicon, came in 1946.

The next generation of cameras had photo conductive (⇒p. 78) instead of photo emissive (⇒p. 78) cells. They included the Vidicon (1952), the Plumbicon (1963), and the Saticon (1974). Charged-coupled devices (⇒p. 164) began to be used in 1980.

Scanning

The clarity of a television picture depends, mainly, on the extent and rate of scanning. Baird's original use of 30 lines and $12^1/_2$ pictures per second, around 1930, gave very low definition and far too much flicker, and when the British Broadcasting Corporation started regular programmes in 1936 it used both an improved Baird system, operating on 240 lines and 25 pictures per second, and a Marconi-EMI system operating on 405 lines and 25 pictures per second. The latter reduced the flicker by using interlaced scanning whereby all the odd-number lines are traced out in one 1/50th second scan and the even numbers in another. The screen is, in effect, scanned 50 times a second though only 25 pictures are transmitted. It took only a few months before the Baird system was abandoned and the superiority of the fully electronic Marconi-EMI equipment was established.

The 405-line system which it used continued in Britain until the acceptance in 1961 of a new standard of 625 lines at 25 pictures per second which had been widely adopted in continental Europe since 1953. In the USA, 525 lines at 30 pictures per second has been used since 1941.

THE ADVENT OF COLOUR

Baird achieved a type of colour television in 1928 by using two Nipkow discs with three different spirals of holes, one covered by a red, one green and one a blue filter, together with three coloured lamps. It did not work at all well but the basic idea of mixing colours was still used when commercial colour television began in the USA in 1951, and in Germany and Britain in 1967. Three incompatible systems developed – the NTSC (National Television System Committee) system is used in the USA and Japan; SECAM (Séquence Electronique Couleur avec Mémoire) in France and Eastern Europe; and PAL (Phase Alternation Line) in the rest of Europe.

Colour cameras

Black-and-white television only requires one camera but in colour television three are used to pick up three separate images of the picture to be transmitted. These are focused, through three mirrors, one of

JOHN LOGIE BAIRD
(1884–1946)

BAIRD, the son of a Presbyterian minister, was born in Helensburgh, Scotland. After training as an electrical engineer at Glasgow University, he worked for the Clyde Valley Electrical Power Co. but had to give up his job because of ill-health in 1918. He then tried his hand at a number of not very successful business enterprises before retiring, still in poor health, to Hastings, England in 1923. It was there that he began his experiments with television.

He had little money, and his first apparatus, set up on a washstand in an attic room, was assembled in a tea-chest and a biscuit tin held together with darning needles and bits of string. Yet, within a year, he had transmitted the outline of a Maltese cross over a distance of a few metres and by 1929 the Baird Television Development Co. was providing experimental programmes for the British Broadcasting Corporation.

However, his dreams were dashed in 1937 when the BBC opted for the rival Marconi-EMI electronic equipment. With hindsight it is remarkable that

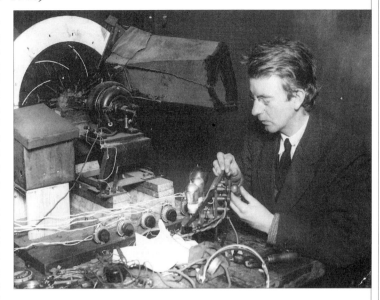

Baird, working almost entirely on his own at the start, managed to achieve so much so early, and it is difficult to assess his contribution fairly when the system which he championed was abandoned. Perhaps he received too little recognition for his achievements during his lifetime, and too much after his death.

J.L. Baird with one of his early transmitters. The rotating Nipkow disc can be seen to the left of the picture

which will transmit red, one blue, and the other green light. Each camera scans its own coloured image with an electron beam so that it is represented by electrical signals. These signals which carry the video information are passed into a cable or superimposed upon a carrier wave transmitted from an antenna.

Receivers

The screen of a colour television receiver is covered with minute dots of red, green and blue phosphors arranged in vertical stripes, and the single electron beam used in black-and-white television is replaced by three beams, one for each colour, coming from the colour camera. Each beam is directed on to its own colour phosphor through holes in a shadowmask, invented in the RCA ($\Rightarrow$p. 190) laboratories in 1949 by a team led by David Sarnoff. The resulting picture is made up of red, green and blue dots (look

at the TV screen through a magnifying glass) but the eye merges them together to give the colour of the original.

OTHER DEVELOPMENTS

The national programmes in most countries, generally paid for by a licence fee, have been supplemented by cable and satellite television programmes which are only available to subscribers. Cable television, with the programme being transmitted to the receiver along a cable, was first used in 1950 in rural areas of the USA where normal reception was poor; it became more widespread in the 1960s. Satellite Television began in Canada in 1979 – programmes are received direct from a satellite via a small, domestic dish aerial.

Video-recording

A video-recorder records both the video

and audio signals from a television programmme either on a magnetic tape or a compact disc. The methods used are essentially the same as for sound recording but because more information has to be handled it is more complex. The first tape recorder was made by the Ampex Corporation of America in 1958 for studio use. The name originates from the initials of the founder, A.M. Poniatoff, plus 'ex' for 'excellence'. The recorder used 2 in (5.1 cm) tape.

Rival video-cassette recorders (VCRs), using $^1/_2$ in (12.7 mm) tape in enclosed cassettes, appeared in the 1970s for domestic use. VHS (video home system), made by JVC, proved to be more popular than the very similar and slightly earlier Betamax, made by Sony. In 1988, Sony introduced the Video Walkman which, whilst weighing only $2^1/_2$ lb (1.2 kg), is both a television and a tape recorder using 8 mm (0.31 in) tape.

Images can also be recorded on a video-cassette inside a portable television camera – a video camera or camcorder.

Videotex systems

Videotex systems are used to transmit information to a television receiver, fitted with a special adaptor. Teletext, for example, transmits pages of up-to-date information from a central computer, alongside the conventional TV signal. The information is generally about news, sport, finance and special events. Typical British services, which began in 1974, are the BBC Ceefax and ITV Oracle.

The Viewdata system, first developed by the British Post Office (now British Telecom) and introduced by the BBC under the name of Prestel in 1975, transmits information to the television set along a telephone line. The telephone connection allows the viewer to interact with the information supplied so that he or she can, for example, buy goods, operate a bank account, or make travel or theatre bookings, all from the comfort of an armchair. It will soon be possible to 'order' a particular film or video pro-gramme to be transmitted to the user's screen, a service already provided in many hotels.

Digital television

Television signals were first converted into a digital form (⇒p. 183) in 1986 and this enables them to be manipulated on a computer so that modified and improved images can be produced. It also allows the application of what is known as data or digital compression in which a picture is divided into parts which don't move, such as a sky background, and parts which do. Because it is only necessary to transmit changes in the latter, more programmes can be sent along the allotted wavebands. In Britain, for example, it is estimated that the new technology will lead to the establishment of at least 18 new television channels when it is fully implemented. However, it will only be possible to receive the new digital services on television sets which have been fitted with an expensive decoder.

Other changes

In the early 1980s, pocket-sized flat-screen television sets using a liquid crystal display (LCD) (⇒p. 80) to show the picture were first made in Japan. Similar screens came to be used in portable or notebook computers (⇒p. 202), and larger ones, up to 40 inches, are just beginning to be marketed for use as wall-hanging television screens.

In 1989, high-definition television (HDTV) began in Japan. The system, known as MUSE, uses 1125 lines, and a similar European system, HD-MAC, uses 1250 lines. In these systems, and elsewhere, there has also been considerable experimentation with the aspect ratio (the ratio of the width to the height) of the screen. This has traditionally been 4 x 3, or 1.33:1, but in wide screens it can fall between 1.65:1 and 2.35:1; 16 x 9 (1.77:1) is popular. In 1990, the BBC adopted a digital stereo sound system, NICAM (Near Instantaneous Compounded Audio Multiplex) for television programmes.

There have also been many attempts, beginning with Baird in 1928, to achieve three-dimensional television pictures to imitate three-dimensional films (⇒p. 169). Methods involving the projection of two images which can be viewed through special glasses, as in films, have been tried with some success, and research is being carried out using liquid crystal displays, and holography, but the problems involved in making a successful commercial set have not yet been solved.

12

COMPUTERS

'Fingers and toes are the most fundamental
digital computing device.'

LANDMARKS IN DIGITAL COMPUTING,
Smithsonian Institution Press

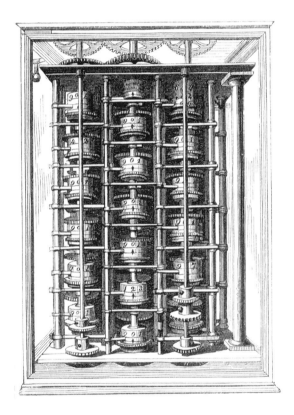

COMPUTERS

THE GERMAN MATHEMATICIAN AND PHILOSOPHER, Gottfried Wilhelm Leibniz, wrote in 1685 that 'it is unworthy of excellent men to lose hours like slaves in the labour of calculation which could safely be relegated to anyone else if machines were used'. He himself invented a mechanical calculator (⇒p. 196), but today's problems are solved much more successfully by the omnipresent electronic computer which has taken over in so many walks of life. In 1853, it took William Shanks 15 years to calculate the value of π to 707 decimal places; in 1945, a computer showed that he had made a mistake in the 528th place; in 1989, the value was calculated to 1,073,740,000 places by a computer at the University of Tokyo.

NUMBERS

Numbers preceded letters and many ancient civilizations invented their own systems some four to five thousand years ago. In Sumeria, the first 60 numbers were each represented by different cuneiform (⇒p. 174) symbols and that base of 60 persists today in the relationship between the hours, minutes and seconds of time, or the degrees, minutes and seconds of angles. But 10 came to be a commoner base number, probably because of the practice of counting on the fingers of two hands. The Egyptians, Greeks, Romans and others used systems in which numbers such as 10, 100, 1000, and 10,000 were represented by their own hieroglyphs or letters.

> **6** *Numbers are the language of nature.* **9**
>
> PYTHAGORAS
> (6th century BC),
> Greek philosopher

Roman numerals
The Romans used a system of seven letters. Although it was cumbersome, had no zero, could not cope with fractions, and was ill-adapted to arithmetical manipulations such as additon, subtraction, multiplication and division, it became so entrenched that its use has survived as, for example, on some clock and watch faces.

The decimal system
Today's numbers – 0, 1, 2, 3, 4, 5, 6, 7, 8, 9, 10 – originated in India about AD 500 and arrived in the West around 1200. Whole numbers were written, as today, with the figures moving from right to left representing in turn, units, tens, hundreds, thousands and so on. However, for many years numbers between whole numbers were expressed as fractions and the decimal point was only invented in 1592 by an Italian mathematician, Magini. When it was used, as for example in 123.456, the figures to the right of it represented, in turn, tenths, hundredths, thousandths and so on.

The index or exponent
Large and small numbers also came to be written more elegantly by using an index or exponent. Thus: 1,000,000 is 10^6, 10,000,000 is 10^7, 0.000001 is 10^{-6}, 0.0000001 is 10^{-7}. The superscript number is the index or exponent; if positive, it indicates how many times the number to which it refers has to be multiplied by itself; or if negative, divided. It is also expressed as the power to which that number has to be raised. On this basis, a large number such as 606,000 can be written as 6.06×10^5 or a small number, such as 0.0000606, as 6.06×10^{-5}.

Logarithms
The logarithm (from the Greek *logos arithmos*, reckoning number) or log of a number is the power to which a specified base has to be raised to produce the number. The idea was invented by a Scot, John Napier, in 1614, and he spent many years in compiling tables of logarithms. The base he chose for what are now called Napierian or natural logs was the number, *e*, which has an

ROMAN SYSTEM		
I	1	For example:
V	5	VI = 6
X	10	IV = 4
L	50	LX = 60
C	100	XL = 40
D	500	XXX = 30
M	1000	CCC = 300

Thus 1996 is written MCMXCVI because it is the sum of M = 1000, CM = 900, XC = 90 and VI = 6.

approximate value of 2.718282.

Shortly after, Henry Briggs, one of England's leading mathematicians, and a Dutchman, Adriaen Vlacq, produced more useful tables of what are now called common logarithms. They have 10 as the base instead of *e*. Thus the log of 1000 to the base 10 is 3 because 10^3 equals 1000; the log of 3 is 0.4771, because $10^{0.4771}$ is equal to 3; the log of 30 is 1.4771 and of 300, 2.4771. Logarithms were widely used, before the advent of calculators, because they enabled multiplication of numbers to be achieved by adding up their logs, and division by subtracting them. For example, 546 multiplied by 3 is 1638; using logs, log 546 (2.7372) + log 3 (0.4771) equals 3.2143 which is log 1638. Dividing 546 by 3 is 182; using logs, 2.7372–0.04771 equals 2.2601 which is log 182.

The binary system

This is a numerical system based on the two numbers, 0 and 1, and was first described in detail by Leibniz in 1679. The system came to be of vital importance in the design of digital computers because the two numbers, 0 and 1, could be represented by a switch being on or off in an electrical circuit, or by there being a higher or a lower voltage.

In the decimal system, the digits in any number, from right to left, represent units, tens, hundreds, thousands, and so on, i.e.,

1000 100 10 1

So that 537 means (5 x 100) + (3 x 10) + (7 x 1). In the binary system, the digits represent units, twos, fours, eights, sixteens, thirty-seconds, and so on, i.e.

32 16 8 4 2 1

So that 10111 means (1 x 16) + (0 x 8) + (1 x 4) + (1 x 2) + (1 x 1), i.e., 23 on the decimal system. Binary 111111 is decimal 63; 100000 is 32; and 10 is 2.

The binary system is less compact than the decimal so that binary arithmetic is a relatively lengthy process, but this is offset by the speed with which computers can work.

Character codes

The binary system allows individual characters such as numbers, letters and symbols to be represented by a code. The widely used American Standard Code for Information Interchange (ASCII) is typical. In its simplest form, it uses seven digits (bits) so that it can represent 128 (2^7) different characters which is adequate for normal English usage. For example,

1000001	A	1100001	a
1000010	B	1100010	b
0110001	1	0110011	3
0110010	2	0110100	4

0101110	for a full stop
0101011	for +(plus)
0101101	for – (minus)

The seven bits may, however, have an eighth written at the front to give them an even or an odd parity, i.e. an even or odd number of 1's. A and a, for example, are expressed as 01000001 or 11100001, respectively, to give them even parity. The purpose is to enable a computer to check the validity of the data entered.

The Extended Binary-coded Decimal Interchange Code (EBCDIC) uses eight bits and can represent 256 (2^8) characters. Unicode, using 16 bits, can represent 65536 (2^{16}) characters and is adequate for all the characters in all the living, and most of the dead, languages.

EARLY CALCULATING MACHINES

The abacus

This probably began as a grooved tray containing pebbles, but a typical development as used in China consists of a rectangular frame, divided into two halves, fitted with nine parallel wires carrying movable beads. The wires, moving from right to left, represent units, tens, hundreds, thousands, etc. The two

Part of an abacus (left), and how it is used to add 321 to 637 (right)

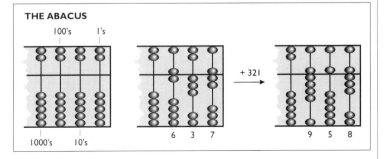

THE ABACUS

NAPIER'S RODS

	2	3	4	5	6	7	8	9			2	4	7		
1	0/2	0/3	0/4	0/5	0/6	0/7	0/8	0/9		1	0/2	0/4	0/7	=	247
2	0/4	0/6	0/8	1/0	1/2	1/4	1/6	1/8		2	0/4	0/8	1/4	=	494
3	0/6	0/9	1/2	1/5	1/8	2/1	2/4	2/7		3	0/6	1/2	2/1	=	741
4	0/8	1/2	1/6	2/0	2/4	2/8	3/2	3/6		4	0/8	1/6	2/8	=	988
5	1/0	1/5	2/0	2/5	3/0	3/5	4/0	4/5		5	1/0	2/0	3/5	=	1235
6	1/2	1/8	2/4	3/0	3/6	4/2	4/8	5/4		6	1/2	2/4	4/2	=	1482
7	1/4	2/1	2/8	3/5	4/2	4/9	5/6	6/3		7	1/4	2/8	4/9	=	1729
8	1/6	2/4	3/2	4/0	4/8	5/6	6/4	7/2		8	1/6	3/2	5/6	=	1976
9	1/8	2/7	3/6	4/5	5/4	6/3	7/2	8/1		9	1/8	3/6	6/3	=	2223

Left: *The numbering on a set of rods.* Right: *How they are used to multiply 247 by 1 to 9. The figures on the rods are added diagonally*

beads in the upper half of the frame each represent five units; each of the five beads in the lower half represent one unit. The type of abacus used in Japan is called a *soroban*; and in Russia, a *schoty*.

Napier's rods or bones
This was a system for multiplying, described by John Napier in 1617. It was, in effect, a set of simple multiplication tables engraved into wood, ivory or bone sticks. In its simplest form, there were nine flat sticks each with a digit of 1 to 9 at its top and with the first nine multiples of the digit in squares below.

The slide rule
In 1620, Edmund Gunter, professor of astronomy at Oxford University, England, replaced printed log tables by etching a line of logs along a 2-ft wooden rule. This could be used for multiplication or division by adding or subtracting lengths measured from the line by dividers. The idea was improved upon, in 1621, by an Englishman, the Revd William Oughtred when he did away with the dividers, by sliding one scale over another. In 1630, this was developed still further into an early type of slide rule by Robert Bissaker. There were fixed and sliding log scales and, later, a sliding cursor. Many more scales were added to slide rules enabling them to be used for many different computations.

The Pascaline
This was a mechanical calculator invented by a Frenchman, Blaise Pascal, in 1642 when he was only 19. It was a box containing a number of cylinders marked with the figures 0 to 9 which could be viewed, one at a time, through small windows. The cylinders, in line from right to left, represented hundredths, tenths, units, tens, hundreds and thousands, or any variation on that theme, and each could be turned one-tenth of a revolution at a time by attached gears operated from an external dial. There was also an ingenious 'carrying' device by which a complete revolution of any cylinder rotated its higher neighbour by one-tenth. To add 1111.11 to the number showing through the window, for example, it was only necessary to turn each cylinder by one tenth.

Pascal's machine was reasonably successful for addition, but it was expensive. Nevertheless, the general idea was copied by Leibniz in 1671, and more successfully by a Frenchman, Charles Xavier Thomas in the arithmometer which he invented around 1820. Two eight-figure numbers could be multiplied in 18 seconds.

Punched cards
Punched cards for feeding information into a machine, pioneered by Jacquard and by Babbage, came to be widely used in tabulating machines as invented by an American, Herman Hollerith, in the 1880s. He was a mining engineer who joined the US Census Bureau just after the 1880 census had been carried out. When he realized how slow the manual analysis of the data was, he designed his first tabulator in which spring-loaded

❛What shall we do to get rid of Mr Babbage and his calculating machine?❜

SIR ROBERT PEEL (1788–1850), English statesman, when Prime Minister, 1842

CHARLES BABBAGE
(1791–1871)

CHARLES BABBAGE, son of a wealthy banker, went to school in Totnes, Devon and completed his education at Cambridge University where, in 1823, he was appointed Lucasian professor of mathematics. Isaac Newton had held that position in 1669, and it is now occupied by Stephen Hawking, the author of *A Brief History of Time*.

Babbage was also an amateur engineer and his two interests led him to improving the early calculating machines of Pascal, Leibniz and others. He therefore began in 1823 to construct what he called his 'difference engine' which was intended to calculate and print more accurate mathematical tables, such as log tables. It had a complex array of interlocking gear wheels and the plans involved 25,000 separate parts made of brass, steel and pewter, many of them machined to previously unheard of tolerances. The project was, however, far too ambitious and was abandoned in 1842 with the engine only partly built. Babbage had spent £6000 of his own money and £17,000 of government money on it. A working replica was built in the Science Museum in London in 1991.

In 1834, Babbage began work on his 'analytical engine', which was of even more complex design with a system of punched cards, as used by Jacquard in his loom (⇒p. 113), added to all the gears. Once again, neither Babbage, nor his son after him, could bring the grandiose plans to fruition. It was all far too much ahead of its time, though it is possible to see now that the general idea contained many of the features of the first electrical computers designed in the 1940s. Babbage may not have been the father of modern computers but he was, perhaps, the grandfather.

> *The whole history of this invention has been a struggle against time.*
>
> CHARLES BABBAGE
> (1791–1871), English
> mathematician

pins, passing through a hole in a punched card, where appropriate, made an electrical contact with a pool of mercury which actuated a counter. It enabled the 1890 census to be analysed much more quickly than the 1880 census, even though the population had increased by nearly 25 per cent.

In 1896. Hollerith set up his own Tabulating Machine Co. to make keyboard-operated mechanical calculators. It was absorbed into the International Business Machines Corporation (IBM) in 1924. Similarly, the British Tabulating Machine Co. Ltd, founded in 1907, became part of British International Computers and Tabulators Co. in 1959. That, in turn, became part of International Computers Ltd (ICL) in 1968, and the Japanese company, Fujitsu, acquired an 80 per cent share in 1990.

Keyboard calculators

In the late 1880s, two Americans, Dorr Felt and William S. Burroughs, took out patents for machines which could add or subtract numbers entered into them, through a system of levers and gears, from a typewriter-like keyboard. Within a few years the machines could print out the numbers concerned. They were sometimes called comptometers and they were used for many years in cash registers and for bookkeeping in offices.

Early computers

The first large electrical computer was built by an American, Dr Vannevar Bush, at the Massachusetts Institute of Technology (MIT) in the USA in 1930, for solving differential equations. It was partly mechanical and partly electrical but it did not use binary code so it was not what is today called a digital computer. Instead, it represented different quantities by different voltages and would nowadays be called an analogue computer. Such computers are still used for special purposes but are not common.

The first digital computer was designed by a German mathematician, Konrad Zuse, in 1938, and later models – Z_2 and Z_3 – were used during World War II for studying the ballistics of rockets. Zuse founded the firm Zuse KG and became honorary professor at Göttingen University in 1966. His computers were operated by electromechanical relays, as was the much larger ASCC (Automatic Sequence Controlled Calculator), Mark I, which an American, Howard Aitken of Harvard University, persuaded IBM to fund and build. It was 15.5 m (50 ft) long and 2.4 m (8 ft) high, had 750,000 parts connected by over 500 miles (800 km) of wire, and data was fed into it from punched cards. It first operated in 1943 and was used during World War II to study the firing of large naval guns.

ELECTRONIC DIGITAL COMPUTERS

Today's computers come in many shapes and sizes but they all function in the same general way. They are, first, programmed so that they will be able to perform the task expected of them. Data (the input) is then fed in and stored in the computer's memory; it is manipulated by the processor; and the final outcome (the output) is displayed on a screen, or printed out on paper. The computer can only handle data if it is supplied in a binary code ($\Rightarrow$p. 195) and this is done using magnetic or optical disks (discs), or by some other method.

Disks

Magnetic disks are coated on both sides with a magnetic material and data can be recorded on them in much the same way as on magnetic tape ($\Rightarrow$p. 171). The disk is divided up (formatted) into sectors and circular tracks, and each bit of data is stored in one particular area. When in use within a computer the disk is rapidly rotated past a magnetic head which can either record (write) data on to it or retrieve (read) data from it. Any particular area can be accessed quickly by rotating the disk into the correct position.

Both hard disks, made of rigid aluminium, and floppy disks, made of flexible plastic, are used. The former are more reliable, hold more data and provide quicker access, but they are more expensive. They are generally fitted permanently within a computer. Floppy disks are put into or taken out of the disk drive in a computer as required. They are generally contained in a protective plastic case and have a diameter of 89 mm (3.5 in) or, less commonly, 133 mm (5.25 in). Compact disks ($\Rightarrow$p. 171) are also used. They can hold considerably more data than a hard disk and come in two main forms – CD-ROM (compact-disk read-only memory) and WORM (write once read many times).

Input devices

A keyboard, similar to that on a typewriter, is the commonest input device to a computer system. Pressing any key, or combination of keys, converts the chosen letter, number or symbol into binary digits according to a character code ($\Rightarrow$p. 195).

A device known as a mouse, because it was originally shaped like one, is also used; it was invented by an American, Douglas Engelbart, at the Stanford Research Institute in the USA, in 1963. Moving it over a flat surface in front of a computer screen to which it is connected causes a sphere, protruding from its base, to rotate, and this controls the position of a pointer on the screen. The data indicated by the item at which it is pointed can be processed in the computer by pressing a switch on the upper surface of the mouse. A similar, but more precise method is adopted in the digitizing pad which enables accurate diagrams or maps to be drawn or traced. It consists of a flat pad fitted with a closely-spaced pattern of wires and any particular point on the pad can be transmitted to the computer screen using a hand-held cursor.

Data can also be transmitted into computers with specially treated screens by using a lightpen to write directly on to the screen or simply by touching designated areas.

Automatic reading devices

Data can be fed into a computer system in a number of ways by reading the original data automatically. They include the scanning of bar codes as in a library book or at a supermarket check-out; the use of magnetic strips as on credit cards, train tickets or building society passbooks; the detection of particular marks on a document, as on a football pool or lottery coupon, or on a multiple-choice examination paper; magnetic ink character recognition (MICR) which can read the magnetic characters on, for example, the bottom of a cheque; optical character recognition (OCR) which can read standard typefaces, as on gas, electricity or telephone bills, and, to some extent, individual handwriting as in clearly written postal codes. Even voice recognition (voice input) can be used for a limited number of words and phrases from a voice that has been 'learnt', but recognition of continuous speech from a stranger is not yet possible.

Programing

A program is a complete set of instructions which ensures that a computer functions in a particular way. To produce the program, a programer must decide in every detail what is required, break the tasks down into a series of logical steps, and then arrange them in the best order.

Originally, programs were written in binary or machine code, but this was slow and cumbersome so that it was replaced by the use of a number of different artificial languages. These are classified as low- or high-level depending on their complexity. They use accepted symbols which are converted into a machine code, before entry into a computer, by another program called a compiler or an interpreter.

Different languages have been invented for different purposes. Examples are provided by FORTRAN (Formula Translation) invented by John Backus in 1957; COBOL (Common Business Oriented Language) by Grace Murray Hopper in 1959; BASIC (Beginners' All-Purpose Symbolic Instruction Code) by John Kemeny and Thomas Kurtz in 1965; C by Dennis Ritchie at the Bell Laboratories in 1972;

and ADA (named after Lady Ada Lovelace, the daughter of Lord Byron, who had worked with Babbage) by Jean Ichbiah in 1979.

Processing

At the heart of every computer there is a central processing unit (CPU) made up of one or more chips ($\Rightarrow$p. 81). It contains an arithmetic and logic unit (ALU) and an operational control unit (OCU). The ALU performs the basic arithmetical and logical operations on the data fed into it. It is here, for example, that 1 and 1 can be added to make 2, or where a list of items can be placed in alphabetical order. The OCU controls the timing and order of the operations. In general, there is a quartz crystal oscillator ($\Rightarrow$p. 50) which moves everything forward with each pulse of electricity, and there may be over 100 million pulses per second (100 MHz).

Popular PCs ($\Rightarrow$p. 202), in the early days, commonly had speeds of 5, 8 or 10 MHz. Today, it is more likely to be 75, 90, 100, 120 or 133 MHz, and the faster the model, the more expensive it is likely to be.

Memory

The information fed into a computer is stored, or memorized, on a collection of chips. Each bit of information is stored in its own individual cell and given an 'address' so that it can be retrieved as required. There are two main types of memory storage. The ROM (read-only memory) is built into the computer during manufacture and cannot be changed. It holds essential operating instructions. The RAM (random-access memory) operates on a more temporary basis and will only work whilst the computer is switched on; it is said to be volatile. To avoid losing all the information within the RAM when a computer is switched off, it must be transferred to a back-up store consisting of magnetic disks. Alternatively, a bubble memory consisting of a series of 'bubbles' on a magnetic surface can be used.

The capacity of a computer memory is measured in bytes, with 1 byte being a group of eight bits ($\Rightarrow$p. 195). It represents an individual character such as a letter, number, punctuation mark or colour. A kilobyte, Kb or K, is 1024 (2^{10}) bytes; it corresponds to about 20 lines of typing at 50 characters per line. A megabyte, Mb or M, is 1024Kb or 1,04,8576 (2^{20}) bytes, and a gigabyte, Gb or G, is 1024Mb. An optical disk can store thousands of megabytes, and one of less than 127 mm (5 in) diameter can accommodate the whole of the *Encyclopaedia Britannica*. A hard magnetic disk holds between 20 and 3000Mb, depending on its size, and a floppy disk, 0.5 to 2 Mb. Early computers had very limited memory capacity. Today, 8 Mb of RAM and 850 Mb of hard disk is common even on a comparatively inexpensive system.

Output

In a small portable computer, the results of the processing are shown in a liquid crystal ($\Rightarrow$p. 80) display. For larger machines, a visual display unit or, in the US, a video display unit (VDU), which contains a cathode ray screen is used. The material showing on the screen can be printed off on paper using a variety of printers ($\Rightarrow$p. 178) or transferred to a microfilm (COM). It is also possible to output the material from a computer in graphical form ($\Rightarrow$p. 203) or by using a speech synthesizer.

COMPUTER MODELS

Modern computers are classified according to their size. The smallest is the microcomputer or personal computer (PC), which is now available in a portable laptop range weighing less than 2 kg (4.4 lb). Next in size come the minicomputer, the mainframe computer, and the supercomputer. They have developed as the thermionic valve or tube has been replaced, first by the transistor and then by chips.

The use of valves or tubes

The first generation of computers contained thousands of valves or tubes and had miles of wiring; they used a lot of power; they got very hot; they were expensive and bulky; and they were built and operated by universities or government departments.

One of the first was a special-purpose machine called Colossus which was used

from the end of 1943 at Bletchley Park in England to break the Enigma code employed by the German armed forces. Its success was a major factor in Germany's defeat. The first general-purpose machine, ABC, was built between 1939 and 1942 by an American mathematician, Professor J.V. Atanasoff, and Clifford Berry, one of his students at Iowa State University. It was followed at the end of 1945 by ENIAC (the Electronic Numerical Integrator and Computer), which was designed by John W. Mauchly and J. Presper Eckert at the University of Pennsylvania. It was used in designing the hydrogen bomb ($\Rightarrow$p. 242).

The next step forward, the incorporation of an internal memory, came with the Manchester University Mark I, built in collaboration with Ferranti Ltd in 1948, and the Cambridge University EDSAC (Electronic Delay Storage Automatic Calculator) in 1949. Other stored-program computers soon followed; they included EDVAC, IAS, ACE, MANIAC, SILLIAC, ORACLE, and WHIRLWIND.

The use of transistors

The second generation of computers, developed during the 1950s, was based on transistors and printed circuits. LEO (the Lyons Electronic Office), used from 1950 by Lyons, a British catering firm, for accounting and stock control, was one of the first. UNIVAC (Universal Automatic Computer), designed by two Americans, John W. Mauchly and John Eckert, was used by the Bureau of the Census in 1951; and by Columbia Broadcasting System (CBS) in 1952 to predict presidential election results. Their success opened up the possibilities of commercial exploitation and IBM marketed their IBM 701 model in 1952. It was followed by IBM 704 (1956) and 1401 (1959), and many more.

The use of chips

Computers based on chips or integrated circuits became very popular in the 1960s. They were sometimes called minicomputers. The first, the PDP-1 (Programmed Data Processor), was built in 1959 in America by the Digital Equipment Corporation (DEC), founded by the Americans, Ken Olsen and Harlan

6To err is human but to really foul things up requires a computer.9

Farmers' Almanac,
1978

The Colossus computer built at Bletchley Park, England, in 1943. It was used to break the Enigma code used by the German armed forces

Anderson. It grew into the successful PDP-8 range, but was overshadowed by the IBM System/360 and ICL 1900 machines, launched in 1964, which both became very popular. Similar minicomputers were used in ballistic missiles (⇒p. 237) such as Minuteman; in spacecraft (⇒p. 249) such as *Gemini* and *Apollo*; and in the electronic calculators which became so popular in the 1970s. Inexpensive, pocket-sized models came from Texas Instruments, where the chip had been invented (⇒p. 81), from Hewlett-Packard in the USA; and from Sinclair Radionics Ltd, founded by Sir Clive Sinclair in Britain.

Microprocessors

The design of chips improved so much in the 1970s that it became possible to make single chips which could carry out all the functions of the central processing unit (⇒p. 199) of a small computer. Such chips came to be called microprocessors or processors and they were applied not only in computers but in automating the operation of many other machines (⇒p. 54) and processes (⇒p. 83).

The first to be widely used, the Intel 4004, was designed in 1971 by an American, Marcian 'Ted' Hoff, working for the Californian firm of Intel, founded by Bob Noyce and Gordon Moore in 1968. It could only handle four bits and was originally intended for use in calculators, but it was followed by 8086 and 8088 (1979), 80286 (1982), Intel 386 (1985), and Intel 486 (1989) processors which could deal with 8-, 16- and 32-bits, and in 1993 by the Pentium, the first 64-bit processor. It is a thin wafer, only about 2 cm (0.8 in) square, yet it contains 3.1 million transistors each 100 times less than the thickness of a human hair. An improved product, the Pentium Pro Processor, was marketed late in 1995.

Intel still dominates the market, but Motorola, a company started in Chicago by Paul V. Galvin in 1928, manufactures a competing 68000 family of processors, and new 64-bit processors, the Power PC family, have recently been developed in collaboration with IBM and the Apple Computer Co.

Micro- or personal computers

Computers containing a microprocessor are called micro- or personal-computers (PCs). The first, the Altair 8800, was designed by MITS (Micro Instrumentation and Telemetry Systems) in 1974, but by 1979 more commercially acceptable models such as TRS-80 from Tandy Radio Shack and PET from Commodore had been launched. They

One of a group of Apple PowerBook computers, the smallest of which weighs 4.2 lb and is 1.4 x 10.9 x 8.5 in, and the largest 7.3 lb and 2.3 x 11.5 x 9.7 in

sold well but new models from the Apple Computer Co., started in California by Stephen Wozniak and Steven Jobs in 1976, and IBM, took the lead.

The first Apple computers were made in 1977 and Apple II was particularly successful. It was followed in 1984 by the first Apple Macintosh model, which was based on a Motorola 68000 processor and was particularly easy to operate. This was achieved by using a mouse (⇒p. 198) to pick out particular items or instructions from a graphical display on the computer screen, instead of following numerous printed commands. This type of 'friendlier' user interface has always been a distinctive feature of Macintosh computers and has now been widely adopted by other makers. Today's models are based on three ranges – Performa for home and individual use; Power Macintosh for business; and the Macintosh PowerBook portable computers. All models either contain Power PC processors or can easily be fitted with them.

IBM entered the market in 1981 and introduced the personal computer (PC) name. Their first model, the PC-XT, used an 8-bit, Intel 8088 processor, and was to be followed by more powerful models using other Intel processors (⇒p. 201) in turn. Today's wide variety of IBM computers is based on the Aptiva range, for domestic use; the PC 300 and upgraded PC 700 ranges, for business use; and the Think Pad 300 and 700 portable models.

Until recently, the Apple Computer Co. has always fought any attempts to copy the individual technicalities of its range, but the components of the IBM models, largely bought from outside sources, were freely available to other companies. So it was that, as early as 1982, the Houston-based firm, Compaq, marketed the first of many copies (clones) of an IBM model and by now there are many other firms producing dozens of imitations described, collectively, as IBM-compatible. That leaves users of Apple Macintosh models in a minority, but it all adds up to a fiercely competitive market and a remarkably wide choice for the ever-increasing number of PC customers, which is currently estimated at over 125 million worldwide and is likely to increase very rapidly in the future.

Supercomputers

These are very powerful mainframe computers designed to tackle complex scientific, design and organizational problems. They achieve speeds of billions of calculations per second by using microprocessors in parallel and, if required, by cooling them down to increase their electrical conductivity ($\Rightarrow$p. 81). Cray-1, designed by an American, Seymour Cray, in 1976, was an early version which was followed by Cray-2 in 1985 and then by Cray Y-/MP 8 and Cray T3D. Other models are made by the Japanese companies Fujitsu, Hitachi and Nippon Electric Co. (NEC), the American Convex, and Meiko, founded in Britain by David Alden and Miles Chesney in 1985.

SOFTWARE

The electrical and mechanical parts of a computer are known as hardware; and software is what is used to make it function as required. The software comes in ready-made packages usually on floppy disks. There are two main types: systems software, or operating systems (OS), augment the operating programme stored inside a computer to control its basic functions; applications software enables the computer to carry out specific tasks. Much of the software produced is designed for use on a particular computer model and cannot be used on other models. As with hardware there is plenty of choice.

The Microsoft Corporation, founded by two school friends, Bill Gates and Paul Allen in 1975, is today's best known manufacturer of software. It began by developing the Microsoft Disc Operating System (MS-DOS) which was used by IBM, under the name of PC-DOS, in its early PCs. After 1990, however, the two organizations went their separate ways with IBM developing OS/2 which was improved as OS/2 Warp in 1994, and Microsoft introducing Windows 3.0 in 1990, Windows 3.1 in 1992 and Windows 95 in 1995.

UNIX, developed in the Bell Laboratories of the American Telephone and Telegraph Co. (AT & T) in 1971 is a widely applicable system which is used in many forms. There is AT & T System V, AIX for use by IBM compatible machines, and A/UX for Apple Macintosh machines. Other systems include the old CP/M (control program/monitor) from Digital Research, founded by Gary Kildall in 1974, and a number of Apple or Macintosh OSs culminating in the Macintosh System 7.5, in 1994.

Applications software is available for almost every human activity. Word processing, keeping accounts, playing games, translating from one language to another, solving crossword puzzles, planning a journey, creating an alphabetical index and stock-keeping are but a few of the myriad examples.

Spreadsheets

These are general-purpose programmes which enter numerical data into rows and columns as done by hand by old-fashioned bookkeepers. The figures can then be manipulated and analysed in a variety of ways to provide financial control and forecasts. The first spreadsheet software, VisiCalc, appeared with Apple-II in 1979. Later versions include Lotus 1-2-3 and Microsoft Excel.

Computer graphics

These packages and devices enable computers to display information in pictorial form which can vary from a simple graph, histogram or pie chart to an apparently three-dimensional drawing which can be used by engineers, architects and others in computer-aided design (CAD). The necessary data is fed into a computer in the form of a mathematical equation; from a bank of pre-drawn patterns; by scanning a picture; by using a light pen or digitizing pad ($\Rightarrow$p. 198); or, particularly in video games, by using a joystick, like the control lever in some aeroplanes, to move a point on a screen in various directions.

Windows

Windowing is a way of making a computer more user friendly. It was pioneered by the Xerox Corporation in the 1970s and popularized in Apple Macintosh computers in the 1980s. It has been extensively developed, particularly by the Microsoft Corporation, and is now commonplace in almost all models.

❢These communication tools are letting us experience things at a distance...❡

BILL GATES,
co-founder and chairman, Microsoft Corporation

Information and instructions on a VDU screen are presented in both words and pictures (icons) which are displayed in different areas (windows) of the screen. Each area can be picked out by using a pointer operated by a mouse (⇒p. 198).

Computer simulation

This uses a computer system to reproduce a real-life situation. The effect of changing different variables can be studied to help design decisions or uncover faults. Alternatively, the simulation can be used for training, as in a flight simulator which allows a pilot to experience all kinds of in-flight situations without ever leaving the ground.

Virtual reality is a more advanced form of simulation giving the viewer an impression of a completely imaginary environment. The viewer wears a head-set which holds small television screens in front of each eye and provides background sound effects. If gloves fitted with sensors are also worn, the viewer can experience the effect of moving objects within the illusory environment. The technique has applications in games, training and design.

NETWORKS

Networks consist of a number of computers linked together by telephone lines. They have been used for some time by, for example, airlines for booking seats, news agencies and banks, and they can be classified according to their scope as local area (LAN) or wide area (WAN) networks. They are operated by special network operating systems such as Novell's NetWare 4.1.

The Internet is the best known, generally available network. It was started in the USA in 1969 to enable scientists and engineers working on vast academic or defence projects to communicate with each other. Then, in the early 1980s, the defence aspects were separated and what remained was made freely available on an international basis.

Anyone with a suitable computer and the necessary software can link in to the network, which is estimated to have 30 million subscribers as compared with a mere 2000 in 1981. Subscribers to the network can make use of the mind-boggling amount of material available, particularly on what is called the World

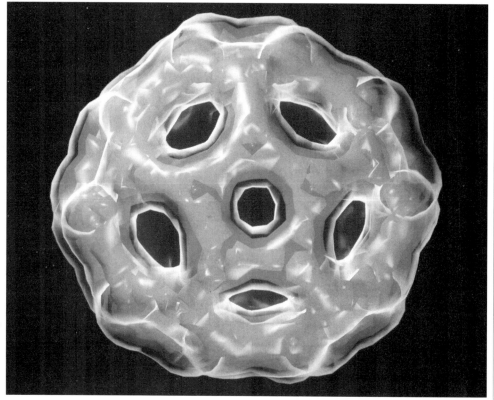

A supercomputer simulation of electron distribution in a single molecule of buckminsterfullerene (⇒p. 38)

Wide Web. A subscriber can obtain programs relating to every form of human activity simply by tapping in the correct code to his or her computer. For example, http;//www.roe.ac.uk/ will produce a program from the Royal Observatory in Scotland of interest to all astronomers.

THE INFORMATION SUPERHIGHWAY

The information superhighway is the name given to a rapidly expanding, international system which uses telephone lines, in conjunction with modems ($\Rightarrow$p. 183) and other accessories, to feed information from a global network, such as Internet, or from other sources, on to an individual computer or television screen. The owner of a television set and a telephone can, for example, receive information through teletext or viewdata systems ($\Rightarrow$p. 192). A computer owner has access to similar services and can also exchange written

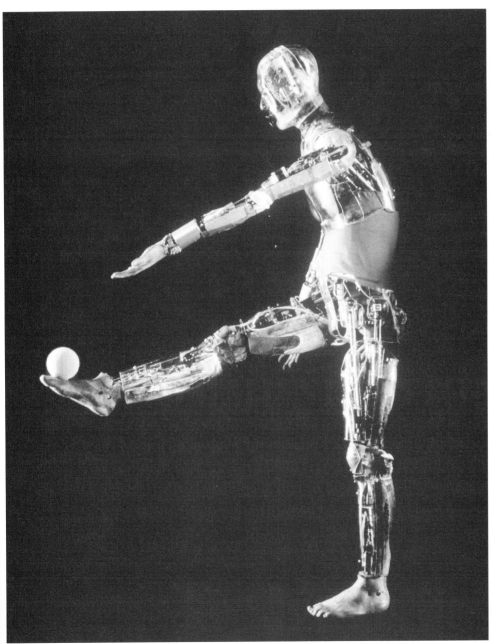

A robotics mannequin, used to simulate a human in testing the suitability of clothing such as space suits or fire-fighting protective equipment. The robot is fully articulated and can simulate sweating and breathing

messages, as in electronic or e-mail, which enables a letter written on his or her computer to be transmitted to another computer anywhere in the world. All that is necessary is to give it the correct e-mail address.

New ways of using the highway are being actively developed. There are, for example, telephones fitted with a screen which can pick up e-mail messages without the need of a computer, and television sets which can be modified to function as computers or vice versa.

The full development of the superhighway is, however, likely to be impeded in many parts of the world by the lack of optical fibre cabling ($\Rightarrow$p. 183). There are also problems, as yet unsolved, about security when the highway is used for passing confidential business information, and about how to control the material which can be fed into the system so that anything undesirable can be avoided.

AUTOMATION

Automation, which has increasingly become widespread since 1946, makes a process more automatic so that it is less reliant on human labour. Early methods included the use of the governor ($\Rightarrow$p. 59) in steam engines around 1790; the use of punched cards in looms ($\Rightarrow$p. 113) in 1805; the use of the thermostat ($\Rightarrow$p. 43) in controlling temperature around 1830; and the use of gyroscopes ($\Rightarrow$p. 62) in the automatic pilot in 1911.

However, it was the invention of the chip that enabled microelectronic automatic control systems to be fitted more widely. Since 1952, for example, the movement of many machine tools has been controlled by numerical programs fed into a computer; it came to be called numerical control. In everyday life, simple microprocessors are fitted to central-heating systems, washing machines and dryers, video-recorders, cameras, sewing machines and ovens, so that they can be set to follow a variety of programs usually by pressing a few buttons. Cars, too, became more and more automated until it is now possible to purchase a model which talks to the driver and which prevents him or her from getting too close to the car in front or straying out of lane.

In other forms of transport there are railway signalling controls; automatic train control, which allows a train to be run safely without driver or guard; and automatic (blind) landing for aeroplanes.

Robots

Chips also made possible the development of robots which can replace a human and which are studied in the new technology of robotics. The first robot was patented by two Americans, George C. Devol and Joseph. F. Engelberger, who founded Unimation Inc., in Danbury, Connecticut in 1961. Their first product was designed to remove parts from a die-casting machine, and material handling is still one of the main uses of robots. It is of particular importance when the materials are noxious as with radioactive chemicals, or when the environment is hazardous as in space, under water or in a coal mine. Robots are also used in the automobile industry for paint spraying, spot- or arc-welding, windscreen fitting, and inspection; in submersibles ($\Rightarrow$p. 239) and guided or remote control vehicles as used for bomb disposal, and for landing on the Moon and other planets; for routine cleaning jobs; for security patrols; and in assembling the very chips on which they all rely.

The main component of any robot is a manipulator which can function as an 'arm' or 'hand'. It is made from flexibly joined metal links, which can be moved in any direction by electric motors or by pneumatic or hydraulic power controlled by a computer program. The 'hand' may be a magnet, a suction cup, a simple two-pronged gripper, or a life-like, five-fingered replica. If mobility is required, a robot is fitted with wheels, tracks, or spider-like 'legs'. Sensors to detect the position of the robot by robotic imitations of the human senses of sight, smell, touch or hearing are commonly fitted.

It is possible to build very life-like robots which can run or play games. It is an ultimate goal of the new computer science of artificial intelligence to build robots which can exhibit a wider variety of human behaviour and, maybe, even come to think for themselves.

13

FARMING *and* FOOD

'Whoever could make two ears of corn, or two blades of grass,
to grow upon a spot of ground where only one grew before,
would deserve better of mankind, and do more essential service
to his country, than the whole race of politicians put together.'

JONATHAN SWIFT (1667–1745),
Anglo-Irish satirist

FARMING AND FOOD

AGRICULTURE BEGAN about 10,000 years ago when people from early civilization, who had been nomads dependent on hunting and gathering wild plants for their food, settled down in small communities where they began to cultivate the ground and rear domesticated livestock. This happened for no very clear-cut single reason in a number of places, particularly the Near East, the Far East and Central America, where there were good supplies of water and fertile soil. As these centres grew, they led to increased building, trade, social organization, and defence. It was the beginning of new civilizations and, for those that have survived, agriculture still plays a pivotal role because the one thing that all men and women must do is eat. There are, however, two kinds of agriculture. In many countries it is still a labour-intensive activity using traditional methods and simple tools. In others it relies on recently developed machines and new farming methods, but employs few people.

> *Agriculture is beyond all doubt, the foundation of every other art, business and profession.*
>
> ARTHUR YOUNG
> *(1741–1820), first secretary, Board of Agriculture*

AGRICULTURAL MACHINES

The plough

The first farmers used pointed wooden sticks, sometimes weighted with a stone, to till the soil, but they could only scratch the surface and this did not produce good crops. These tools developed, however, into today's hoes, spades and forks, in all their variety – and, as early as 3500 BC, into the greatest basic invention in agriculture, the plough. A typical model was made of wood in the shape of a narrow letter A, curved at its pointed end so that it made a furrow in the ground when it was dragged along, steered by the ploughman walking behind. The dragging was done initially by men and then, in turn, by oxen, horses, steam engines and tractors.

By 500 BC the pointed end of the plough had been replaced by an iron blade or ploughshare which cut a deeper furrow and lasted longer, and, by AD 1000, wheels had been fitted to give better control; a cutter or coulter, ahead of the share, sliced the soil to loosen it; and a shaped mouldboard, behind the share, turned it over.

The coulter, the share and the mouldboard are still the basic components of any plough but over the years many variations have been introduced to meet local conditions. Ploughs suitable for tilling the dry soils of Mediterranean countries, for example, could not cope with the soils of northern Europe or the American prairies; and so it was that new models were invented. The Rotherham plough, based on a Flemish design, was manufactured on a large scale in Rotherham, England from 1760; Robert Ransome began to manufacture an all-iron plough in Ipswich, England in 1783; and in 1837 an American, John Deere, designed a plough in which the share and the mouldboard were constructed in one piece from steel. Around 1860, some wealthy farmers in England tried pulling their ploughs over the fields using a length of wire wound on to a drum by a steam engine, but many others were still using wooden ploughs.

A modern plough is pulled by a tractor. It can dig 12 furrows simultaneously and till 4 hectares (10 acres) in an hour. One thousand years ago, a single-furrow plough drawn by a team of eight oxen would have taken 30 days to do the same work.

The tractor

The first tractors appeared at the end of the 19th century. Early models, invented by C.W. Hart and C.H. Parr in the USA, and by D. Albone in England, were superseded when Henry Ford (⇒p. 136) began mass production of Fordson tractors in 1916. Ten years later he was making 70,000 a year and monopolized the market. But competition, and much patent legislation, came with the invention of the Ferguson tractor in 1933.

Harry George Ferguson (1884–1960) was born in County Down, Northern Ireland, and went to work on his father's farm when he was 14, before joining his brother in running a garage four years later. In 1909, he made the first flight from Irish soil in a homemade aeroplane. His tractor, designed for use on small farms, was much lighter and less cumbersome than the Fordson; it was much easier to get in and out of the lower driving seat; and it had pneumatic rubber tyres instead of the earlier ridged-steel ones. It was particularly versatile because the engine drove not only the wheels but also another shaft which projected at the rear. This could be linked to any of the various implements that could be towed by the tractor, and there was a hydraulic control system which enabled the tractor driver to manipulate and operate the implement from the cab. It was launched in England in 1936 and, in collaboration with Ford, in the USA in 1939. In 1946 a new model, the TE-20, began to be manufactured at Coventry in England; 500,000 were made in ten years and some are still in use today. Ferguson sold out to Massey-Harris in 1953 and, thereafter, tried unsuccessfully to market a revolutionary design of car.

Preparing the soil

Ploughing leaves large clods of earth and, before seed can be sown, the ground has to be harrowed, cultivated and rolled. In Roman times, the clods were broken down by being hit with mallets or by dragging a rudimentary harrow over the field; it consisted of thorn branches mounted on a framework, or a log of wood fitted with wooden or iron spikes. Today's harrows are triangular or rectangular frames holding flexible chains, discs or protruding tines of varying shapes and sizes.

Cultivators serve the same purpose as harrows. They contain strong curved tines mounted on a framework between two wheels. The tines may be rigid or spring-loaded; they can be fitted with differently shaped points at their lower ends; and their height above the ground can be adjusted. In a rotary cultivator, the tines are rotated about a vertical or horizontal axis as the cultivator is moved forward.

Rolling was originally done with stone cylinders and they are still used. Other rollers are made of ribbed or toothed, cast iron or steel sections. The Crosskill roller, patented in Great Britain by William Crosskill, as a clod-crusher in 1841 is typical; its sections are toothed.

Seed drills

Attempts to mechanize the sowing of seeds were made around 1000 BC in Mesopotamia when ploughs were fitted with a separate piece of wood containing a hole through which the seeds were dropped from a tube. The first efficient seed-drill was invented by an Englishman, Jethro Tull, who, after reading law at Oxford University, devoted his life to studying soil fertility. He was a keen organist and the seed-drill, which he invented in 1701, was based on the arrangement of the groove, tongue and spring in the sound-board of an organ. The drill was pulled along by a horse and the seeds dropped from hoppers down tubes in such a way that they were sown in rows. This enabled him to use a special hoe, which he also invented, between the rows. He grew above-average crops from fewer seeds over many years, without using any manure.

His drill was complicated, but it was the prototype on which modern drills are based. Seeds and fertilizer are stored in a hopper from which tubes lead down to the soil. Ahead of each tube there is a steel prong and, as the drill moves forward, the prong makes a hole into which the seed falls through mechanically operated shutters. A light harrow, behind the drill, covers the seed with soil.

Reapers and mowers

The first stage of harvesting a cereal crop is to cut (reap) it. This was originally done by hand using a sickle (reaping-hook) or a scythe. The sickle began, before 4000 BC, as a straight knife made from sharp flints embedded in a wooden handle. By 3000 BC, today's crescent-shape had been adopted by setting the flints into the teeth sockets in an animal's lower jaw. Later, bronze and iron blades

❝I suppose you know that only one invention in ten thousand succeeds. The reason is that there is no plan behind the failures. The one that succeeds has a plan behind it.❞

HARRY FERGUSON (1884–1960), Irish engineer

❝Hoeing once well done is twice done.❞

JETHRO TULL (1674–1741), English agriculturalist

Replica of an 1831 McCormick reaper

❛ This cross between an Astley chariot, a wheel barrow and a flying machine. ❜

Description of McCormick's reaper from THE TIMES, *1851*

were fitted on to shaped wooden handles.

From Roman times, as it became possible to make larger metal blades, the scythe began to replace the sickle. It had a long, curved wooden handle set at right angles to the blade and, operated by two hands, it could cut a much wider swathe than the one-handed sickle.

It required a lot of men to cut a field of corn with scythes and sickles, and during the 1st century AD Pliny descibed a mechanical reaper, but the first commercial machines were invented by a Scotsman, the Revd Patrick Bell (1826) and by the Americans Obed Hussey (1833) and Cyrus McCormick (1834). They all used revolving horizontal blades at the front of the machine to hold the stalks vertical whilst they were being cut at ground level by an upper row of toothed blades moving to-and-fro across a lower one. McCormick's model won the day and at the Great Exhibition in London in 1851 it was described as being 'worth the whole cost of the Exposition'.

Cylinder mowers, for cutting lawns, were invented by Edwin Budding in 1830, and manufactured by Ransomes of Ipswich, England, in 1832. They used a rotating cylinder of blades which moved

across a fixed horizontal blade. Rotary mowers employ a spinning cutter, which may also be shaped to function as a fan so as to lift the machine on a cushion of air, as in the Flymo invented in Sweden, in 1963, by Karl Dahlman.

Threshers

Threshing, the process of separating the grain from the straw and the husks, was traditionally carried out by flailing. This involved hitting the corn with a flail, a wooden rod loosely attached to a handle. The first attempt to mechanize the process came from a Scotsman, Andrew Meikle. His machine, patented in 1788, had an internal revolving drum surrounded by a close-fitting cylinder, and the ears of grain were rubbed off as they passed between the two. Chaff was separated from the grain by the old-fashioned method of winnowing in which an air blast from a fan blew the lighter chaff away.

The combine harvester

The combine harvester is today's most powerful agricultural machine. It is a reaper, thresher and binder all in one, which can cut a swathe 5.5 m (18 ft) wide

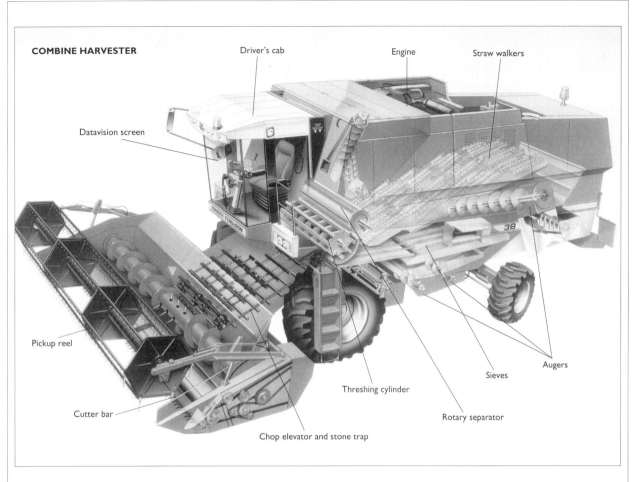

COMBINE HARVESTER

Driver's cab

Engine

Straw walkers

Datavision screen

Pickup reel

Cutter bar

Chop elevator and stone trap

Threshing cylinder

Rotary separator

Sieves

Augers

---

in a field of corn and convert 12 hectares (30 acres) into sacks of wheat in one day. The first machine, drawn by horses, was invented by Hyram Moore and J. Hascall in the USA in 1836. Today's models are self-propelled. The crop is cut about 75 mm (2.95 in) above the ground and the stalks are threshed in a spiked cylinder. The grain passes on to a vibrating plate and the chaff is blown away by a blast of air from fans. The cleaned grain falls through sieves into a chute and on to an auger for off-loading into sacks or a nearby wagon. The straw is carried to the rear on moving racks where it is baled.

FARMING METHODS

Irrigation

Because crops need water to grow, the earliest agricultural settlements were in river basins such as the Nile in Egypt, the Tigris and Euphrates in Mesopotamia, and the Yangtze and Yellow rivers in China. At first, it was the perennial flooding of these great rivers that rendered large tracts of land fertile but, later, the water was used in more controlled irrigation systems best suited to the local needs. These involved the building of dykes, ditches, canals, aqueducts, dams and wells.

It was easiest if the flow of water could be controlled by gravity but, if it had to be lifted, this could be done by using the shaduf, an Archimedean screw or a bucket-chain. The shaduf, invented around 1500 BC, consists of a horizontal pole pivoted at its centre on the top of a vertical pillar some 2 m (6.5 ft) high. The pole carries a leather bucket at one end and a counter-weight at the other. The human operator fills the bucket by lowering it into a supply of water and then swings it up and empties it into a container or channel at a higher level. A series of shadufs can be arranged one above the other. The Archimedean screw raises water by rotating a screw inside a cylinder. The same principle applies in moving grain in the auger of a combine

Cut-away of a modern Massey Ferguson combine harvester

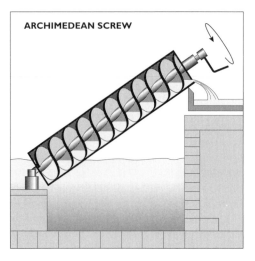

ARCHIMEDEAN SCREW

> 6 *The fixation of nitrogen is vital to the progress of civilized humanity.* 9
>
> SIR WILLIAM CROOKES, *(1832–1919), English scientist, in 1898*

harvester (⇒p. 210), or in a household mincing machine. A chain of buckets passing round a wheel can be used to lift water from a well.

Many of the older methods of irrigation are still in use today, but others depend on pumps (⇒p. 55), first used in the 3rd century BC, distributing water through sprinklers or trickle-feed arrangements. Over the years, millions of acres of arid land have been made fruitful by irrigation, and there is still much more waiting to be done.

Fertilizers

The Greeks and the Romans used farm manure and vegetable waste as fertilizers to replace the chemicals which are extracted from soil by growing plants, and such natural products were used for many centuries. There is, indeed, an old Norfolk farming proverb that 'muck is the mother of money'. Eventually, however, as more intensive cultivation of the available land was required to feed increasing numbers, the 'muck' began to run out. The importing of South American guano (the droppings of seabirds) into England, from 1840, helped to meet the need but by then it had been established that nitrogen, phosphorus and potassium were the key elements so that it became possible to replace natural by synthetic fertilizers.

The widespread use of phosphate fertilizers was largely due to the work of Sir John Bennet Lawes. After being educated at Eton College and Oxford University in England, he ran the family estate at Rothamsted which he had inherited when he was eight years old. Using one of the bedrooms as a laboratory, he turned his attention to agricultural experiments and in 1843, with his partner, Sir John Gilbert, he founded the now world-famous Rothamsted Experimental Station. Three years before, he had patented a process for making superphosphate, a successful phosphatic fertilizer. It involved treating calcium phosphate, which occurs in bones and in the mineral, rock phosphate, but which was too insoluble to be very effective as a fertilizer, with sulphuric acid. The resulting, soluble superphosphate was manufactured by Lawes at a factory in Deptford and by Messrs Fison, Packard and Prentice in Ipswich. Later, reaction between rock phosphate and phosphoric acid produced double or triple superphosphates with higher phosphorus contents.

Sodium nitrate, imported from Chile, and ammonium sulphate, a by-product from coal-gas manufacture, were used as nitrogenous fertilizers from around 1880, but in 1910, Fritz Haber, a German chemist, found that ammonia gas could be made from a mixture of nitrogen and hydrogen. The process was known as the fixation of nitrogen. Pressures between 150 and 350 bar, temperatures of 400 to 500°C, and a catalyst were required to get good yields of ammonia, and Haber developed new methods of operating a chemical plant at high pressure.

The ammonia can be liquefied and injected under pressure into soil. Alternatively, it is converted into ammonium sulphate, ammonium nitrate, carbamide (urea), or into ammonium phosphates which provide both nitrogen and phosphorus. Haber directed Germany's gas warfare organization during World War I, and, after the war, invented a process for extracting gold from sea water. Alas, like others before and after, he found that it could only be done at a price that rapidly led to bankruptcy. He was forced to leave Germany in 1933, and he died in Switzerland in 1934.

Potassium-containing fertilizers have been mined and used since about 1860. Potassium chloride, abundant in the Stassfurt deposits in Germany, is the most common.

Most modern fertilizers are compound fertilizers, which are mixtures providing nitrogen, phosphorus and potassium together with trace elements such as magnesium. They have sustained the intensive system of agriculture required to feed the world but there has been a price to pay because they are not cheap and they can be harmful particularly if wrongly used – so much so that there has been a distinct move back to 'organic' farming.

Rotation of crops

Rotating the crop which is grown on any piece of ground is advantageous because different crops take different nutrients out of the soil; changing the crop prevents any build-up of specific diseases; and some leguminous crops, such as peas, beans and clover, actually put nitrogen back into the soil from the air. Rotation has been practised since the 3rd century BC and was much used by the Romans who usually adopted a three-year rotation – a grain crop one year; beans, peas or lupins the next; and then an uncropped (fallow) year.

Similar systems lasted until new methods, avoiding the fallow year, which were pioneered, particularly in the Netherlands from 1650, formed the basis of what became known as the Norfolk four-course rotation. It was introduced and popularized, during the 18th century, by Viscount 'Turnip' Townshend. He was a wealthy English landowner and statesman, who farmed in Norfolk, and rotated turnips, barley or oats, clover and wheat over a four-year period. The leguminous clover regenerated nitrogen in the soil and, together with the turnips, provided fodder for more animals so that more natural manure was available. It proved to be a very successful system, which is still used, in modified forms, today.

Hydroponics

An Englishman, John Woodward, found in 1699 that plants could be grown in water but that they grew better the less pure the water was. It is now realized that it was the impurities in the water that provided nutrients for the plants. Hydroponics is the modern technique of growing plants without soil, by keeping their roots in a solution containing the correct chemicals, or in sand or gravel through which such a solution is passed. This seems a very attractive proposition because the conditions under which the plant grows can be controlled so closely, but attempts to use it commercially have met with very limited success because it is costly.

Insecticides

Until the 1940s, the main insecticides contained pyrethrum, the powdered leaves of a daisy-like chrysanthemum which was first used in China during the 1st century AD, or derris dust, obtained from the roots of a Far Eastern shrub. But, when their supply was cut by Japanese conquests during World War II, many newer synthetic products began to be used.

The most notable was DDT, a white powder, which was first made in 1873 but only patented as an insecticide by a Swiss chemist, Paul Müller, in 1940. As it was cheap and effective against many insects, it became so widely used as to pose a threat to wildlife and this led to it being banned in most countries during the 1970s and 1980s. It was replaced by another chlorinated hydrocarbon, BHC or Lindane, and, later, by organophosphates such as malathion and chlorpyrifos, or carbamates such as pirimicarb and carbaryl. Chemicals which attract insects sexually and lure them into traps or disorient them, and hormones that retard the development of insects in their larval stage, have also been used. There are, by now, very many commercial products available, marketed under a variety of trade names. Many of them are highly selective, killing only certain insects, and some of them can be used as systemic insecticides, which are absorbed into a plant through its leaves and are then ingested by sap-sucking insects.

Fungicides

Fungal attacks such as potato blight, wheat rust, and wine mildew do at least as much damage to crops as insects. Older methods of control include fumigation by sulphur vapour, mentioned by Homer in the 8th century BC; dusting with powdered sulphur; and

‘Clover and turnips are the pivots on which agricultural progress must revolve.’

CHARLES TOWNSHEND, *(1674–1738), English statesman*

spraying with Bordeaux mixture (copper sulphate and lime). Newer products include thiram, captan, benomyl, carbendazim and triforine.

Herbicides and weedkillers

Many chemicals will kill all plants if used in high enough concentrations, but sodium chlorate is the commonest all-purpose weedkiller. However, it persists in the soil so that any new planting has to be deferred. Paraquat, patented by ICI in 1959, does not have that disadvantage. It kills all plants by contact with their foliage, but is inactivated within the soil. Other similar products contain glyphosphate or diquat; they are known as non-residual or post-emergence weedkillers. For longer weed-free periods it is necessary to use a residual or pre-emergence weedkiller which will linger in the soil killing new weeds as they germinate; simazine and dichlobenil are typical.

Selective weedkillers will kill only broad-leaved plants, such as plantains and docks, but will not affect grasses or cereals. The best known are 2,4-D, which was developed during World War II, MCPA, dicamba, dichloroprop and mecoprop.

Breeding

Today's plants and animals have been bred over the years from wild species with a view to achieving greater variety, increased yields, better quality and less disease. The aim is to enhance the desirable characteristics of one species in its offspring. Artificial insemination, the introduction of male semen into the female by indirect means, was originally carried out on a dog in 1785 and developed commercially by Ilya Ivanovitch in Russia in 1901. It allows large numbers of offspring to be produced from the semen of a selected sire, and, if necessary, the semen can be treated and refrigerated for storage. Genetic engineering holds out hopes of facilitating a number of breeding processes.

FOOD TECHNOLOGY

Food technology is concerned with improving the quality of food; protecting it against chemical deterioration and the ravages of bacteria, enzymes and fungi; and storing it. The methods used have been so successful that much of what we eat was harvested many weeks ago in some foreign land, yet it remains edible and safe to eat today.

An English cannery in 1852

PRESERVATION OF FOOD

Canning

In 1795, Napoleon offered a prize of 12,000 francs to anyone who invented something better for preserving food than the old methods of drying, smoking, salting, and pickling in vinegar. It was won by a French confectioner, Francois Appert, when in 1810 he heated food to destroy harmful bacteria and then hermetically sealed it in a container. Appert used champagne bottles, with wired-on corks, but tin-plated cans were patented by an Englishman, Peter Durand, in 1810, and used when Bryan Donkin, a paper-maker (⇒p. 22) set up his canning factory in Bermondsey, England in 1811.

The canned food was tried out on servicemen and explorers, and, though there were some early disasters when it was found to be bad on opening, a

number of improvements rendered the process much safer. The temperature of sterilization was increased by using water boiled in a pressure cooker (⇒p. 98) or a boiling solution of calcium chloride. The manufacture of the can by hand, with one man only able to make ten cans in a day, was slowly automated. Better methods for the final sealing of the can by soldering were also introduced. Canned meat was exported from Australia in 1847 and large canning factories were set up, particularly in the Chicago area of the USA, in the 1860s.

At first, cans had to be opened by using a hammer and chisel and it has provided a fruitful field for inventors ever since. The simple claw-shaped opener came in 1855, and the ring-pull on many of today's canned drinks is a particularly successful modern device invented by the American Can Co., in the early 1970s.

Pasteurization
This is a method of partially sterilizing milk by storing it at a temperature around 64°C for not less than 30 minutes. It kills off bacteria, such as those causing tuberculosis and brucellosis, and lowers the number of those responsible for the milk going sour, without having much effect on the taste or the nutritional value of the milk. It was originally invented by Louis Pasteur (⇒p. 222), in the 1860s, as a method of preventing the souring of maturing wines.

Irradiation
Both Röntgen and Becquerel suggested in 1896 that X-rays or radiation from a radioactive source could be used for preserving food, but the idea was not put into practice until the 1980s. The process is, however, still controversial; it is banned in some countries and only allowed in others under strict controls.

Additives
Some foods are preserved by incorporating synthetic additives which are given an E number between 200 and 297. Sorbic acid (E200) in processed cheese and fruit yoghurt; and potassium nitrate (E252) in canned meats, bacon and ham are typical. Antioxidants (E300 –321), which prevent oxygen in air having harmful effects on food, are also used, for example ascorbic acid (E300) in jams and sausages. Other additives include colourings (E101–180) and emulsifiers (E322–495).

FERMENTATION

It has been known for many years that complex chemical changes can be brought about by micro-organisms originating from either plants or animals. The enzymes in malt, for example, can convert starches in cereals, such as barley, into sugars, which can then be changed into ethanol by other enzymes in yeast. Likewise, sugars present in grapes are converted into ethanol by enzymes present in the moulds that grow on their skins. These conversions of sugars into ethanol, known as fermentations, have been used all over the world for very many years to make ale, beer, wines and spirits. Similar processes are involved in the use of yeast in making bread, and the conversion of milk into cheese and yoghurt by the action of bacteria.

It was not, however, until around 1900, some 40 years after Louis Pasteur (⇒p. 222) had founded the new science of bacteriology, and around the time of the first isolation of enzymes, that living organisms were used on a wider scale. Then, for example, acetone and butyl alcohol were first made from starch; citric acid from sugars; and methane from sewage. The isolation of penicillin (⇒p. 215) from the mould *penicillium notatum* by a Scottish bacteriologist, Alexander Fleming, in 1928, opened up further possibilities of making other medical chemicals, and what began as fermentation in a few very old established trades has now become today's biotechnological industry.

REFRIGERATION

Ice has long been the traditional, natural cooler and, as the demand for it grew during the first half of the 19th century, blocks were cut from frozen lakes and rivers in New England, USA for export to hotter countries such as India and Australia. Such trade continued until machines for making ice began to be patented from the 1830s. They were bulky, steam-driven plants depending on

⁶M. Appert has found the art of fixing the seasons. At his hands, spring summer and autumn live in bottles...⁹

From COURIER DE L'EUROPE, 1809

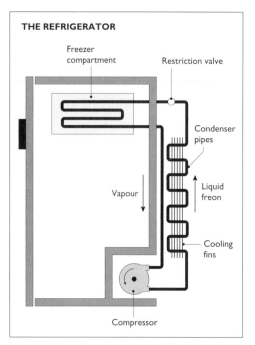

THE REFRIGERATOR

Freezer compartment

Restriction valve

Condenser pipes

Vapour

Liquid freon

Cooling fins

Compressor

The freezing compartment of a refrigerator is cooled by the drop in temperature as the pressurized liquid freon expands into a vapour on passing through a restriction valve. The vapour is then reconverted into a liquid by being compressed, and cooled in condenser pipes on the back of the refrigerator. Heat is transferred from inside the refrigerator to the room outside

6 *There is a crank down in Apalachicola, Florida who claims he can make ice as good as God Almighty.* **9**

THE NEW YORK TIMES, 1851

the fall in temperature when cold, compressed air was allowed to expand (decompress) through a valve, or when a liquid, such as ether or, later, liquid ammonia, evaporated. The first were made by Jacob Perkins (1834) and Dr John Gorrie (1850) in America; by James Harrison (1851) and Thomas Mort (1861) in Australia; and by Ferdinand Carré (1858) in France. They were used for making blocks of ice, air-conditioning, freezing meat, and cooling beer so that it could be brewed in hot weather. They enabled frozen meat to be shipped from Argentine to Le Havre in 1877 and from Australia to London in 1879. It was timely because the consumption of food in Europe was growing apace and there were signs that the countries might no longer be able to feed themselves.

Further progress was made by a German engineer, Karl von Linde. In 1871, he fitted an industrial refrigerating system into a Munich brewery; in 1879, he adapted the system into a small domestic model which sold well in Germany and the USA; in 1895, he designed a plant which cooled air below –196°C so that it liquefied; and in 1902 he added a fractionating column (⇒p. 31) which separated the oxygen from the nitrogen. The two gases came to be widely used in many different industries.

The first electric refrigerator for domestic use, the Domelre, was marketed in Chicago in 1913, and other models such as the Electrolux, Frigidaire and Kelvinator followed, though they were not sold in Britain until 1924. The first dual temperature refrigerator, with a deep freeze storage compartment, appeared in 1939, and domestic deep freezers which could freeze fresh food came in 1955.

Freons
Liquid ammonia was widely used as the refrigerant in refrigerators until 1930 when it was replaced by a less toxic group of compounds known as Freons or Arctons. They are chlorofluorocarbons, for example CCl_2F_2, and were first synthesized by an American, Thomas Midgely Jr, working for the Du Pont Co. They unexpectedly found a different role when they came to be used as the dispersant in aerosols (⇒p. 64), but the deleterious effect they had on the ozone layer has led to them being banned.

Frozen food
Refrigeration not only allows food to be stored; it allows it to be frozen on a commercial scale. This was first started by an American leather and fur merchant, Clarence Birdseye, who had spent much of his early life in Labrador, Canada where he saw how frozen fish and meat was stored. He realized that the secret lay in freezing the food quickly to avoid the formation of large ice crystals which broke down the cell structure of the food and made it soggy. It took him eight years to perfect his process, before he marketed packets of frozen foods, particularly peas, in 1924. The range was widened when he sold out to the Postum Co. in 1929. They used Birds Eye as a trade name and introduced the first pre-cooked frozen foods in 1939, and fish fingers in 1955.

Freeze drying
Bacteria cannot thrive without water so that drying food has long been a means of preservation. Prunes, sultanas, raisins and dried apricots are typical. For many foods, however, slow drying destroys both flavour and texture. This can be avoided by using freeze-drying which

involves a rapid freezing by immersion in, say, isopentane at −190°C. The product is then heated in a high vacuum so that the ice is removed by conversion into a vapour (sublimation) without first melting into water. The technique was first applied by two Frenchmen, Arsène d'Arsonval and George Bordas, in 1900, using Linde's refrigerating system. They used it for drying meats, but it did not have much impact until the 1940s when it was applied to the manufacture of medical products such as blood plasma and vaccines and, shortly after, for foods. It is now used very successfully for making, for example, instant coffee, first marketed as Nescafe, in 1939, by Nestlé; dried spices; and powdered soups.

Vacuum or Thermos flask

This is an open-mouthed, double-walled, glass vessel designed to keep hot things hot, or cold things cold, by limiting the transfer of heat from inside to outside, or vice versa. This is achieved by silvering the walls on the insides, and by extracting the air between them to create a vacuum. The silvering reduces heat loss by radiation, and the vacuum minimizes heat loss by conduction and convection. The vessel is, generally, cylindrical in shape and is protected by an external metal or plastic container. The mouth of the flask is sealed by a cork or plastic stopper.

The inventor of the flask, Sir James Dewar (1892), used it for storing liquefied gases made by the Linde process and in that role it was called a Dewar flask. The idea was patented in 1904 by a German glass-blower, Reinhold Burger, who had helped Dewar put it into practice – the name Thermos was suggested by a member of the public in a competition. The flask was used for storing liquid oxygen in rockets such as the V-2 during World War II and in everyday life it is still widely used by picnickers and travellers for carrying hot or cold drinks.

SOME SPECIFIC FOODS

Margarine

This was invented by a Frenchman, Hippolyte Mège-Mouriès, as a result of a competition set up by Napoleon III in 1869 to find 'a clean, cheap fat, with good keeping qualities, suitable to replace butter'. Today, it is made from a mixture of animal and vegetable fats churned into a semi-solid emulsion with milk, vitamins A and D, and colourings. Some of the fats are made from liquid oils, such as sunflower and whale oils, by reaction with hydrogen (hydrogenation), a process invented by the Frenchmen, Paul Sabatier and Jean-Baptiste Senderens, in 1897. By adjusting the mixture of solid fats and liquid oils it is possible to make a hard or soft margarine and the proportion of saturated and unsaturated fats it contains can be controlled by choosing different raw materials and varying degrees of hydrogenation.

Sugar

Honey was the main sweetener until it was replaced, from about 1700, by sucrose which was extracted from sugar cane. At that time, the cane was cultivated mainly in the West Indies, but Napoleon established the sugar-beet industry in Europe to provide an alternative souce of supply in about 1800. In England, Henry Tate, the founder of the Tate Gallery, and Abram Lyle, both built sugar refineries around 1860 and eventually joined together as Tate and Lyle in 1921. As it became

Sugar cane plants are one of the main sources of sugar. They are cultivated in the West Indies, Australia, the southern USA and other tropical or semi-tropical regions

SIR JAMES DEWAR
(1842–1923)

Sir James Dewar, the son of a wine merchant, was born at Kincardine-on-Forth, Scotland and attended Dollar Academy until, when he was only ten, his education had to be continued at home because he was stricken with rheumatic fever. He did, nevertheless, begin to study physical science at Edinburgh University in 1859 and, later, became a demonstrator. After a period as a teacher at the Royal Veterinary College in Edinburgh, he was appointed professor of Natural Experimental Philosophy at Cambridge University in 1875 and, two years later, he also became professor of Chemistry at the Royal Institution.

His early work was concerned with establishing the chemical structures of compounds such as benzene, pyridine and quinoline; and with spectroscopy. But he is best remembered for his invention of the Dewar, or vacuum, flask in 1872. This helped him in his work on liquefying gases at low temperature because the products which he was studying, such as liquid oxygen, could be stored in the flask. The equipment he designed enabled him to liquefy hydrogen at -252.8°C in 1898, and to solidify it at -259°C in 1899. Thereafter he achieved a temperature (-272°C) within a degree of absolute zero.

Between 1888 and 1891, whilst serving on a government committee on explosives, he invented cordite in collaboration with Frederick Abel.

He was a short, brusque man with unusual and diverse experimental skills. He was elected a fellow of the Royal Society in 1877; knighted in 1904; and occupied both his professorial chairs until his death.

more readily available, sugar was used as a preservative in making jellies and jams which became very popular towards the end of the 19th century.

Because sucrose is not suitable for diabetics and is generally regarded as fattening, a number of substitutes have been made. Saccharin was synthesized by the American chemists, Constantin Fahlberg and Ira Remsen, in 1879; cyclamates by Dr Michael Sveda in 1937; and aspartame by the Searle Laboratories in 1965.

Milk

Milk does not keep well unless it is condensed, dried or ultra-heat-treated (UHT). The first condensed milk was made by Gail Borden, an American inventor, in 1860. He evaporated the milk in a vacuum and sold the product in open containers. Today's product is evaporated in the same way but sugar is added as a preservative before it is canned. Dried milk was made in England in 1855 and, in a purer form, in the USA around 1900. UHT milk is sterilized at a very high temperature which affects the taste slightly, as in today's long-life milk.

Nowadays, both milk and fruit juices are commonly sold in TetraPaks made of waxed paper or plastic laminated with aluminium. The pack was invented by a Swede, Ruben Rausen in 1951, and has been a great commercial success even though it is difficult to open reliably.

Potatoes

When potatoes were imported into Europe from South America, around 1550, they became the staple diet for many people. The crop was for many years stored by piling the potatoes up into clamps which were tightly covered with straw and earth. Potato crisps, thinly sliced pieces cooked in oil, originated in France but were manufactured from 1920 in England by Frank Smith, the manager of a wholesale grocery company. He sold a packet, containing some salt, for 2d and crisps have gone from strength to strength. A newer company, Golden Wonder, which began in a small Scottish bakery in 1948, introduced flavoured crisps in 1962. A dry, powdered potato product which can be converted into mashed potato simply by adding hot water was first made in the 1960s.

14

MEDICINE

'I swear by Apollo the healer, by Asclepius, by Hygeia, by Panacea and by all the gods and goddesses, making them my witness, that I will carry out, according to my ability and my judgement, this oath and this indenture.'

Introduction to the Hippocratic Oath, HIPPOCRATES
(c. 460–c. 377BC), Greek physician

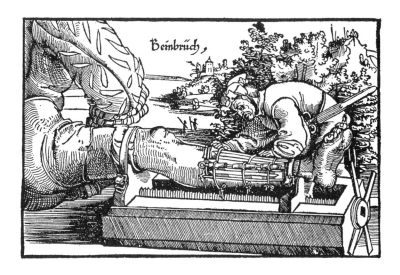

MEDICINE

MODERN MEDICINE has grown out of ancient magic as epitomized in the witch doctors in many tribal societies. In the past, the sick may have been treated with herbal remedies and even by crude surgery using sharp flints, but it must all have been very hit or miss and progress came in fits and starts as more was learnt about human anatomy and the causes of disease. Then, as specific diseases were recognized, cures for them were worked out, and the materials and equipment for treating them were discovered or invented. So that today many older diseases which, like the plague, were a scourge in their day have been almost completely wiped out, and overcoming the pain of arthritis by a hip replacement is commonplace in many developed countries.

BLOOD

⁶Not even medicine can master incurable diseases.⁹

SENECA, THE YOUNGER
(4 BC–AD 65), Roman
philosopher

Sir William Harvey, who was born in Folkestone, England, established in 1628 that the heart acts as a pump which circulates blood around the body by muscular action. The flow depends both on the rate of pumping (beating) of the heart and the pressure at which the blood is pushed through the arteries and veins. The use of pulse-counting, to measure the heart beat, was introduced by an Englishman, John Floyer, in 1707 and he invented a special watch for the purpose. Blood pressure is measured on a sphygmomanometer, invented by an Italian, Dr Scipione Riva-Rocci, in 1896.

The sphygmomanometer

This consists of a narrow rubber tube which is connected to a mercury manometer ($\Rightarrow$p. 44) at one end and to a rubber bulb at the other. In use, a broad arm band in the tube is wrapped around the upper arm and inflated, by compressing the bulb, to apply pressure. The doctor recognizes when the pulse beat at the wrist stops, momentarily, both by feeling it and by placing his stethoscope ($\Rightarrow$p. 228) above the inner surface of the elbow so that he can also hear it. As he slowly releases the pressure in the tube he records the pressure on the manometer when the first signs of the pulse beat return; this is called the systolic pressure. He then records the diastolic pressure when the beat becomes steady. Blood pressure is therefore expressed as two figures, for exaample

120/80, representing 120 mm of mercury for the systolic and 80 mm for the diastolic pressures. These are the normal readings for a young, healthy person, but the values are affected by exercise, emotion, illness and age. Abnormal blood pressure can generally be controlled by drugs.

Blood transfusion

Blood was successfully transferred from one dog to another in 1666, but early transfusions involving human blood were as likely to kill as to cure. The reason for this only became apparent in 1901 when an Austrian, Karl Landsteiner, discovered that there were four main types of human blood. They came to be known as group A, B, AB or O, and they were not all compatible. For successful transfusion, as first practised in America in 1905 by Dr G.W. Crile, it is therefore necessary to match the blood groups of the recipient and the donor. Human blood transfusion involves the collection and storage of blood from donors. It could be greatly simplified if a synthetic blood substitute was available, and there has been some success in developing such a product.

VACCINATION

Smallpox was for many years one of the deadliest of all diseases but, like many others, it has been largely eradicated by vaccination. The procedure probably originated in China, but it was first introduced into Britain in 1718 by Lady

*A Gillray cartoon
showing an
inoculation, c. 1796*

Mary Wortley Montagu, the wife of the British Ambassador to Turkey. Healthy people were inoculated with some of the pus from a sore on the body of a smallpox sufferer. In many cases, this gave the healthy person a mild form of smallpox but prevented them from catching the disease again. In modern terms, they were immunized against smallpox.

The treatment was, however, somewhat hazardous and more reliable results were obtained by Edward Jenner (1749–1823), a country doctor in Gloucestershire, England. It is said that a milkmaid told him when he was a medical student that she would never catch smallpox because she had already suffered from cowpox, a similar but much less deadly disease which afflicted cattle. Jenner saw the possibility that immunization from smallpox might be achieved more safely by inoculation of the pus from a cowpox rather than a smallpox sufferer. So in 1796 he took some pus from a sore on the arm of a cowpox sufferer and used a thorn to scratch it into the arm of a local eight-year-old boy. The boy developed a sore on his arm but had no other symptoms and, later, when he was injected with real smallpox pus, he did not catch the disease.

Thereafter, Jenner vaccinated many local people, including his own son, but for a while he had to contend with some violent opposition. By 1802, however, the practice was so obviously successful that it was made compulsory by an Act of Parliament, and Jenner was awarded £30,000 for his invention.

BACTERIOLOGY

Jenner had no idea why vaccination worked. At the time, the spread of disease was thought to be associated with 'bad air' – the Italian *'mal aria'*. That it was really due to micro-oganisms did not become apparent until the middle of the 19th century. A Dutchman, Antoni van Leeuwenhock, had observed germs or bacteria under his microscope (⇒p. 156) around 1675 but he had not associated them with disease. The first move in that direction came when Louis Pasteur (⇒p. 222) suggested that fermentation and putrefaction were initiated by airborne micro-organisms. Later, he suggested that each specific disease was probably caused by one particular bacterium. If that bacterium was extracted from a diseased animal, it would pass on the disease if injected into another. But Pasteur discovered, rather by chance in 1879, that bacteria could be made less

❛Do not think, but try; be patient, be accurate.❜

Advice from JOHN HUNTER (1728–93), Scottish surgeon, to his pupil Edward Jenner

LOUIS PASTEUR
(1822–95)

PASTEUR, the only son of a tanner, was born in Dôle, France, and though his school record was not good he became professor of chemistry at Lille in 1854, and at the Sorbonne in Paris in 1867. He was the founder, with Robert Koch, of the new science of bacteriology.

After Robert Koch's isolation of the anthrax bacillus, Pasteur began his own experiments and found that he could make a vaccine by weakening (attenuating) the bacillus by storing it at a temperature between 42° and 43°C. Pasteur demonstrated the efficacy of his new vaccine in a public test. Twenty-five sheep were inoculated twice, at intervals, with the vaccine, whilst 25 others were left untreated. After about a month, both groups of sheep were injected with anthrax and, two days later on 2 June 1881, Pasteur found that all the unvaccinated sheep were dead or dying but the vaccinated animals were fit and well.

Pasteur followed this by making a vaccine for rabies or hydrophobia, which he tested successfully on 50 dogs. But would it work on humans? By chance, it was put to the test on 6 July 1885. A nine-year-old boy, Joseph Meister, who had been bitten 14 times by a mad dog, was brought to Pasteur by his mother, pleading for help. Doctors said that the boy would die but Pasteur agreed to give him a course of vaccinations, and he survived.

Like Jenner before him, Pasteur had to withstand severe criticism from antivivisectionists but, in 1886, 2671 rabies patients were treated and only 25 died. In 1888, the first Pasteur Institute was set up in Paris by public subscription to perpetuate his memory and work. Joseph Meister was employed as a caretaker.

> **'Chance favours only the prepared mind. '**
>
> LOUIS PASTEUR
> *(1822–95),*
> *French chemist*

Louis Pasteur in his laboratory

virulent (attenuated) by storing or heating them. The product was called a vaccine. If it was injected into an animal, it would pass on the original disease only very mildly and, in so doing, would protect the animal against it.

Pasteur's ideas were supported by the work of a German, Robert Koch. He

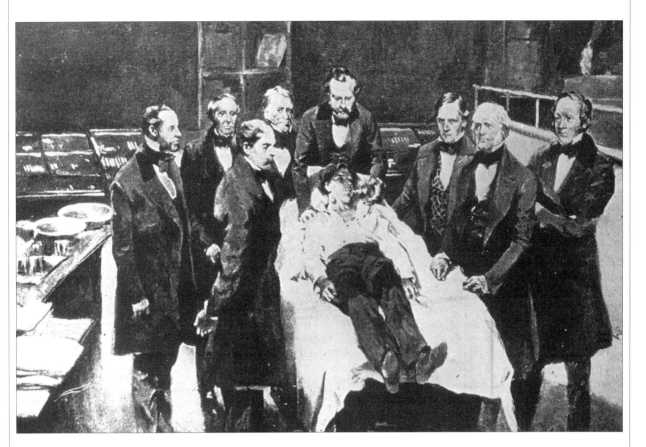

pioneered the method of growing bacteria, on gelatin or agar-agar to which nutrients had been added, in a flat glass dish designed by his assistant, J.R. Petri. In 1876, he isolated a rod-shaped bacillus which caused anthrax, and five years later Pasteur made a vaccine for that disease. It was followed by many more so that vaccination or immunization is nowadays a part of everyday life.

Antigens and antibodies

Bacteria cause disease because they are covered with protein molecules called antigens which disrupt the body's normal functioning. Their impact is, however, resisted by the body's immune system through which, in a complex process within the bone marrow, they produce antibodies which link up with the antigen and destroy it. Each particular antigen produces an antibody peculiar to itself so that the antibody generated by, say, smallpox has no effect on typhoid. Many diseases can only be contracted once because the antibodies specific to that disease, and generated by it, remain in the blood and prevent further infection.

Similarly, vaccination against a disease prevents it by building up the necessary antibodies, though the treatment may sometimes have to be repeated.

Very exciting possibilities were opened up by the invention of a method of making large quantities of pure, specific antibodies, known as monoclonal antibodies (MAB), in 1975. This was achieved in the Laboratory of Molecular Biology at Cambridge University, England, by an Argentinian, César Milstein, and a German, George Köhler. The MABs are made by injecting a mouse with a particular antigen and, after some time, removing some of its cells which are producing the required antibody. They are then fused with myeloma (cancer) cells to give hybrid cells which can survive indefinitely, and from which a continual supply of the original antibody can be obtained.

ANAESTHETICS

Until the middle of the last century, surgical operations were only carried out in dire circumstances and it was only the

From a painting of one of the first public demonstrations of the use of ether as an anaesthetic by W.T. Morton at the Massachusetts General Hospital, Boston, USA, on 16 October 1846

use of, first, anaesthetics, such as ether, nitrous oxide (laughing gas) and chloroform, and, later, antiseptics that made surgery more tolerable.

Dr C.W. Long, an American surgeon, first used ether, in 1842, when he removed a cyst from the neck of a boy. In 1844, an American dentist, Horace Wells, inhaled nitrous oxide before having one of his teeth extracted by Dr John Riggs; and in 1846, James Young Simpson, the professor of midwifery at Edinburgh University, began to use chloroform in childbirth. That roused violent passions with many thinking that the Bible had decreed – 'In sorrow thou shalt bring forth children' – that pain in labour was a divine necessity. But attitudes changed when chloroform was administered to Queen Victoria at the birth of Prince Leopold in 1853.

Those early anaesthetics are classified as general anaesthetics because in the correct dose they produce complete unconsciousness. They were administered by inhalation and were all used until well into the 20th century before being replaced by better, synthetic products, many of which can be injected. Local anaesthetics, injected into a particular area of the body, can render that area insensitive and they are, for many purposes, more satisfactory than general anaesthetics. Cocaine was the first chemical to be used for this purpose in 1884, when Carl Koller, a Czech ophthalmologist, working in America, carried out an eye operation. Cocaine occurs naturally in the leaves of the Peruvian coca tree, which have long been chewed to deaden aches and pains. It is, however, an addictive drug so that once its molecular structure was worked out in 1898, attempts were made to modify it to produce more acceptable, synthetic products. In epidural anaesthesia, the anaesthetic is injected into the lower part of the spine; it was first used by two Germans, August Bier and August Hildebrand, in 1883.

ANTISEPTICS

Anaesthetics made surgery much less traumatic but there was still a high risk of contracting some form of blood-poisoning, which could be fatal, until antiseptics were introduced by Sir Joseph Lister, the professor of surgery at Glasgow University in 1865. When, luckily, a colleague drew his attention to Pasteur's work he realized that the sepsis from which so many of his patients suffered might also be caused by bacteria. To prevent it, he dressed their wounds with an antiseptic, carbolic acid to kill off any bacteria that might be present. Later, in 1887, when he had moved to King's College Hospital in London, he began to replace his antiseptic technique, designed to kill bacteria, by aseptic methods aimed at excluding them. This involved the sterilization of anything – the air, hands and clothes of medical staff, instruments, and dressings – that might come into contact with a wound during an operation. It is the foundation-stone of modern surgery.

Soon, a very large number of chemicals which would kill bacteria more effectively than carbolic acid were made. They were known as bactericides, antiseptics or disinfectants and they were used in every walk of life. Cleanliness began to be placed next to godliness, and it has been a much harder life for bacteria ever since.

CHEMOTHERAPY

Carbolic acid and most of the early antiseptics were toxic to a wide range of bacteria, but their medical use was limited because they were also toxic to healthy animal cells. In 1907, a German bacteriologist, Paul Ehrlich, coined the name chemotherapy for the use of synthetic drugs which not only had a specific action against only one type of disease but could also be taken internally with safety.

Beginning in 1887, he painstakingly investigated the bactericidal properties of a vast number of chemicals by injecting them into infected mice. The 606th compound that he made, in 1910 – arsphenamine, Salvarsan or simply '606' – was a very effective cure for syphilis. Others followed for treating sleeping-sickness, bilharzia, kala-azar, amoebic dysentery, and yaws. These were all common tropical diseases transmitted by insect bites and caused, not by bacteria, but by micro-organisms called protozoa.

Take of opium, mandragora and henbane in equal parts, pound and mix them with water. When you want to saw or cut a man, dip a rag in this and put it to his nostrils.

Medieval prescription for surgeons

Geduld, Geschick, Geld und Glück

PAUL EHRLICH (1854–1915), German bacteriologist, was fond of quoting the four big Gs (patience, ability, money, luck) as essential ingredients of any achievement

Then, in 1932, Gerhard Domagk, a German biochemist, made a red dye called prontosil which could cure streptococcal diseases such as scarlet fever, puerperal fever and erysipelas. Investigation showed that the prontosil actually spilt up inside a human body into a simpler chemical called sulphanilamide and that this was the active agent. It had in fact been known since 1908 without its bactericidal properties being recognized and its structure was modified, mainly by the research chemists at the British firm of May and Baker, into a group of drugs known as sulphonamides. Like Ehrlich, they had to synthesize many chemicals before they found what they wanted and their first success, made in 1938, was the 693rd compound which they tried. Named sulphapyridine, or M & B 693, it was particularly effective in treating pneumonia, and many other similar drugs were synthesized, which in their day were remarkably effective in treating a wide range of diseases until they were, in many cases, replaced by improved products.

Antibiotics

Antibiotics are particular types of chemotherapeutic agents derived from moulds or other living sources. The first one, penicillin, was discovered in 1928 by a Scot, Sir Alexander Fleming, who was the professor of bacteriology at St Mary's Hospital in London. He was preparing a culture of staphylococci when the Petri dish in which he was doing it became contaminated with an airborne mould. Much to his surprise, he noticed that the bacteria around the patches of mould were dying off and he concluded that the mould must be producing some bactericidal substance. It came to be called penicillin because the scientific name for the mould was *Penicillium notatum*, but it was not until 1939 that a team of Oxford University scientists, led by an Australian, Dr Howard Florey, and a German, Dr Ernst Chain, were able to isolate a sample of pure penicillin from the mould. Because it showed such remarkable bactericidal properties, large-scale manufacture was undertaken in the USA and there was enough penicillin available to treat many World War II casualties. It saved thousands of lives.

That was just the beginning. Many other forms of penicillin, and other types of antibiotics have been made by chemical or biological methods. They include chloramphenicol, tetracyclines, cephalosporins, erythromycin, amino-glycosides and 4-quinolines. All the products have, or have had, their individual use and it is important to keep up the search for new ones, because the more they are used the more quickly bacteria become resistant to them.

RADIOGRAPHY

X-rays were discovered by Wilhelm Röntgen in 1895 (⇒p. 77) and he used the fact that they would pass through soft body tissues, but not through denser bones, to take an X-ray of his wife's hand

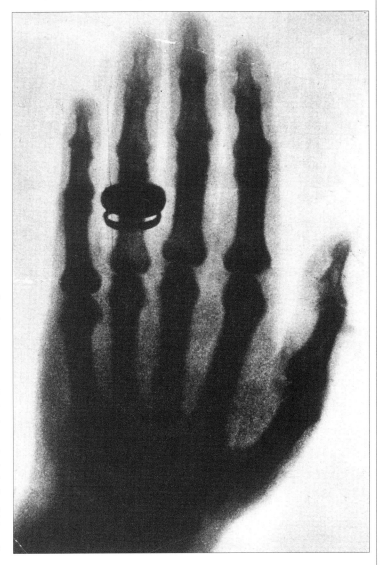

One of Röntgen's first X-ray photographs taken on 23 January 1896

– it showed that she was suffering from arthritis. Since then, X-rays have been widely used in medical diagnosis; the technique is known as radiography. The 'picture' can be shown up on a fluorescent screen or on photographic film.

Bones, and fractures in them, or solid objects show up very clearly but, in some cases, a pre-treatment is required before a successful X-ray can be taken. The barium meal, for example, was invented by an American doctor, Walter Bradford Cannon, in 1897. The patient swallows a suspension of barium salts, which is opaque to X-rays, so that the digestive system can be investigated. Other parts of the body can be rendered opaque to X-rays by injection.

Large doses of X-rays will damage living tissue and the early workers suffered ill effects from over-exposure. This is avoided nowadays by careful control and by the use of lead shields which are particularly impermeable to the rays.

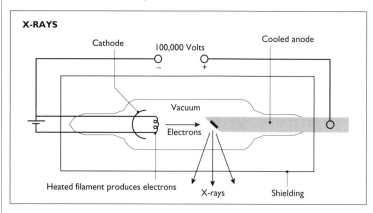

X-RAYS

Cathode

100,000 Volts

Cooled anode

− +

Vacuum

Electrons

Heated filament produces electrons

X-rays

Shielding

X-rays are produced when a beam of electrons impinge on a metal target

RADIOTHERAPY

The deleterious effect of X-rays on living tissue can be put to good use because it may be possible to destroy a localized cancerous growth by directing a beam of X-rays on to it, particularly if high energy X-rays, obtainable from particle accelerators, are used. The procedure is known as radiotherapy.

In many cases, the X-rays can be replaced by gamma rays from radioactive materials. This was done, originally, using radium, isolated by Madame Curie from pitchblende (⇒p. 76) in 1898, as the source of the gamma rays. The radium

was placed in a sealed glass tube which was embedded in, or close by, the growth. That was successful for many years but, nowadays, it may be replaced by synthetic radioisotopes such as cobalt-60 or radioactive iodine.

TOMOGRAPHY

The word tomography is derived from the Greek *tomos* (a slice) and *graphein* (to draw). It is a modern technique for obtaining 'pictures' of different 'slices' of the head or body and it has improved and extended the use of X-rays for internal diagnosis. It provides, for example, much better detail than a routine X-ray. In a CAT (computerized axial tomography) scanner, invented by the British engineer Godfrey Newbold Hounsfield and the South African physicist Allan McLeod Cormack in 1973, a thin beam of X-rays is rapidly rotated around a patient's head or body as it is moved slowly through the scanner. Detectors pick up the transmitted X-rays, which are of varying intensity depending on the nature of the tissues they have passed through, and a computer converts the signals into 'pictures' which by 1979 could be obtained in colour.

In positron emission tomography (PET), the patient is placed in a scanner after inhaling or being injected with a radioactive material. The radiation emitted is then examined in much the same way as in a CAT scanner. It is particularly useful in diagnosing mental illnesses such as schizophrenia.

TRANSPLANTS

Skin-grafing, within one individual, is both the oldest and the commonest form of transplanting. It was first attempted in the 17th century and it has been of particular value to plastic surgeons. Two New Zealanders, Sir Harold Gillies and Sir Archibald Macindoe, for instance, developed new techniques in their treatment of severe burns during World War II.

Attempts to graft skin from one body on to another, excepting identical twins, were not at first successful because the skin was rejected. It was only the realization that extensive 'tissue typing' had to be carried out, to ensure compatibility between donor and recipient, that made transplanting possible. The background work on cell structures was done first by Sir Peter Medawar (England) and Sir Frank Macfarlane Burnet (Australia), and later by Drs Baruj Benacerraf (Venezuela), Jean Dausset (France) and George D. Snell (USA). The former pair shared a Nobel Prize in 1960; the latter three, in 1980. The 1990 prize went to two Americans, Drs Donnall Thomas and Joseph Murray, for their discoveries concerning organ and cell transplantation.

Much of the progress has centred around the discovery of immuno-suppressive drugs which lower the chance of transplant rejection. Cyclosporin-A, extracted from a Norwegian mushroom, in 1972, and corticosteroids, secreted by the adrenal cortex or made synthetically, are typical. They are difficult to use, however, because they lower the body's resistance to infection.

Nevertheless, transplants of the liver, kidney, cornea, and bone marrow are reasonably common, and those of a testicle, and parts of the brain, muscles and nerves have been undertaken. But it is heart transplants, originally carried out by Dr Christiaan Barnard in Cape Town, South Africa, that have aroused the greatest interest. His first patient, Louis Washkansky (December 1967), survived for only 18 days, but a second, Philip Blaiberg (January 1968), lived for 594 days. Some later patients have lived for many years.

PROSTHESIS

This is the use of man-made aids to correct a bodily malfunction. It was originally limited to external attachments such as splints, crutches, spectacles, hearing aids, dentures and artificial limbs, but has recently been extended to include internal parts such as hip and knee joints, tendons, eye lenses, hair, skin, kidneys, and parts of the ear, heart and even the brain. Some of these modern 'spare parts' are of bionic (biological electronic) design so that they can be controlled by movements of the body muscles.

Hearing aids

Conical-shaped ear trumpets, first introduced in the 18th century, were replaced from the start of the 20th century by electrical devices involving microphones and amplifiers. One of the first, the Acousticon, invented by an American, M.R. Hutchinson, was used by Queen Alexandra, who had been deaf since childhood, at the coronation of King Edward VII in 1902. It was very bulky and the main aim, thereafter, was to reduce the size of the aid. The smaller Amplivox came in 1935, but it was the first commercial use of the newly discovered transistor by the American Sonotone Corporation in 1952 that marked the way forward. Modern aids, using micro-electronic circuits, are so compact that they can be fitted into spectacle frames or worn behind the ear. Bionic cochlea implants, entirely enclosed within the ear, were first fitted in the 1980s.

Dentures

The first false teeth, as early as the 4th century BC, were made from animal teeth or from ivory; they were attached to existing teeth by gold wires. Later, similar teeth were mounted on a gold plate, fashioned to fit the mouth. They remained an expensive luxury until Goodyear's invention of vulcanite (⇒p. 36) in 1844. This provided a suitable material for making a plate, fashioned from a plaster cast of the inside of the mouth, to which porcelain teeth were attached. Today's dentures, worn by millions of people, have a plastic or metal base and plastic teeth.

Artificial limbs

Wooden legs were described by the Greek historian Herodotus, in the 5th century BC, and Pliny mentions artificial hands, 400 years later, but the first major advances were made by a Frenchman, Ambroise Paré (1510–90), sometimes described as 'the father of modern surgery'. He was an army doctor who invented artificial legs and arms which could bend at the knee and elbow. They were rather grotesque metal devices, made by armourers, whereas today's much more sophisticated fittings both look and function more like natural limbs and can be of bionic design.

❝I dressed him and God cured him. ❞

AMBROISE PARÉ (1510–90), French surgeon

Kidney machines

The kidneys purify the blood by removing waste materials, such as urea, and passing them into the bladder as urine. This involves separating the small molecules, like those of urea, from the much larger ones of the proteins, such as haemoglobin. A similar process can be carried out in a dialyser, an apparatus containing a special membrane through which small, but not large, molecules can pass. It was invented by a Scot, Sir Thomas Graham, in 1850, and applied to the treatment of damaged kidneys by Willem Kolff, a Dutchman working in the US in 1943. He passed the blood of a patient through a dialyser, in what came to be known as a kidney-machine, before reintroducing it into the body. By 1964, many patients could treat themselves by periodically connecting their blood supply, via a plastic fitting in their forearm, to a kidney machine in their own home.

Hip replacement

Hip replacements were attempted as early as 1890 but they could not be carried out successfully until an Englishman, Sir John Charnley, perfected the technique at Wrightington Hospital in Lancashire, in the 1950s and 1960s. His work, which involved designing new artificial joints and developing new surgical methods of fitting them, meant that hip replacement is nowadays commonplace. Recent advances have centred around the use of new materials in making the replacement and in extending the techniques to other joints such as the knee and the shoulder.

Heart replacement

There are a number of possible ways of avoiding or delaying a heart transplant. An irregular heart beat can be corrected by implanting pacemakers, which operate by imparting electrical impulses to the heart muscles. The first were invented in the 1950s and ran off small batteries. In the 1980s, microprocessors ($\Rightarrow$p. 201) were incorporated to control their functioning, and in 1988 a nuclear pacemaker, powered by a small pellet of plutonium, was used for the first time.

A damaged heart valve can be replaced by an artificial one. An early example was invented in 1952 by an American surgeon, Charles A. Hufnagel, and a more widely used valve, consisting of a plastic ball which can move within an alloy cylinder, was designed by two other Americans, Dr Albert Starr, a heart specialist, and M.L. Edwards, an aircraft engineer, in 1960. A portion of an artery can also be replaced by a length of special plastic tubing; a constriction within an artery can be widened by using angioplasty ($\Rightarrow$p. 229); or a vein from the leg can be grafted around an arterial blockage in a so-called coronary bypass operation first carried out at the Cleveland Clinic, Ohio, USA, by Dr Rene Favaloro in 1967.

In 1970, Robert Jarvik, at the University of Utah, invented an artifical heart, the Jarvik-7, which was operated by compressed air. From 1982, some 90 patients were fitted with such 'hearts' but they were not universally successful and their use was banned in the USA in 1989. They are now being replaced by new devices made by the American firms of Baxter Novacor and Thermo Cardiosystems Inc. (TCI). They are implanted alongside the heart to assist its functioning and operated by batteries carried in a pack round the waist. They were originally intended as a stand-by whilst the patient waited for a complete transplant but, in October 1995, one was permanently fitted into a 64-year-old man who was regarded as too old for a transplant. The operation was carried out at the John Radcliffe Hospital in Oxford, England by Stephen Westaby and the patient survived for six months. It could be that these electrical 'hearts' will become as commonplace as pacemakers but many problems still have to be solved.

Since 1953, heart surgery has been carried out whilst blood circulation is maintained by passing it through an apparatus called a heart-lung machine, containing both a pump and an oxygenator. The first was invented by an American surgeon, John. H. Gibbon, in 1935.

MISCELLANEOUS PROCEDURES AND EQUIPMENT

The stethoscope

When a doctor taps the chest of a patient with his fingers, he hears one noise if the patient is healthy and another if there is any abnormality. This method of diagnosis, known as percussion, was invented by an Austrian, Leopold Auenbrugger, in 1761, and it led to the invention of the stethoscope by a French doctor, René Laënnec, in 1816. Unable to get any helpful response from percussion from a particularly fat girl, he rolled a piece of paper into a tube and used it to listen to her heart beat. The roll of paper was soon replaced by a wooden, horn-shaped tube and, towards the end of the 19th century, by the present-day type of stethoscope which has two rubber tubes, each fitted with an ear-piece, leading from the listening head. The method is, nowadays, called auscultation (the act of listening).

Magnetic resonance imaging

Hydrogen atoms placed in a strong external magnetic field will absorb radiation; the phenomenon is known as nuclear magnetic resonance. For a given field strength, the precise frequency absorbed depends on the environment of the hydrogen atom. It is different, for example, for a hydrogen atom in an O – H bond than in a C – H bond. Moreover, for any type of hydrogen atom, the amount of radiation absorbed increases as the number of atoms does.

In magnetic resonance imaging (MRI), a body is surrounded by very strong electromagnets and scanned with narrow beams of radiation. By measuring the frequency of radiation absorbed, and its amount, for particular field strengths, it is possible to examine the nature and quantity of the hydrogen-containing molecules within the body. The same applies to molecules containing fluorine and phosphorus atoms. 'Pictures' of cross-sections of a head or body can be built up by computers and they may provide better detail than a CAT scanner (⇒p. 226). The procedure, moreover, is safer because it does not involve X-rays.

In vitro fertilization

In vitro fertilization (IVF) involves growing an embryo, in a test tube, from sperm provided by a male and an egg taken from a female. The embryo is then implanted into the womb of the female where it can grow into a normal baby.

The technique, pioneered by Drs Robert Edwards and Patrick Steptoe at the Oldham Hospital in England, produced the first 'test tube' baby, Louise Joy Brown, in 1978. Thousands of others have been born since but, despite the successful use of frozen embryos and eggs in the 1980s, the success rate is low.

Catheters

A catheter is a narrow tube which can be inserted into the body. It is most commonly used for draining urine from the bladder, but Drs W. Forssman (Germany), A.F. Cournand (USA) and D.W. Richards (USA) won a Nobel Prize in 1956 for using catheters to study the interior of the heart. They invented the technique of introducing radio-opaque materials into the blood vessels (angiography), and their work, which involved carrying out dangerous experiments on themselves, contributed greatly to the advances in heart surgery. Catheters are also used to implant pace-makers; and a balloon catheter can be inserted into an artery and inflated to stretch a constriction. The latter technique, angioplasty, was first used by a Swiss doctor, Andreas Grüntzig, in 1977.

Thermography

This involves measuring the heat emitted by the body using an infra-red camera. Small temperature differences can be detected and can indicate, for example, the existence of damaged or cancerous tissue. The technique was developed in the 1970s.

Endoscopy

The inside of a body can sometimes be examined, visually, through an endoscope, of which the ophthalmoscope, for viewing the eye, was the first. It was invented by a German physiologist, Hermann von Helmholtz, in 1851, and it directs a beam of light into the eye and on to the retina, at the rear of the eye-ball, which can then be examined through a lens. Similarly, the larynx can be viewed through a laryngoscope, and the ear through an otoscope.

There is also a whole family of other endoscopes. The gastroscope for the stomach; the bronchoscope for the lungs; the nephroscope for the kidney; the

❛The total destitution of sound over one whole side is generally a fatal sign.❜

LEOPOLD AUENBRUGGER
(1722–1809),
Austrian physician

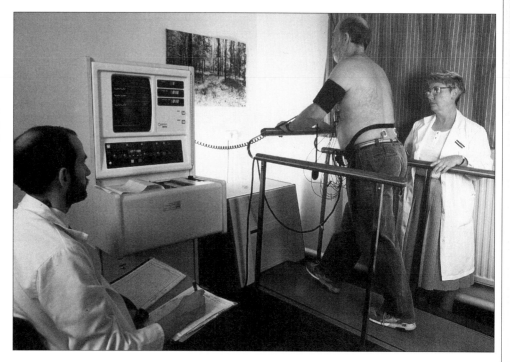

*A patient undergoing
an electrocardiograph
whilst taking exercise*

laparascope for the abdomen; the foetuscope for the foetus; and the cystoscope for the bladder. Their use was originally limited by their rigidity but, today, they generally consist of a flexible outer tube containing two inner tubes of glass fibres terminating in lenses. A beam of light is passed down one of the tubes to illuminate the area to be examined, and it is viewed or photographed through the other tube. In many cases, the endoscope may also be fitted with other channels to give access for laser beams or for tiny, remote controlled instruments which allow tissue samples to be taken or operative procedures to be carried out.

ECG and EEG
Electrocardiography (ECG) studies the functioning of the heart in a machine which monitors the minute electric currents associated with its beating. Electrodes are positioned on the chest or, possibly, in the oesophagus or within the heart itself, and the currents flowing between them are recorded. Early ECG techniques were invented by a Dutch physiologist, Willem Einthoven, in 1903; he won the Nobel Prize for Medicine for his work in 1924.

A similar procedure, electro-encephalography (EEG), with electrodes placed on the scalp, is used in the diagnosis of neurological disorders. The necessary EEG machine was invented by a German psychiatrist, Hans Berger, in 1929.

Alternative and complementary medicine
These are methods of medical treatment, which are not fully accepted by all orthodox practitioners but which have their own champions. Acupuncture, originating in China 5000 years ago, is the oldest. It involves inserting needles into specific points on the body depending on the illness being treated. A Japanese treatment, shiatsu, applies finger-pressure to similar points; and herbalism, treatment by plant extracts, is another ancient form of medicine.

More recently, amongst others, there have been homoeopathy (Samuel Hahnemann, Germany, 1810) which, on the principle that 'like cures like', treats patients with a small amount of a substance known to cause their illness; osteopathy (Andrew Taylor Still, USA, 1892) and chiropractic (D.D. Palmer, USA, 1897), which rely on manipulation, particularly of the spine, to correct stresses caused by misalignments; and the Alexander technique (F.M. Alexander, Australia, 1900) which emphasizes the importance of posture.

CHAPTER

15

WARFARE

'If the Germans had succeeded in perfecting these new weapons
[the V1 and V2 rockets] six months earlier and putting them
into action as opportunity arose, it is possible that our invasion
of Europe would have come up against tremendous difficulties,
and in certain circumstances might have been impossible.'

GENERAL DWIGHT EISENHOWER,
US President (1953–61)

WARFARE

INVENTIVE GENIUS HAS BEEN APPLIED TO WAR as much as to peace so it is not surprising that the spears, the slings, the bows and the arrows have given way to the atom bomb and intercontinental missiles. The progress, if that be the right word, has been relentless, but there are three outstanding landmarks of change – the invention of gunpowder, the unleashing of atomic energy, and the development of computerized guidance systems.

PRE-GUNPOWDER

Prehistoric weapons, made at first of wood or stone but then of bronze or iron, were intended to deliver a blow with a blunt instrument, a sharp point or a cutting edge. They were operated by human muscle power and included the stick or club, the knife or axe, the sling, the bow and arrow, the spear and the sword. They developed in various ways. Thus, the simple spear became a lance and a pike, and, in the halberd, it had an axe-head and a pointed hook attached to it. It survives as the bayonet probably first used in Bayonne, in France, in the 17th century.

As body armour improved, heavier weapons were used, and their range was lengthened by bolstering human muscle power. So it was that the bow and arrow had such a long history, and that such vast machines for hurling various missiles were made.

The bow and arrow

Bows and arrows were probably first used in warfare around 3000 BC as newly formed cities in Western Asia began to fight each other. A short or hand bow, about 4 ft (1.2 m) across and using 3 ft (0.9 m) arrows was used by the Assyrians in the 8th century BC. It was, even then, sometimes made of laminated wood or wood and horn to give greater flexibility, and was light enough to be used by skilled horsemen. The arrows had flint heads, sometimes barbed, and possibly tipped with poison. Foot soldiers used a heavier long bow, commonly made of yew, which was developed in Wales around 1150 into a particularly formidable weapon. It could shoot twelve 3 ft (0.9 m) arrows a minute, and in

> **6In the hands of the English the bow had become, in the form of the long bow, the most deadly and formidable weapon of its time.9**
>
> *J.W. FORTESCUE (1859–1933), English military historian*

battles such as those at Crécy, Poitiers and Agincourt, in the early years of the 15th century, a few thousand British archers routed the French cavalry.

The crossbow, with a bow resting on a stock, sometimes used a mechanical aid such as a lever or a winding mechanism to draw back the bow string into a catch which could be released by a trigger. It could be fired like a gun, and had a longer range than a long bow but reloading was slow.

Siege engines

Siege engines were used between about 500 BC and AD 1450 to attack fortified cities under siege. They included wheeled scaling ladders, battering rams, and ingenious machines for launching arrows, cannon balls or rocks at a low trajectory against the walls of a city or lobbing them into its heart. The ballista was like a giant crossbow. The mangonel was a massive catapult in which a throwing arm, held at its base between two twisted strands, possibly made from human or horse hair, was pulled back and released. The trebuchet was like a see-saw, with the missile at one end and a counterweight at the other. The missile was launched by hauling its end down by ropes and then letting go.

Greek fire

Greek fire was a liquid incendiary mixture which could float on water. It was used to defend the Byzantine Empire and its capital, Constantinople, for over 800 years. The composition of the mixture is not known with any certainty but it was probably made by refining locally occurring rock-oil and dissolving substances such as resin and sulphur in the product. The secret of how to do this

Greek fire being used by the Turks from ships in an assault on Constantinople in 1453

was brought to Constantinople by an architect, Kallinikos, in AD 673. On land, the Greek fire was either hurled from ballistae in large tubs with the mixture already alight, or projected in pots and then ignited by incendiary arrows. At sea, it was ejected through tubes.

Armour

Ancient civilizations used shields and a variety of body armour to defend themselves against the weapons of the day. At first it was made of leather, but then of bronze and iron. There were three main types – scale armour, chain-mail and plate. Scale armour, dating from around 2000 BC, consisted of overlapping, heart-shaped pieces of metal. In chain-mail, popular at the time of the Norman Conquest (1066), metal rings were interlocked and sometimes sewn on to a leather or linen backing. It was reasonably flexible and could be made into 'shirts' or 'coats' with sleeves. Plate armour had been tried in earlier times, but reached its peak during the 15th and 16th centuries. It was made of large pieces of metal, sometimes tailor-made for an individual, and held together by chain-mail or strapping. It was very expensive and heavy and was therefore, in the main, limited to mounted knights.

The use of body armour declined with the arrival of effective guns, but cuirasses – back- and breast-plates joined together – persisted, and are still worn in the ceremonial dress of the Household Cavalry of the British Army. Today's steel helmets, riot gear, bullet-proof vests and flak jackets are modern forms of body armour.

GUNS

The first guns appeared in China around 1280 and in Europe some 50 years later. The larger ones were called cannon or bombards and developed into today's field artillery and naval guns. The smaller, hand guns became hackbuts, arquebuses, muskets and rifles. They all worked on the same principle. Gunpowder was placed in a smooth cylindrical barrel, open at one end (the muzzle) but closed at the other apart from a small vent hole. Spherical shot, at first made of stone but later of iron, was loaded into the barrel through the muzzle and the gunpowder was ignited by touching the train of powder passing

❛Guns will make us powerful; butter will only make us fat. ❜

HERMANN GOERING (1893–1946), German politician

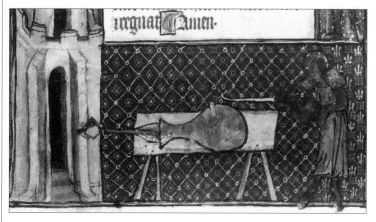

One of the earliest guns, c. 1326

Percussion caps

Everything began to change in 1807 when a Scottish clergyman, Alexander Forsyth, who was an ardent wildfowler, patented a new system in which a gun was fired by the flash from a mixture of chemicals, such as potassium chlorate, charcoal and sulphur, when it was struck by a sharp blow. Soon after, the chemicals were packaged in paper or metal containers to make what came to be called percussion caps or just caps. They revolutionized both the firing of guns and of explosive charges in mining. Their invention was claimed by most contemporary gunsmiths but an English landscape artist, Joshua Shaw, who went to America in 1817, probably deserves most credit.

through the vent with a red-hot rod or a slow-match held in a linstock.

Firing mechanisms

Hand guns developed more slowly than cannon because they were more difficult to operate since one hand had to be used for igniting the powder leaving only the other for holding the gun. This was eventually avoided by fitting a firing- or flash-pan, which could hold some fine gunpowder, as priming, on the outside of the barrel adjacent to the touch-hole, and a number of mechanical ways of igniting the priming were invented. The matchlock, dating from around 1410, was the first. A slow-match was held in an arm so that its glowing end was positioned just above the priming in the pan. On pulling the trigger of the gun, the arm was released to ignite the priming. In the wheel-lock system, invented in Germany around 1520, pulling the trigger released a spring-loaded wheel which had previously been wound up. Its serrated edges rubbed against a piece of pyrites and the resulting sparks ignited the priming. The French flintlock (1610) produced sparks by causing the sharp edge of a flint to strike against a roughened plate and it was the most widely used system between 1700 and 1850.

New ammunition

During the 16th century, the correct quantity and quality of gunpowder for each type of gun was packaged in a cartridge made of waterproof paper for muskets or cloth bags for cannon and this was loaded into the gun barrel, through the muzzle, with the shot on top of it. In 1812, a Swiss gunmaker, Samuel Pauly, went a stage further when he invented a cylindrical, cardboard cartridge, which contained the powder but also had a built-in bullet at its head and a percussion cap in its base. The ammunition invented by a Frenchman, Captain Minié, in 1847 was even more effective. It had an elongated bullet, with a hollow in its base, and, on firing, the base expanded to fit tightly into the barrel.

The solid projectiles fired by the larger guns were replaced at the end of the 18th century by hollow metal shells packed with incendiaries or explosives. The early shells were set off by slow-burning fuses or clockwork mechanisms. Later, around 1850, percussion and concussion fuses were invented. The former operate by the shock of impact with a target; the latter by the shock of discharge on firing.

Rifling

Sportsmen had known, since the 16th century, that a rifle, a gun with a grooved barrel which imparted spin to a projectile, was more accurate than a smooth bore gun. But it was only possible to make general use of this after 1850 when the necessary engineering skills had

The detonation of the sensitive explosive in the percussion cap explodes the propellant, which ejects the bullet from the cartridge case

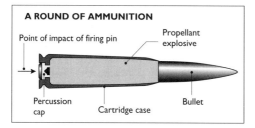

A ROUND OF AMMUNITION

Point of impact of firing pin

Propellant explosive

Percussion cap

Cartridge case

Bullet

SIR HIRAM STEVENS MAXIM
(1840–1916)

MAXIM, the son of a farmer, was born in Sangerville, Maine in the USA and left school at 14 to become an apprentice to a carriage maker. Thereafter, he practised a number of other trades, including pugilism, before working in his uncle's engineering firm in Fitchburg, Massachusetts, and eventually becoming chief engineer to the United States Electric Light Co., the first company formed in the USA.

Maxim represented that company at the 1881 Paris Exhibition where he heeded the advice of a friend that the most lucrative field for invention was in weapons of war. In 1881 he set up a laboratory in Hatton Garden, London, and by 1884 he had made the first Maxim machine-gun. It had a single water-cooled barrel, a belt of ammunition carrying 250 rounds, and a rate of fire of 11 rounds per second. The gun was adopted by all the major powers and it was so successful that he became world famous. His own firm became part of Vickers Ltd in 1896; he became a naturalized British subject in 1900; and he was knighted by Queen Victoria in 1901.

His strong personality and his arrogance made him very intolerant and even his younger brother, himself an expert on explosives, could not work with him. But his inventive genius was demonstrated in the 149 British and 122 US patents he took out during his lifetime. These included a hair-curling iron; the Maxim lamp; a steam-driven aeroplane which took, just, to the air; and a mousetrap. His son was also a successful inventor.

An early model of a Maxim machine-gun

---

developed and new ammunition became available. The P/51, based on the French Minié rifle and made at the Royal Small Arms Factory in Enfield, England from 1851, was particularly successful for British forces in the Crimean War (1854-56), and when rifles also proved their superiority in the American Civil War (1861-65) they soon took over from smooth-bore guns.

At the same time, two English engineers, William Armstrong and James Whitworth, also began to make rifled cannons using shells which were fitted, first with external studding and later with driving bands to engage with the rifling in the barrel.

Breech loading

Breech-loading, through the rear end of a gun barrel, was another important advance because it greatly increased the rate of firing. It was first achieved by a German, Johann Dreyse, in 1837, using a Pauly-type cartridge which was pushed into the firing chamber from the rear by a sliding bolt which closed the breech behind it and was locked in position when given a half turn. The Dreyse gun was adopted by the Prussian army in 1842 and was followed by, for example, the American Snider and Springfield, the French Chassepot, the German Mauser, and the British P/53 Enfield and Martini-Henry rifles.

Breech-loading for cannons was also introduced around 1850 with the breech being closed or opened by screwing a breech-block in or out. Its use was, however, controversial, particularly in Britain where it was not fully adopted until 1880.

❛Whatever happens, we have got the Maxim gun, and they have not.❜

British soldier's chant during the conquest of the Sudan (1896–98)

Repeater rifles

Single-shot rifles were replaced by repeaters from around 1860 when gunsmiths introduced a magazine which could hold a number of rounds of ammunition. It was generally positioned below the breech and its top round was loaded when the rifle bolt was pushed forward. After firing, the empty case was ejected as the bolt was pulled backwards, and springs in the magazine pushed the next round into position for loading as the bolt was pushed forward again. Repeater rifles gave increased rates of fire of up to 30 shots per minute and were the main type used by all participants in World War I. Typical examples were the French Lebel (1886), the German 1898 Mauser, the American .30 M 1903 Springfield and the British .303 Lee-Metford and .303 SLE (Short Lee-Enfield).

Machine-guns

A machine-gun goes on firing automatically so long as the trigger is pressed; it is generally mounted on a portable tripod or similar support, and ammunition is fed in from a magazine or a belt. Today, a rate of fire of 500 rounds per minute is commonplace.

The first successful model was invented by an American doctor, Richard J. Gatling, in 1862. In his gun, up to ten parallel barrels were manually rotated across a single firing point into which ammunition was fed by gravity. The French mitrailleuse had up to 25 barrels, but these hand-operated weapons were very cumbersome and they were replaced by automatic guns in the 1880s.

One of the first was invented by Hiram Maxim in 1884. The ammunition was held in a canvas belt and as each round was fired, through a single barrel, its recoil was used to move a spring-loaded bolt backwards and, in the process, to eject the spent cartridge. As the bolt sprang forward again, it fed another round into the barrel and fired it. The Maxim was followed by the Browning (1885), the Lewis (1911), the Vickers (1912), the Hotchkiss (1914) and the Bren (1938).

Sub-machine guns, smaller versions of the real thing, which can be fired from the hand, include the German MP

Bergmann, used in World War I; the American Tommy gun (1921); the British Sten (1941) and Sterling (1953); and the Australian Owen (1942). These weapons were deadly at short range because of their high rate of fire, but they were never very accurate and have, nowadays, largely given way to assault rifles and automatic pistols.

Automatic rifles

Semi- or fully-automatic rifles operate on the same principle as the machine-gun. The first semi-automatic rifle, the .30 M1, was invented by John C. Garand in the USA and adopted by the US Army in the 1930s. After firing one round, another was fed in from a magazine, so that the gun was ready for firing on the next pull of the trigger. The gun proved itself during World War II and over five million were manufactured before it was replaced in the 1950s by fully automatic rifles.

Automatic rifles go on firing so long as the trigger is held down and are sometimes called assault rifles. One of the first was the German MP-44 rifle, designed by Hugo Schmeisser, which proved itself towards the end of World War II. It was developed in Russia by Mikhail Timofeyevich Kalashnikov, into the AK-47, with a curved magazine holding 30 rounds, and in the 1970s into the AK-74. Other recent examples are provided by the American Armalite AR 15, alias the M-16, and the M-16 A2; the Belgian FN FAL rifle which was adopted by NATO; the SA-80 of the British Army; and the French FA MAS.

Pistols and revolvers

These are small guns which can be held and fired in one hand and which were originally intended for use by horsemen. Until 1835 they could only fire one shot but then an American, Samuel Colt, applied an old idea to the design of a repeating pistol which came to be called a revolver. Six rounds of ammunition were held in a cylinder which could be rotated to allow each round to be fired in turn. Colt's gun was not a commercial success until one thousand were ordered for use during the Mexican–American War in 1846. Thereafter, he built a factory in Hartford, Connecticut, and produced a

6 It bears the same relation to other firearms that McCormick's reaper does to the sickle, or the sewing machine to the common needle. 9

R.J. GATLING (1818–1903), American inventor on his gun

Above left: *The German V2 rocket was the first successful ballistic missile*
Above right: *A modern missile. A Hawk anti-aircraft missile of the US Marine Corps being prepared for action during the 1991 Gulf War*

series of firearms which made him one of the richest men in America.

Revolvers are still favoured by some police forces but, for military purposes, they have been replaced by automatic pistols which operate like small sub-machine guns. The first was invented in 1893 by an American, Hugo Borchardt. His original model, improved by a German, Georg Lüger, was adopted by the German army in 1908. Others include the German Mauser and Walther P38; the American Derringer, Browning and M1911 Colt; the British Webley; and the Italian Beretta. A modern Beretta, the M9, has recently been adopted by the US Army and by NATO forces.

MISSILES

Military missiles are pilotless, self-propelled vehicles, which carry an explosive or nuclear warhead and are powered by a rocket or jet motor. The German V1 and V2 (⇒p. 247) were the first, but today there is a wide variety, classified in a number of ways. Strategic missiles are designed for long-range attack on an enemy's territory; tactical missiles are for use in the course of a battle. In ballistic missiles, the engines cut out shortly after launch; in aerodynamic types they provide power throughout the flight. They are also broken down according to their use into surface-to-surface (SSM), surface-to-air (SAM), air-to-air (AAM), air-to-surface (ASM), anti-tank, and ship-to-ship missiles.

The warhead is fitted with a contact or proximity fuse which operates either when the target is hit or approached, and its impact may also be increased by using multiple re-entry vehicles (MRVs) or multiple independently targetable re-entry vehicles ((MIRVs). In the former, the warhead splits into several smaller units after launch to confuse any defences and to spread the damage. In the latter, a single missile launches a number of warheads each aimed at a different target.

The giants are the intercontinental ballistic missiles (ICBMs) with a range of up to 13,000 km (8080 miles) which are launched from underground silos; they include the American Minuteman (USA, 1962), Peacemaker (USA, 1986); the French SSBS (*sol-sol ballistique stratégique*, 1960s); and the SS-18 (USSR, 1974). Then come intermediate range ballistic missiles (IRBMs) and submarine-launched ballistic missiles (SLBMs) with ranges up to 10,000 km (6200 miles). The US Polaris (1960) and Trident (1979), as used by the British navy; the Russian SS-19 (1980); and the French M-4 (MSBS, *met-sol ballistique stratégique*, 1965) are typical. Cruise missiles, which are of the aerodynamic type not unlike an unmanned aircraft, can be launched from land, sea or air, and include the American Tomahawk (1979), the French ASMP (*air-sol moyenne portée*) and the Russian SSC-X-4 (late 1980s).

Other well known missiles include the French Exocet (ship-to-ship, 1972); the British Blowpipe (SAM, 1975); and the American Sidewinder (AAM, 1956), Lance (SSM, 1972), Pershing (SSM, 1972), Patriot (SAM, 1983), Stinger (SAM, 1984), and Harm (ASM, 1984).

Guidance systems

Guided, or smart, missiles have sophisticated guidance systems which function for all or part of their flight to ensure that they reach their target accurately. For short ranges, the system may depend on direct guidance from the launch pad by wire or radio links; on the missile following a radar beam; on the detection of infra-red, acoustic, electrical or magnetic emissions from the target; or on picking up the reflection of radar or laser beams directed on to the target either from the missile itself or from some other source. Inertial guidance systems are used for longer ranges. They depend on gyroscopes (⇒p. 62) to maintain the alignment of a platform within the missile on which accelerometers are fitted. These measure the horizontal and vertical movements of the missile, in relation to the fixed platform, and feed that data into a computer enabling the missile to be guided along a predetermined course. Thus a cruise missile can hug the Earth's surface and avoid detection by radar whilst being directed up or down, or to the right or left, as necessary. It is rather like feeding a route map into the missile's computerized system.

SUBMARINES

Early submarines were all driven by hand-operated propellers. The first was a one-man craft, called *Turtle*, built by an American, David Bushnell, in 1776. It was made of oak and shaped like a coconut; fitted with buoyancy tanks, which were filled with water for sinking or pumped out for rising; and it carried an external explosive charge. Other features of modern submarines – a fish-shape, hydroplanes to guide the vessel up or down, and a supply of compressed air – were fitted to the *Nautilus* built by another American, Robert Fulton, in 1800. In 1863, the *H.L. Hunley*, named after its designer, and driven by eight men turning a crankshaft, became the first submarine to sink a ship when it rammed the USS *Housatonic* with an explosive charge carried on a pole jutting out from its bow. Alas, the submarine could not free itself and also sank.

Manual methods of propulsion were eventually replaced by the use of electric motors powered by on-board batteries, but at first they could only be recharged in port. The problem was solved, however, in 1898, by an Irish-born American, John P. Holland, in his *Holland VI* submarine. It was driven by batteries whilst submerged but, when on the surface, an internal combustion engine was used both for propulsion and for recharging the batteries. His submarine also carried ballast tanks on its surface which could be filled with sea-water or air to adjust the depth, and was fitted with a retractable periscope (⇒p. 154) and torpedo tubes (⇒p. 243). Holland's craft convinced the navies of

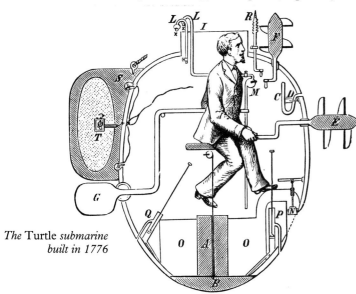

The Turtle *submarine built in 1776*

the world that submarine warfare must be taken seriously and his basic design, with external guns added during World War I, lasted until 1944. Then, a Dutch invention, the Schnorkel, became very popular. It was a flexible tube which could be raised to the surface to allow air in and exhaust gases from the engines out.

The first atomic powered submarine, still another *Nautilus*, was launched in the USA in 1955. An atomic pile (⇒p. 90) is used to provide heat to raise steam which is then used to drive a steam turbine to turn the propellers and generate electricity. Nuclear submarines can remain submerged almost indefinitely and, when fitted with interballistic missiles, they provide a formidable, hidden fire power. In Britain, HMS *Resolution*, carrying *Polaris* missiles, was launched in 1967, and HMS *Vanguard*, carrying *Trident* missiles, in 1994. In France, *Le Triomphant*, carrying M5 missiles, went into service in 1996.

Submersibles

These are small craft used in oceanography, salvage operations and pipe laying. The bathysphere, built for observational purposes by two Americans, William Beebe and Otis Barton, was a steel sphere, fitted with portholes and a powerful searchlight, which was lowered into the ocean on a cable. Its designers descended to a world record depth of 3028 ft (923 m) in 1934. It was followed by a different type of craft called a bathyscape built by a Frenchman, Auguste Piccard, and his son, Jacques. It consisted of a strong observation cabin which hung below a larger bouyancy tank, filled with gasoline. The rate of descent and resurfacing were controlled by allowing water to enter air ballast tanks and by discarding metal ballast held in place by electromagnets. The bathyscape reached a depth of 10,917 m (35,820 ft) in 1960. Modern variations on the theme include the French *Nautilus* (1985) and *Saga* (1987); the American *Jason Jnr* (1986); and the Japanese *Shinkai 6500* (1989).

Three other main types of equipment are in use today. In the first, individual divers wear a suit and are provided with air either through a pipe from the surface

HMS Vanguard, *launched in 1994 at Barrow, England. The submarine carries Trident missiles*

or, in a self-contained suit, from attached cylinders. Such suits were brought into practical use by a German, Augustus Siebe, from 1829. Today, some of the suits are armoured, and fitted with a visor and robot arms, so that they can withstand the pressures at greater depths. Second, divers live under pressure for up to 15 days at a time in a decompression chamber on board a ship. As required, they are transferred into a submersible pressurized chamber, like a diving bell, and this is either lowered to their place of work on a cable, or carried to and fro by a second chamber which is operated by a pilot under normal atmospheric pressure. The necessary equipment is known as a lock-out submersible. Third, an unmanned submersible, fitted with television cameras, photographic equipment and robot arms is used under control from the surface.

TANKS

Tanks, or armoured fighting vehicles, came to prominence in World War I, but they were only adopted very reluctantly when it became clear that something had to be done to try to break the stranglehold of trench warfare, the machine-gun, the barbed wire and the mud.

The idea for what became the modern tank was floated at the start of the 20th century and was a consequence of the invention of the internal combustion engine and the caterpillar track, both of which were being used in early farm tractors. Indeed, the first British prototype for a practical tank, nicknamed Little Willie, was built from a tractor by William Foster and Co. Ltd in Lincoln in 1915. Big Willie, which became the British Mark I tank, followed later in the year, and similar Renault FT tanks were built in France. These early models were cumbersome and slow, and not particularly successful when first deployed in action. By the end of the war, however, when the speed and range of the tank had been almost doubled, and when side-mounted guns had been replaced by guns mounted in a rotating turret on the top, the new weapon had proved its worth. Britain and France had built more than 6000; Germany had about 40.

However, the Germans learnt their lesson and, during the 1930s, they built up a force of 3000 tanks (*Panzerkampfwagen*) with which they had so much success in the early stages of World War II. It was in that war, particularly in the actions in the North African desert, that tanks came to dominate ground warfare. They were also used for a variety of purposes. There were flail tanks, with long whirling chains beating the ground ahead of them to detonate mines; amphibious tanks, which approached a beach like a boat before reverting to their normal land role; and assault vehicles which could carry a bridge for laying down over any barrier or an explosive charge for placing against any obstacle.

There has also been a continuous improvement in the general performance of tanks and in the strength of their armour. In 1915, the British Mark I weighed 28.4 tonnes, had a top speed of 4 mph (6.4 km/h) and carried two 57 mm (2.25 in) guns and three machine guns. A modern tank, such as the British *Challenger* weighs 60 tonnes, has a speed of 35 mph (56 km/h) and carries 120 mm (4.7 in) rifled guns. Comparable vehicles include the German *Leopard II*, the American *M1 Abrams*, the Israeli *Merkava*, and the Russian *T 80*.

The armour plating on tanks has been improved in three main ways. First, by

> **❝*I will make covered chariots, safe and impregnable, which may enter among the enemy and his artillery and so defeat any body of men...*❞**
>
> *LEONARDO DA VINCI
> (1452–1519), Italian
> painter and engineer*

A Big Willie tank built by W. Foster and Co., England, in 1915

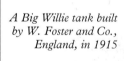

using thicker and tougher steel. Second, in the 1970s, by using Chobham armour, a laminated structure of steel, titanium and ceramics, invented at Chobham in England. Third, in the 1980s, by using reactive armour, which covers the most vulnerable places of a tank's armour with external explosive charges. The idea is that their detonation by any incoming missile will not damage the tank but will disrupt the missile and prevent it from penetrating the tank.

Anti-tank weapons

To counter the increasingly strong tank armour with which tanks were protected during World War II, special anti-tank weapons were invented which used shaped, hollow or cavity-charge shells. They have a conical hole, lined with metal, drilled into the leading edge of their explosive charge and this has the effect of concentrating the shock wave in a forward direction as though it was a beam of light. Using this type of projectile, the British PIAT (Projectile Infantry Anti-Tank), the American Bazooka, the Russian Simonov and the German Panzerfaust, which were reasonably light weapons fired from across the shoulder, enabled infantrymen to cripple tanks. They were replaced in the 1960s by the American M72 LAW (light anti-tank weapon) which fired a 66 mm rocket projectile, the Russian RPG-7, and the German Armbrust launcher.

The Franco-German Milan (*Missile d'infanterie léger anti-char*), introduced in the 1970s, is typical of today's weapons. Its 115 mm warhead is guided by a wire and has a two-stage rocket motor which gives a speed of 200 m/s (447 mph) at a range of 2 km (1.24 miles); it is effective against almost 1 m (3.2 ft) of armour. There are also the British LAW 80; the French Strim *LRAC 89* and Apilas; the American TOW 2 (Tube-launched, Optically-tracked, Wire-guided); the Franco-German HOT (*Haut-subsonique Optiquement Téléguide*); and the Russian AT-4 Spigot anti-tank weapons.

These weapons generally fire either HEAT (high explosive anti-tank) or HESH (high explosive squash head) missiles. The former have shaped charges designed to penetrate a tank's armour. In the latter, the head of the charge is made of plastic explosive, and it is hoped that this will first spread out on the external surface of the armour and then dislodge a lethal scab of armour from the inner surface when it is detonated.

The counter-measure to reactive armour is to use a warhead containing one shaped charge behind the other. The first will detonate the protective explosive on the tank whilst the second, fired microseconds later, will penetrate the main armour. Another recent ploy has been to attack the more thinly protected top of a tank by firing a special shell, such as a Bofors BILL (Bofors, Infantry, Light, Lethal), just over it. The shell is detonated by a proximity fuse which detects its position.

NUCLEAR WARFARE

Nuclear warfare began on 6 August 1945 when an American B-29 bomber dropped the first ever atomic bomb on the city of Hiroshima in Japan. It was cylindrical in shape and about 3.05 m (10 ft) long and 0.76 m ($2^1/_2$ ft) in diameter; it weighed only about 4 tonnes but it had the same explosive power as 12,700 tonnes of TNT ($\Rightarrow$p. 27); its code name was Little Boy and it was made from ^{235}U ($\Rightarrow$p. 89). Because the Japanese government did not surrender, a second bomb was dropped, on Nagasaki, three days later. It was egg-shaped, about 3.65 m (12 ft) long, with a maximum diameter of 1.52 m (5 ft); it weighed about $4^1/_2$ tonnes and was equivalent to 22,300 tonnes of TNT; its code name was Fat Man and it was made from plutonium, ^{239}Pu.

The Manhattan project

On 25 July 1941, a British committee, chaired by G.P. Thomson and code-named Maud to try to conceal its acivities, issued a report which concluded that building an atom bomb was a practical proposition, and that it would 'lead to decisive results in the war'. Its recommendations were accepted by the British Prime Minister, Winston Churchill, in August. When American scientists supported the findings of the Maud committee, President Franklin Roosevelt established the Manhattan Project to harness all the various

❛The committee considers that the scheme for a uranium bomb is practicable and likely to lead to decisive results in the war.❜

THE *MAUD* COMMITTEE, 24 *July* *1941*

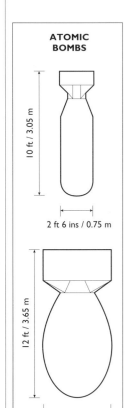

ATOMIC BOMBS

10 ft / 3.05 m

2 ft 6 ins / 0.75 m

12 ft / 3.65 m

5 ft / 1.5 m

The shape of Little Boy (top) and Fat Man (bottom). Little Boy weighed 4000 kg (8818 lb) and Fat Man 4500 kg (9920 lb)

activities. General L.R. Groves, then a Colonel in the Corps of Engineers, was put in charge, and he chose Robert Oppenheimer, a distinguished professor of science at the University of California and California Institute of Technology, to direct a new central laboratory where the bomb would be designed and built. It opened at Los Alamos in April 1943, and Oppenheimer gathered a formidable international team around him. It included Enrico Fermi (Italy), Leo Szilard (Hungary), Edward Teller (Hungary), Otto Frisch (Austria), Niels Bohr (Denmark), Mark Oliphant (Australia) and many others. It was a unique team effort that brought the whole fantastic enterprise to fruition.

Little Boy

The first problem to solve in making Little Boy was how to obtain adequate supplies of ^{235}U. Early in 1940, an American, Alfred Nier, working at the University of Minnesota, had separated small amounts of it from the ^{238}U with which it occurred in natural uranium, but it was a Herculean task to do it on a large scale. There was only 0.7 per cent of ^{235}U present in the natural uranium and it differed in mass from ^{238}U by only 1.26 per cent. It was likened to a blind man trying to find one black sheep amongst 140 white ones. Because so little was known about how to tackle the problem, and because of the urgency, three different methods were adopted – electromagnetic separation, gaseous diffusion and thermal diffusion – on a site at Oak Ridge, in Eastern Tennessee, which had been bought in September, 1942. In less than three years 40 kg (88 lb) of about 80 per cent pure ^{235}U had been obtained and was passed to Los Alamos for making into a bomb.

The general idea in making Little Boy was to assemble two sub-critical (⇒p. 90) pieces of ^{235}U at opposite ends inside a gun barrel. To set off the bomb, one of the pieces would be fired into the other, using a traditional explosive charge, to form a super-critical mass and, at the same time, to trigger off a source of neutrons. The actual critical size for ^{235}U had, therefore, to be measured, and this was done in a series of dangerous experiments in which small blocks of the

material were built up into a small pile until the critical size was just reached. Because there was not much ^{235}U available and because the team were confident in their design, the finished bomb was never fully tested before it was used.

Fat Man

Some of the ^{238}U atoms in a pile (⇒p. 90) capture neutrons and are transformed into heavier plutonium, ^{239}Pu, atoms which, like ^{235}U atoms, have unstable nuclei so that they can also be made into a bomb. To make the plutonium in sufficient quantities, three huge piles were built, beginning in August 1943, alongside the Columbia River at Hanford in the State of Washington. After the piles had operated for about seven weeks the uranium in them contained about 250 parts per million of plutonium, and this was extracted by a lengthy, complex chemical process carried out in vast, concrete containers, which were called 'Queen Marys', after the huge British passenger liner of that name. Early in 1945, enough plutonium had been extracted to make two bombs.

The 'gun' method of shooting two pieces of ^{235}U at each other would not work for two pieces of plutonium because they could not be pushed together quickly enough. Instead, a much trickier implosion method had to be adopted. The idea was that two touching hemispheres of plutonium, forming a sphere which was below the critical size, would be compressed, by surrounding explosive charges, into a sphere about half the original size. This would be super-critical because its density would be so much higher, which would bring its atoms much closer together. Because of some lingering doubts as to whether such a radically new design would work, a full-scale test on a prototype Fat Man bomb was carried out on the edge of the Alamogordo bombing range, in New Mexico, on 16 July 1945. It was successful.

The hydrogen bomb

This bomb, which is also called a super, thermonuclear or fusion bomb, depends, not on the fission of large atoms such as uranium and plutonium, but on the fusion of small atoms such as the isotopes of hydrogen. The problem is that such fusion will only take place at very high temperatures, as in the Sun. But, in 1942, the idea occurred to both Enrico Fermi and Edward Teller that a fission bomb might be used to heat a mixture of small atoms to such a high temperature.

There was, at first, little enthusiasm for trying to build a hydrogen bomb, but, after the USSR had exploded its first atom bomb in 1949, Roosevelt's successor as President, Harry Truman, decided that work should go ahead. After some setbacks, Teller, with the assistance of Polish-born Stanislaw Ulam, came up with an idea which involved a 'fusion mixture' of the two isotopes of hydrogen, deuterium, ^2H, and tritium, ^3H. When it was tested in 1952 at Eniwetok it was found to be equivalent to over 10 million tonnes of TNT and more than 500 times more powerful than Fat Man. It was not, however, a practical proposition for a bomb because it weighed 65 tonnes, mainly because of the refrigeration equipment required to keep the deuterium-tritium mixture below –253°C so that it remained liquid.

A practical 'dry' bomb only came when the deuterium-tritium mixture was replaced by lithium deuteride, a compound between a lithium-6 isotope and deuterium. This was a solid and, when it was bombarded within a bomb by neutrons, some of the ^6Li atoms were transformed into tritium atoms, which together with the deuterium atoms already present created a satisfactory mixture for fusion. These types of bomb can, nowadays, be made small enough for fitting into many missile systems. They have an awesome power, up to 50 megatonnes, with 1 megatonne being equivalent to 1 million tonnes of TNT.

WEAPONS AND DEVICES

The torpedo

The torpedo is a cigar-shaped underwater guided missile which was invented by a British engineer, Robert Whitehead, in 1866. His first design was about 4.26 m (14 ft) long and 36 cm (14 in) in diameter. It carried an 8.16 kg (18 lb) warhead of dynamite, was powered by a propeller driven by a compressed air engine, and was held at a set depth by a hydrostatic valve which operated horizontal rudders at the rear. Vertical rudders, controlled by a pre-set gyroscope to give lateral steering, were fitted in 1896.

The early torpedoes were launched from specially designed torpedo-boats. Today they are also launched from submarines and aircraft. They are commonly driven by battery-operated electric motors; have guidance systems like those of guided missiles ($\Rightarrow$p. 238); and may carry a nuclear warhead.

The depth charge

A depth charge is a canister of explosive which was first used as an anti-submarine weapon by the British navy in 1915. The canisters were originally dropped or thrown from the stern of a ship in a pattern of five. The explosive, detonated by a hydrostatic fuse set at a particular depth, caused serious damage even if it exploded some way from the submarine because the pressures built up by underwater explosions are much greater than those in air. Today, computerized launching systems are used, the canisters are propelled over greater distances, and they may carry nuclear charges which can destroy a submarine up to 1.61 km (1 mile) away from the explosion.

Bombs

A bomb is a container filled with explosives, or with some explosive mixed with an incendiary material, a smoke producing mixture, or a poison gas. If dropped from an aircraft, it is set off by timed or contact fuses, or, if it is a modern smart bomb, it is directed to its target like a guided missile ($\Rightarrow$p. 238). If placed in position, as for example by terrorists, it is set off by timed fuses, by remote control, or by some booby trap mechanism.

In World War II, Sir Neville Barnes Wallis, an English aeronautical engineer and inventor, made a 'bouncing bomb' with which to attack the Möhne and Eder dams in Germany. It was shaped like a barrel about 1.5 m (5 ft) in length and diameter. Before it was dropped on to the water, crosswise, ahead of the dam, it was given a back-spin by an electric motor so that on impact it skimmed

❛What was gunpowder? Trivial. What was electricity? Meaningless. This atomic bomb is the Second Coming in Wrath.❜

WINSTON CHURCHILL (1874–1965), English statesman

across the water surface until it hit the dam. The spin then moved it downwards into the water before it exploded.

Grenades

These are small bombs which can be thrown by hand or shot from a rifle. They were first used during the 17th century by special units of elite troops, the grenadiers, and they played an important role in the trench warfare of World War I. The British Mills grenade, invented in 1915 by Sir William Mills, was typical. It was of a convenient size to hold in the hand, and when thrown, an external lever, with its safety pin removed but still held down by the hand, flew free and activated a timed fuse. The resulting explosion broke the corrugated cast-iron casing of the grenade and scattered the lethal fragments.

Barbed wire

This was used extensively, particularly during World War I, to impede troop movements. It had originally been invented by an American, Joseph Glidden, in 1874 for fencing purposes. It is commonly replaced today by razor wire in which the barbs are replaced by sharp-edged pieces of metal.

The Molotov cocktail

This is a home-made petrol bomb, first used as an anti-tank weapon during the Spanish Civil War in 1936, and by partisans and terrorists ever since. It is named after the Soviet Foreign Minister of the day, and is made by filling a glass bottle with petrol and oil or tar. A paraffin-soaked rag, tied round the neck of the bottle, is ignited and the whole is hurled at the target.

The Shrapnel shell

This shell was invented in 1784 by the British Lieutenant (later General) Shrapnel. It was a shell with a thin casing containing both musket shot and gunpowder, which was fused to burst in the air over the heads of enemy troops. When it did so, the scattered shot inflicted many casualties.

Mines

These are bombs placed underwater (naval mines) or underground (land mines) to damage ships, vehicles or troops. The first effective naval mines were made by Alfred Nobel's father who, at the time, was working in Russia. They were used during the Crimean War (1854–56), when they were moored in shipping lanes to sink craft which came into contact with them. This type of contact mine remains in use today, together with other more sophisticated types which were invented during World War II. The magnetic mine is triggered by the magnetic field of a passing ship; the acoustic mine by the sound of it; and the pressure mine by the small changes in pressure the ship causes.

Land mines only became common during World War II. There are two main types: heavier anti-tank mines designed to destroy tanks or other vehicles; and lighter anti-personnel mines aimed at troops. They are both set off by pressure. Many earlier models, with metal casings which, could be picked up by metal detectors have been replaced by plastic mines.

The ejector seat

This is a device invented by a British engineer, James Martin, which, when operated by the pilot of a high-speed aeroplane in an emergency, ejects him and his seat from the plane. A small attached parachute maintains the seat in its correct position and retards its fall, whilst a larger one pulls the pilot out of the seat and enables him to make a normal parachute descent. The compressed springs, used in the first trials in 1946 by the British Martin-Baker Co., were soon replaced by explosive charges.

Flame throwers

The old use of flame throwing (⇒p. 238) was resurrected by the Germans in 1915. Oil or gasoline from a container was forced along a hose by compressed nitrogen and was ignited as it passed through a triggered nozzle. Much more efficient weapons were developed by the Americans in 1942. They burnt napalm, a gel made from inflammable oils and soaps or, more recently, plastics. It can be projected over longer distances than oil or gasoline, burns more intensely, and sticks to anything it touches.

16

SPACE

'Now is the time to take longer strides – time for a great new
American enterprise – time for this nation to take a clearly
leading role in space achievement, which in many ways may
hold the key to our future on Earth.'

*JOHN F. KENNEDY, US President (1961–63),
in a speech to Congress, 25 May 1961*

SPACE

For centuries, people have stared at the stars and fantasized in literature and films about space travel. This became a reality when Neil Armstrong first set foot on the Moon on 29 July 1969. The 769,000 km (477,000 miles) journey, there and back, took about a week and represented one of the greatest human achievements of all time; its planning and implementation involved around half a million people; and it was made possible by the development of powerful rockets.

ROCKETS

Rockets were probably invented in China during the second half of the 12th century. They were made from hollowed out bamboo cane filled with gunpowder. The bamboo was sealed at one end and it was the escape of the hot gases from the other end, when the gunpowder burnt, that provided the thrust to propel the rocket. They were originally intended mainly as fireworks to drive away evil spirits but, by the 14th century, they were being used sporadically for military purposes both in the East and the West. They were not, however, very effective until used by the Prince of Mysore and his son Tippu Sultan in battles against the British at Seringapatam in 1792 and 1798. Their metal-cased rockets, with a range of about 900 m (984 yd), carried incendiary or explosive charges. They could kill three or four men on landing, had a very alarming effect on horses, and both surprised and impressed the British army.

Congreve rockets

The British response to these rockets was to ask Colonel William Congreve to produce something better. He was an experienced inventor and, working at Woolwich, England, he had by 1805 built a rocket with a cast-iron case which was 40 in (1.02 m) long and $3^1/_2$ in (89 mm) in diameter. It was fitted with a 16 ft (4.9 m) long guide-stick, had a range of 1968 yd (1800 m), and carried an incendiary missile. Congreve built up a range of similar rockets and they were

Use of Congreve rockets in 1827 – repelling cavalry (top) and bombarding a town from ships (bottom)

used with some limited success in various engagements including the Battle of Waterloo in 1815. However, they competed with traditional artillery, were not very reliable, did not appeal to the Duke of Wellington, and were soon discarded.

There was, however, a spin-off. The rocket-launched ship-to-shore life-line was invented and developed by three Englishmen, Thomas Trengrouse (1807), John Dennet (1826) and Colonel Boxer (1855) and rockets were also used successfully in whaling harpoons and in firing sound, light and smoke signals.

Increasing the power

Gunpowder does not burn very rapidly so that it can provide only a limited thrust for a rocket, and a Russian teacher of mathematics, Konstantin Ziolkovsky, first suggested in 1815 that more powerful rockets could only be made if it was replaced as the propellant by a liquid fuel system which would burn more quickly. At the time, that was more easily said than done, and it was not until 100 years later that an American, Robert Goddard, professor of physics at Clark University in Massachusetts, and a Hungarian, Hermann Oberth, working in Germany, made any real progress.

Goddard wrote *A Method of Reaching Extreme Altitudes* in 1919, and in 1926 made a rocket using a fuel mixture of gasoline and liquid oxygen. On its first test it only rose 184 ft (56 m) but by 1937 it had reached 1.8 miles (3 km). Goddard took out over 200 patents before he died in 1945 and, because many of them were infringed by the government, his widow was awarded $1 million in 1966.

Oberth wrote *The Rocket into Interplanetary Space* in 1924 and founded The Society for Space Travel in 1927. Wernher von Braun was one of its early members, and he went on to play a leading role in the development of the German V1 and V2 ballistic missiles (⇒p. 237). The V2 was fuelled by a mixture of ethanol and liquid oxygen; it carried a 1 tonne explosive warhead over a distance of 350 km (217 miles) at a speed of over 5500 km/h (3400 mph); and, in 1944, more than 2000 were directed on to Belgium and southern England.

Today's rockets

At the end of World War II, some of the German rocket workers moved to the USA and some to the USSR, and the highly competitive rocket development

6And the rockets' red glare, the bombs bursting in air.9

FRANCIS SCOTT KEY (1780–1843), American poet, in The Star Spangled Banner describing the use of rockets against Fort McHenry, near Baltimore, in 1814

WERNHER von BRAUN
(1912–77)

WERNHER Magnus Maximilian von Braun, the son of a Baron who had been a government minister, was born in Wirsitz (then Germany now Poland). He was educated at the Institutes of Technology in Zürich and Berlin and was awarded a PhD in 1934 for a thesis on rockets fuelled by liquids.

The German government was already taking an active interest in rockets because it was not covered by any of the limitations on armaments in the Treaty of Versailles, and there was a military research station near Berlin directed by General Walter Dornberger working on rockets fired by solid fuels. Von Braun was helped by the Society for Space Travel to begin his own experiments nearby, and in 1936 the two were brought together at a new centre set up by Hitler at Peenemünde, on an island off the Baltic coast. Von Braun was the technical director and, with the help of Oberth and others, he designed and built both the V1 and V2 rockets.

At the end of World War II, he and many of his team surrendered to the Americans and moved to the USA to continue their work. He began at the US Army Ordnance Corps testing grounds at White Sands, New Mexico, and then became, in turn, Director of the US Army's Ballistic Missile Agency at Huntsville in Alabama, and of the Marshall Space Flight Centre. He was responsible for the development of both the *Jupiter* rocket, which put the first American satellite, *Explorer 1*, into orbit in 1958, and the *Saturn* rocket which sent men to the Moon in the *Apollo* missions betweeen 1969 and 1972.

programmes of both countries were based on the V2 design. Different fuels were tried; bigger and bigger rockets were made; and more power was achieved by having two- and three-stage systems. Amongst others, the *Korolev, Soyuz, Yanguel* and *Chelomei* came from the USSR; the *Viking, Jupiter, Atlas, Titan, Delta* and *Saturn* from the USA. Their work was augmented by the joining together of 13 European countries in 1972 into the European Space Agency (ESA). Its launch site is at Kourou in French Guiana in South America and the first *Ariane* rocket was fired in 1979. Japan, China and India also have rocket launching sites.

INTO ORBIT

To launch an Earth satellite, a rocket has to propel it with a speed above 7.9 km/s (17,640 mph) to lift it beyond the height of the Earth's atmosphere. It can then encircle the Earth because its forward motion, keeping it up, just balances the downwards pull of gravity on it and it stays in its orbit indefinitely because there is no air resistance.

The first satellite, *Sputnik I*, was launched on 4 October 1957, in the USSR by a *Korolev* rocket. It was a steel sphere 58 cm (22.8 in) in diameter and weighing 84.5 kg (186 lb); it carried only a radio which transmitted identification signals. A month later, a capsule containing a dog was put into orbit, and another, launched in August 1960, and containing two dogs, was returned to Earth by parachute.

The scene was set for the first manned flight which was made on 12 April 1961 by Yuri Gagarin, a 27-year old Soviet pilot. His spherical, pressurized capsule, *Vostock 1*, was linked to a service module which provided him with air and which was fitted with its own rockets enabling it to slow down and manoeuvre the capsule at the end of its mission for return to Earth. Gagarin was protected from the heat generated as the capsule entered the Earth's atmosphere by an external heat shield, and after re-entry the module was discarded and the capsule descended to the ground by parachute. The mission, which included one orbit of the earth, took 1 hr 48 mins.

> *Space isn't remote at all. It's only an hour's drive away if your car could go straight upwards.*
>
> FRED HOYLE (1915–),
> English astronomer

Meanwhile, the Americans had also been active and, on 20 February 1962, an *Atlas* rocket launched *Friendship 7*, which took Lt-Col. John Glenn three times round the Earth before returning by parachute into the Atlantic Ocean. The mission lasted almost 5 hours.

Today's satellites

Today, there are over 400 artificial satellites in orbit serving a number of peaceful and military functions. They relay telephone and television signals; they gather covert intelligence information; they are used by map-makers, meteorologists, astronomers and environmentalists; and they provide a platform on which to site a wide range of scientific instruments out in space.

A number of individual countries design and make satellites and have them launched elsewhere if they have no launch facilities of their own. It might well come to be called the satellite age.

MAN ON THE MOON

In 1961, shortly after the Soviets had put Yuri Gagarin into orbit, President Kennedy set American scientists the task of landing a man on the Moon and returning him safely to Earth before the end of the decade. Many thought it an impossible target, but the Apollo programme, controlled by the National Aeronautics and Space Administration (NASA), was set up to try to achieve it and an inexorable build-up of space activity began.

The preliminaries

At first, unmanned craft were used to gather information about the Moon's surface to try to assess what reception any visitors might get. The Soviet *Luna-3* craft had already flown past the Moon in 1959 and photographed its far side. In 1965, the American Edward White and the Soviet Alexei Leonov had both walked in space in special space suits. In the same year, the American *Gemini 6* and *Gemini 7* rendezvoused in space. A year later the docking of two craft was achieved and, in 1967, *Saturn* launched its first unmanned satellite. Over Christmas 1968, *Apollo 8*, with a three-man crew, orbited the Moon ten times.

The landing

On 16 July 1969, the Apollo 11 spacecraft was launched by *Saturn V*. It was manned by Neil Armstrong, Edwin (Buzz) Aldrin and Michael Collins, and it was made up of a command module in which the three astronauts spent most of their time, a service module supplying oxygen, electricity and water, and a lunar module for landing on the Moon. The first-stage of the *Saturn* rocket lifted it to a height of about 60 km (40 miles), in 2¹/₂ minutes, before being jettisoned into the ocean. The second-stage rocket, burning for six minutes, raised it to 180 km (110 miles) before it, too, was discarded. The third-stage, in two firings, took *Apollo 11* first into an Earth orbit, and then carried it at a speed of 40,000 km/h (25,000 mph) into a lunar orbit before being ditched.

Whilst Collins kept the spacecraft orbiting round the Moon, Armstrong and Aldrin descended to its surface, in the lunar module. After two hours they returned to the lunar module and were fired back into the original Moon orbit by a small rocket, to dock with the main spacecraft. The lunar module was then discarded and crashed on to the Moon's surface, whilst the command and service module headed back to Earth. The latter was discarded before re-entry into the Earth's atmosphere, and the command module landed safely by parachute.

Five more *Apollo* missions, all launched by *Saturn* rockets, put a further ten men on the moon between 1969 and 1972, and a folding electric four-wheeled vehicle was driven on the Moon in the last three. The Soviets have not put a man on the Moon but they did land two radio-controlled vehicles (*Lunakhods*) in 1971 and 1973.

SPACE STATIONS

Space stations are large spacecraft, big enough to allow crews of two or three astronauts to stay in space for some time and to work and live in some comfort as compared with the cramped conditions in earlier craft. The crews can also be replaced every so often by a new team which arrive in another capsule which docks with the space station. The Soviet *Salyut 1* was put into orbit in 1971; it was

A Saturn V *rocket as used to launch the Apollo 11 mission which landed the first men on the Moon in 1969*

14 m (46 ft) long. The American *Skylab*, almost twice as long, followed in 1973.

Skylab was manned by three different crews for a total of 172 days before it eventually fell to Earth in 1979. *Salyut 1* was only occupied for 23 days and the crew were killed on return to Earth, but it was followed by six other improved models, before a new type of Soviet station, *Mir*, was launched in 1986. It has six docking ports so that extra modules can be attached temporarily or permanently; it is kept supplied by an unmanned craft which brings new stores and takes old rubbish away; and it has so many facilities such as a washroom, lavatory and separate bedrooms, that it is something like a hotel in space. Astronauts have lived in it for more than a year.

An international space station built

❝That's one small step for man, one giant leap for mankind.❞

NEIL ARMSTRONG (1930–), American astronaut, on landing on the Moon, 21 July 1969

mainly by Japan, Canada and the USA, at an estimated launch cost of $27 billion, is being planned. Different parts of it will be launched separately for joining together in space.

SPACE SHUTTLES

These are reusable, rocket-launched aeroplanes intended to eliminate the waste involved in using a separate rocket for each satellite launch. They can carry up to four satellites in a vast pay-load bay. Alternatively, the bay can be occupied by *Spacelab*, a well-equipped research unit built by the European Space Agency.

A typical lift-off is achieved by using the shuttle's main engines together with two rocket boosters which are attached externally. After two minutes, the boosters are released and dropped into the sea on parachutes; they are recovered for reuse. After eight minutes, the main engines are shut down and a huge fuel tank, now empty, is discarded. Two smaller rocket engines then manoeuvre the shuttle into orbit, and when its mission is completed, they direct it back to Earth. They are switched off before landing and the shuttle glides safely to the ground.

The first shuttle, *Columbia*, took off on its test flight from the Kennedy Space Centre at Cape Canaveral in Florida, USA on 12 April 1981. It was followed by *Challenger* (1983), *Discovery* (1984), *Atlantis* (1985), and *Endeavour* (1992), and the Soviet shuttle, *Buran* first flew in 1988. There was a set-back in 1986 when *Challenger* exploded and the crew were killed, but successful missions began again 32 months later. In 1989, *Atlantis* launched *Magellan* on its journey to orbit Venus; in 1992, *Columbia* undertook the longest space shuttle mission of almost 14 days; and in 1995, first *Discovery* and then *Atlantis* rendezvoused with the Russian space station, *Mir*. Meanwhile, a half-way house had also been tried by launching small satellites from a *Pegasus* rocket aboard a converted B-52 bomber.

LIVING IN SPACE

Life in space is very different from that on Earth. Within a pressurized spacecraft such as the flight deck of a shuttle, or in *Spacelab*, air is provided similar to that on Earth and casual clothing can be worn, but astronauts still have to contend with the weightlessness caused by the lack of gravity which means that anything which is not tied down simply floats away. Astronauts have always to hang on to something, can only move by pulling or pushing themselves along, have to eat with care and drink from a straw, and sleep in a bag attached to a wall.

In a space walk, outside a container, conditions are even less friendly. It is extremely hot in the sun and extremely cold out of it and there is also some danger from radiation or from tiny rock fragments. A special suit is needed. The innermost part, next to the body, can be inflated so that a constant pressure is maintained to prevent the blood from boiling. That is surrounded by a cooling garment containing a network of narrow tubes through which water is circulated. The outer suit, made of several layers of material, has a hard top half and a more flexible lower one. Air is provided, and carbon dioxide removed, via a backpack; there is a head-piece with a visor and built-in communication equipment; special 'gloves' which allow some finger movement; and attached cameras. A unit, on the back, has a number of small jets from which nitrogen gas can be propelled, to allow the astronaut to control his movements.

EXPLORING OUTER SPACE

Astronomers have traditionally peered into the heavens through optical telescopes situated on the ground, but their work has now been extended by siting them, and other instruments, in space; by using radio telescopes; and by space probes.

Radio telescopes
Radio astronomy involves the detection and analysis of the radio waves, of widely different wavelengths, which permeate the universe. There is a general background radiation known as cosmic radiation, together with more specific radio waves emitted by the Sun, Jupiter, and nebulae, galaxies, pulsars and quasars.

❛It was like threading a needle.❜

Robert Gibson, Captain of Atlantis *when it docked with* Mir, *29 June 1995*

The first radio telescope was invented in 1932 by a Czech, Karl Jansky, working in the USA for the Bell Laboratories. He was using his receiver to investigate interference with radio-telephone messages in the North Atlantic when he picked up a 'continuous whistle' from the Milky Way. Modern telescopes consist of a parabolic curved dish which can be moved to scan the whole of the sky and which focuses radio waves on to an antenna at its focal point ($\Rightarrow$p. 152) so that their intensity and spectrum can be studied. A giant telescope with a 76.2 m (250 ft) dish was built at Jodrell Bank, near Manchester, England in 1957; a radio interferometer, using three telescopes one mile apart, was built at Cambridge, England in 1964; a very large array (VLA) telescope at Socorro in New Mexico, USA, in 1980; and in 1986 NASA established the largest ever radiotelescope by linking aerials in Japan and Australia to one on a satellite.

Astronomical satellites

The use of satellites for astronomical purposes began, somewhat accidentally, when in 1958 J.A. Van Allen attributed the failure of radiation counters on the satellite, *Explorer 1*, to the presence of rings of radiation encircling the Earth, now known as the Van Allen belts. Since then, numerous other astronomical satellites have been launched carrying radio telescopes, and X-ray, γ-ray, ultraviolet and infra-red detectors. In 1990, the Hubble space telescope, named after the American astronomer, Edwin P. Hubble, was launched in a collaborative venture between NASA and ESA. A fault was found in one of its mirrors, causing it to give blurred pictures, but that was righted in a remarkable space mission in 1993 and the telescope can now see seven times more deeply into space than telescopes on Earth.

Space probes

Unmanned probes are constantly exploring the heavens. Typical Russian examples are provided by *Venera 7* which landed on Venus in 1970; by *Mars 2* which went into orbit around Mars in 1971; and by *Vega 1* which passed close to the comet Halley in 1985. American achievements include *Surveyor 1* which

landed on the moon in 1966; *Pioneer 10* which flew past Jupiter in 1973; *Viking 1* and *2* which landed on Mars in 1975; *Pioneer 11* which flew past Saturn in 1979; *Voyager 2* which left the earth in August 1977 and flew by Jupiter (1979), Saturn (1981), Uranus (1986) and Neptune (1989); and *Galileo* which entered the atmosphere of Jupiter in 1995.

The ESA launched *Giotto*, in 1986, to observe Halley's Comet, and *Hipparcos*, in 1989, to examine over 100,000 stars. *Ulysses*, built jointly by Germany and France, was launched in 1990 to investigate the nature of emanations from the Sun and Jupiter.

Alas, the hazards associated with any space mission were highlighted on 4 June 1996, when *Ariane 5*, launched by the ESA, veered off course shortly after lift-off and had to be blown up by its ground controllers only 66 seconds into its flight.

The spacecraft Magellan *being launched from the space shuttle* Atlantis *in May 1989. The craft orbited Venus 15,000 times and mapped 98 per cent of its surface by transmitting radar pictures back to Earth. Its mission was ended when it was destroyed by directing it into Venus's atmosphere*

2000 YEARS OF INVENTION (1883–present)

DATE	INVENTION	INVENTOR	ORIGIN OF INVENTION
1883	Petrol engine	Gottlieb Daimler	Germany
1884	Linotype machine	Ottmar Mergenthaler	America
	Steam turbine	Charles A. Parsons	England
	Petrol engine	Karl Benz	Germany
	Safety bicycle	J.K.Starley	England
	Fountain pen	Lewis E. Waterman	America
	Nipkow disc	Paul Nipkow	Germany
1885	Motor car	Karl Benz	German
	Dry plates/Film	George Eastman	America
1886	Motor car	Gottlieb Daimler	German
	Making aluminium	Charles Hall	America
		Paul Héroult	France
	Keyboard calculator	Dorr Felt/W.S.Burroughs	America
1887	Esperanto	Ludwig L. Zamenhof	Poland
1888	Kodak camera	George Eastman/W.H.Walker	America
	Induction motor	Nikola Tesla	America
	Disc record player	Émile Berliner	Germany
1890	Punched card tabulator	Hermann Hollerith	America
	Pneumatic tyres	John Boyd Dunlop	Scotland
	Kinetograph	T.A.Edison/W.K.L.Dickson	America
1891	Kinetoscope	Thomas Alva Edison	America
	Gliding	Otto Lilienthal	Germany
1892	Diesel engine	Rudolph Diesel	Germany
	Automatic loom	James H. Northrop	America
	Escalator	Jesse W.Reno/George A.Wheeler	America
	Vacuum flask (Thermos)	James Dewar	England
1893	Shorthand	J.R.Gregg	America
1895	X-ray tube	Wilhelm Röntgen	Germany
	Safety razor	King Camp Gillette	America
	Radio communication	Guglielmo Marconi	Italy
	Cinematography	L. and A. Lumière	France
	Photogravure	Karl Klic	Austria
	Automatic exchange	Almon B. Strowger	America
1896	Sphygmomanometer	Scipione Riva-Rocci	Italy
1897	Cathode ray tube	Ferdinand Braun	Germany
		J.J.Thomson	England
1898	Magnetic sound recorder	Valdemar Poulsen	Denmark
	Bottle making machine	M. J. Owens	America
1900	Airship	Ferdinand von Zeppelin	Germany
	Freeze drying	Arsène d'Arsonval/George Bordas	France
1902	Motorcycle	Eugene and Michael Werner	France
1903	Aeroplane	Orville and Wilbur Wright	America
	Electrocardiography	Willem Einthoven	Netherlands
1904	Diode valve	John Ambrose Fleming	England
1905	Hydrofoil	Enrico Forlanini	Italy
1906	Triode valve	Lee de Forest	America
	Broadcasting	R.A.Fessenden	America
1907	Chemotherapy	Paul Ehrlich	Germany
	Colour photography	L. and A. Lumière	France
1909	Bakelite	Leo Baekeland	America
1913	Zip fastener	Gideon Sundback	Sweden
1915	Depth charge	British Navy	England
	Military tank	William Foster and Co. Ltd	England
		Renault company	France
1916	Tractors	Henry Ford	America
1918	Electric clock	Henry Warren	America
1923	Autogyro	Juan de la Cierva	Spain
	Microphone	W.H.Schottky/Erwin Gerlach	Germany
	Iconoscope	Vladimir Zworykin	Russia
1924	Frozen food	Clarence Birdseye	America
1926	Television	John Logie Baird	Scotland
	Liquid-fuel rocket	Robert Goddard	America
1927	Quartz crystal clock	J.W.Horton/W.A.Marrison	America
1929	Electroencephalography	Hans Berger	Germany
1930	Early analogue computer	Vannevar Bush	America
	Jet engine	Frank Whittle	England
1931	Electron microscope	Ernst Ruska/Max Knoll	Germany
	Electrostatic generator	Robert van de Graaff	America